Digest of United Kingdom Energy Statistics 2003

Production team:	Mike Janes (Managing editor)
	James Achur (Production editor)
	Rebecca Martyn
	Hina Vekria
	Clive Sarjantson
	and chapter authors

A National Statistics publication

London: The Stationery Office

Digest of United Kingdom Energy Statistics

Enquiries about statistics in this publication should be made to the contact named at the end of the relevant chapter. Brief extracts from this publication may be reproduced provided that the source is fully acknowledged. General enquiries about the publication, and proposals for reproduction of larger extracts, should be addressed to the Production Editor, James Achur, at the address given in paragraph XXVII of the Introduction.

The Department of Trade and Industry reserves the right to revise or discontinue the text or any table contained in this Digest without prior notice.

About TSO's Standing Order Service

The Standing Order Service, open to all TSO account holders, allows customers to automatically receive the publications they require in a specified subject area, thereby saving them the time, trouble and expense of placing individual orders, also without handling charges normally incurred when placing ad-hoc orders.

Customers may choose from over 4,000 classifications arranged in 250 sub groups under 30 major subject areas. These classifications enable customers to choose from a wide variety of subjects, those publications which are of special interest to them. This is a particularly valuable service for the specialist library or research body. All publications will be dispatched immediately after publication date. A Standing Orders Handbook describing the service in detail and a complete list of classifications may be obtained on request. Write to TSO, Standing Order Department, PO Box 29, St Crispins, Duke Street, Norwich, NR3 1GN, quoting reference 12.01.013; Alternatively telephone 0870 600 5522 and select the Standing Order Department (option 2); fax us on 0870 600 5533; or finally e-mail us at book.standing.orders@tso.co.uk.

National Statistics

National Statistics are produced to high professional standards set out in the National Statistics Code of Practice. They undergo regular quality assurance reviews to ensure that they meet customer needs. They are produced free from any political interference.

You can find a range of National Statistics on the Internet – www.statistics.gov.uk

---

Contents

Monthly and quarterly data are also available for Energy, Solid fuels and derived gases, Petroleum, Gas and Electricity at: www.dti.gov.uk/energy/inform/energy_stats/

Information on Energy Prices is available at: www.dti.gov.uk/energy/energyprices/prices/

A list of tables

Introduction

I   This issue of the Digest of United Kingdom Energy Statistics continues a series which commenced with the Ministry of Fuel and Power Statistical Digest for the years 1948 and 1949, published in 1950. The Ministry of Fuel and Power Statistical Digest was previously published as a Command Paper, the first being that for the years 1938 to 1943, published in July 1944 (Cmd. 6538).

II   The current issue updates the figures given in the Department of Trade and Industry's *Digest of United Kingdom Energy Statistics 2002*, published in July 2002.

III   This printed and bound issue consists of seven chapters and four annexes. The first chapter deals with overall energy. The other chapters cover the specific fuels, combined heat and power and renewable sources of energy. The annexes cover major events in the energy industries, calorific values and conversion factors, a glossary of terms and further sources of information.

IV   This Digest is also available on the Internet. Some additional information appears on the Internet only. The tables provided on the Internet are provided in Microsoft Excel format. Most Internet versions of the tables include data for earlier years which are not provided in the printed copy publication. For example commodity and energy balances (see VII and VIII, below) for 1998 and 1999 are included on the Internet, and tables that show five years in this printed version show 7 years in their Internet form because page sizes are not a limiting factor. In addition, the following appear on the Internet version only:

Long term trends text and tables
Major events from 1990 to 2000 - Annex D
(only Major events for 2001 to 2003 appear in the printed and bound version)
Energy and the environment – Annex E
UK oil and gas resources - Annex F
Foreign Trade – Annex G

V   Annual information on prices is included in the publication *Quarterly Energy Prices*. This is available together with *Energy Trends* on subscription from the DTI. Further information on these publications can be found in Annex C.

VI   Where necessary, data have been converted or adjusted to provide consistent series, however, in some cases changes in methods of data collection have affected the continuity of the series. The presence of remaining discontinuities is indicated in the chapter text or in footnotes to the tables.

VII   Chapters 2, 3, 4, 5 and 7 contain production and consumption of individual fuels and are presented using *commodity balances*. A commodity balance illustrates the flows of an individual fuel through from production to final consumption, showing its use in transformation (including heat generation) and energy industry own use. Further details of commodity balances and their use are given in the Annex A, paragraphs A.7 to A.42.

VIII   The individual commodity balances are combined in an *energy balance,* presented in Chapter 1, Energy. The energy balance differs from a commodity balance in that it shows the interactions between different fuels in addition to illustrating their consumption. The energy balance thus gives a fuller picture of the production, transformation and use of energy showing all the flows. Expenditure on energy is also presented in energy balance format in Chapter 1. Further details of the energy balance and its use, including the methodology introduced a year ago for heat, are given in Annex A, paragraphs A.43 to A.58.

IX   Chapter 1 also covers general energy statistics and includes tables showing energy consumption by final users and an analysis of energy consumption by main industrial groups. Fuel production and consumption statistics are derived mainly from the records of fuel producers and suppliers.

X   Chapters 6 and 7 summarise the results of surveys conducted by Future Energy Solutions (part of AEA Technology) on behalf of the Department of Trade and Industry. These chapters estimate the contribution made by combined heat and power (CHP) and renewable energy sources to energy production and consumption in the United Kingdom.

XI   Some of the data shown in this Digest may contain unpublished revisions and estimates of trade from additional sources.

Definitions

XII   The text at the beginning of each chapter explains the main features of the tables. Technical notes and definitions, given at the end of this text, provide detailed explanations of the figures in the tables and how they are derived. Explanations of the logic behind an energy balance and for commodity balances are given in Annex A.

XIII   Most chapters contain some information on 'oil' or 'petroleum'; these terms are used in a general sense and vary according to usage in the field examined. In their widest sense they are used to include all mineral oil and related hydrocarbons (except methane) and any derived products.

XIV   An explanation of the terms used to describe electricity generating companies is given in Chapter 5, paragraphs 5.45 to 5.46.

XV   Data in this issue have been prepared on the basis of the Standard Industrial Classification (SIC) 1992 as far as is practicable. For further details of classification of consumers see Chapter 1, paragraphs 1.54 to 1.58.

XVI   Where appropriate, further explanations and qualifications are given in footnotes to the tables.

Geographical coverage

XVII   The geographical coverage of the statistics is the United Kingdom. Shipments to the Channel Islands and the Isle of Man from the United Kingdom are not classed as exports, and supplies of solid fuel and petroleum to these islands are therefore included as part of United Kingdom inland consumption or deliveries.

Periods

XVIII   Data in this Digest are for calendar years or periods of 52 weeks, depending on the reporting procedures within the fuel industry concerned. Actual periods covered are given in the notes to the individual fuel sections.

Revisions

XIX   The tables contain revisions to some of the previously published figures, and where practicable the revised data have been indicated by an 'r'. The 'r' marker is used whenever the figure has been revised from that published in the printed copy of the 2002 Digest, even though some figures may have been corrected on the Internet version of the tables.

Energy data on the Internet

XX   Energy data are held on the energy area of the DTI web site, under "information and statistics". The Digest is available at www.dti.gov.uk/energy/inform/dukes/ . Information on further DTI energy publications as in both printed copy and on the Internet are given in Annex C.

XXI   Short term statistics are published:

- monthly, by the DTI on the internet at www.dti.gov.uk/energy/inform/energy_stats/ .
- quarterly, by the DTI in paper and on the internet in *Energy Trends,* and *Quarterly Energy Prices*: www.dti.gov.uk/energy/inform/energy_stats/ .

- quarterly, by the DTI in Statistical Press Release which provides a summary of information published in *Energy Trends* and *Quarterly Energy Prices* publications: www.gnn.gov.uk/gnn/national.nsf/TI/ .

- monthly, by the Office for National Statistics in the *Monthly Digest of Statistics (The Stationery Office)*.

To subscribe to *Energy Trends* and *Quarterly Energy Prices,* please contact Clive Sarjantson at the address given at paragraph XXVII.

Table numbering

XXII   Page 10 contains a list showing the tables in the order in which they appear in this issue, and their corresponding numbers in previous issues.

Symbols used

XXIII   The following symbols are used in this Digest:

..	not available
-	nil or negligible (less than half the final digit shown)
r	Revised since the previous edition

Rounding convention

XXIV   Individual entries in the tables are rounded independently and this can result in totals which are different from the sum of their constituent items.

Acknowledgements

XXV   Acknowledgement is made to the main coal producing companies, the electricity companies, the oil companies, the gas pipeline operators, the gas suppliers, Transco, the Institute of Petroleum, the Coal Authority, the United Kingdom Iron and Steel Statistics Bureau, the National Environmental Technology Centre, Future Energy Solutions, the Department for Environment, Food and Rural Affairs, the Department for Transport, OFGEM, Building Research Establishment, HM Customs and Excise, the Office for National Statistics, and other contributors to the enquiries used in producing this publication.

Cover photograph

XXVI The cover illustration used for this Digest and other 2003-2004 DTI energy statistics publications is from a photograph by David Askew. It was a winning entry in the DTI News Photographic Competition in 2002.

Contacts

XXVII For general enquiries on energy statistics contact:

Clive Sarjantson on 020-7215 2698,   Rebecca Martyn on 020-7215 3839
(E-mail: clive.sarjantson@dti.gsi.gov.uk) (E-mail: rebecca.martyn@dti.gsi.gov.uk)
or

> Department of Trade and Industry
> Bay 232
> 1 Victoria Street
> London SW1H 0ET
> Fax: 020-7215 2723

Enquirers with hearing difficulties can contact the Department on the DTI Textphone: 020-7215 6740.

XXVIII For enquiries concerning particular data series or chapters contact those named on page 9 or at the end of the relevant chapter.

James Achur, Production Editor
July 2003

Contact List

The following people in the Department of Trade and Industry may be contacted for further information about the topics listed:

Chapter	Contact	Telephone 020 7215	E-mail
Total energy statistics	Julian Prime	6178	Julian.Prime@dti.gsi.gov.uk
Solid fuels and derived gases	Mike Janes	5186	Mike.Janes@dti.gsi.gov.uk
	James Achur	2717	James.Achur@dti.gsi.gov.uk
Oil and upstream gas resources	Clive Evans	5189	Clive.Evans@dti.gsi.gov.uk
	Martin Young	5184	Martin.Young@dti.gsi.gov.uk
North Sea profits, operating costs and investments	Suhail Siddiqui	5262	Suhail.Siddiqui@dti.gsi.gov.uk
	Philip Beckett	5260	Philip.Beckett@dti.gsi.gov.uk
Petroleum (downstream)	Ian Corrie	2714	Ian.Corrie@dti.gsi.gov.uk
	Martin Young	5184	Martin.Young@dti.gsi.gov.uk
Gas supply (downstream)	Mike Janes	5186	Mike.Janes@dti.gsi.gov.uk
	John Castle	2718	John.Castle@dti.gsi.gov.uk
Electricity	Mike Janes	5186	Mike.Janes@dti.gsi.gov.uk
	Joe Ewins	5190	Joe.Ewins@dti.gsi.gov.uk
Combined heat and power	Mike Janes	5186	Mike.Janes@dti.gsi.gov.uk
Prices and values Industrial, international and oil prices	Lesley Petrie	2720	Lesley.Petrie@dti.gsi.gov.uk
	Sara Atkins	6532	Sara.Atkins@dti.gsi.gov.uk
Renewable sources of energy	Mike Janes	5186	Mike.Janes@dti.gsi.gov.uk
Calorific values and conversion factors	Julian Prime	6178	Julian.Prime@dti.gsi.gov.uk
	Martin Young	5184	Martin.Young@dti.gsi.gov.uk
General enquiries (energy helpdesk)	Rebecca Martyn	3839	Rebecca.Martyn@dti.gsi.gov.uk
	Clive Sarjantson	2698	Clive.Sarjantson@dti.gsi.gov.uk

All the above can be contacted by fax on 020 7215 2723

Tables as they appear in this issue and their corresponding numbers in the previous three issues

Chapter	2000	2001	2002(1)	2003(1)
ENERGY	-	-	-	1.1
	-	-	1.1	1.2
	-	1.1	1.2	1.3
	1.1	1.2	1.3	-
	1.2	1.3	-	-
	1.3	-	-	-
	-	-	-	1.4
	-	-	1.4	1.5
	-	1.4	1.5	1.6
	1.4	1.5	1.6	-
	1.5	1.6	-	-
	1.6	-	-	-
	1.7	1.8	1.8	1.8
	1.8	1.9	1.9	1.9
	1.9	1.10	1.1.1	1.1.1
	1.10	1.11	1.1.2	1.1.2
	1.11	1.12	1.1.3	1.1.3
	1.12	1.13	1.1.4	1.1.4
	1.13	1.14	1.1.5	1.1.5
	1.14	1.15	1.1.6	1.1.6
	1.15	1.16	1.1.7	1.1.7
	1.16	1.17	1.1.8	1.1.8
	A9.1	1.7	1.7	1.7
SOLID FUELS & DERIVED GASES	-	-	-	2.1
	-	-	2.1	2.2
	-	2.1	2.2	2.3
	2.1	2.2	2.3	-
	2.2	2.3	-	-
	2.3	-	-	-
	-	-	-	2.4
	-	-	2.4	2.5
	-	2.4	2.5	2.6
	2.4	2.5	2.6	-
	2.5	2.6	-	-
	2.6	-	-	-
	2.7	2.7	2.7	2.7
	2.8	2.8	2.8	2.8
	2.9	2.9	2.9	2.9
	-	2.12	2.10	2.10
	-	2.13	2.11	2.11
	2.10	2.10	2.1.1	2.1.1
	2.11	2.11	2.1.2	2.1.2
PETROLEUM	-	-	-	3.1
	-	-	3.1	3.2
	-	3.1	3.2	3.3
	3.1	3.2	3.3	-
	3.2	3.3	-	-
	3.3	-	-	-
	-	-	-	3.4
	-	-	3.4	3.5
	-	3.4	3.5	3.6
	3.4	3.5	3.6	-
	3.5	3.6	-	-
	3.6	-	-	-
	-	-	-	-
	3.7	3.7	3.7	3.7
	-	-	-	-
	3.8	3.8	3.8	3.8
	3.9	3.9	3.9	3.9
	3.10	3.10	3.10	3.10
	3.11	3.11	3.1.1	3.1.1
	3.12	3.12	3.1.2	3.1.2

Chapter	2000	2001	2002(1)	2003(1)
NATURAL GAS	4.1	4.1	4.1	4.1
	4.2	4.2	4.2	4.2
	4.3	4.3	4.3	4.3
	4.4	4.4	4.1.1	4.1.1
	A9.1(2)	-	-	-
ELECTRICITY	5.1	5.1	5.1	5.1
	5.4	5.4	5.4	5.4
	5.2	5.2	5.2	5.2
	5.5	5.6	5.6	5.6
	5.3	5.3	5.3	5.3
	5.6	5.5	5.5	5.5
	5.7	5.7	5.7	5.7
	5.8	5.8	5.8	5.8
	5.9	5.9	5.9	5.9
	5.10	5.10	5.1.1	5.1.1
	5.11	5.11	5.1.2	5.1.2
	5.12	5.12	5.1.3	5.1.3
	-	5.13	5.10	5.10
	A9.1(2)	-	-	-
COMBINED HEAT AND POWER	6.1	6.1	6.1	6.1
	6.2	6.2	6.2	6.2
	6.3	6.3	6.3	6.3
	6.4	6.4	6.4	6.4
	6.5	6.5	6.5	6.5
	6.6	6.6	6.6	6.6
	6.7	6.7	6.7	6.7
	6.8	6.8	6.8	6.8
	6.9	6.9	6.9	6.9
RENEWABLE SOURCES	-	-	-	7.1
	-	-	7.1	7.2
	-	7.1	7.2	7.3
	7.1	7.2	7.3	-
	7.2	7.3	-	-
	7.3	-	-	-
	7.4	7.4	7.4	7.4
	7.5	7.5	7.5	7.5
	7.6	7.6	7.6/7.1.1	7.6/7.1.1
ANNEX A CALORIFIC VALUES	A.1	A.1	A.1	A.1
	A.2	A.2	A.2	A.2

(1) Tables highlighed in blue appear on the DTI energy statisics web site only: www.dti.gov.uk/energy/inform/energy_stats/

(2) Table A9.1 is now Table 1.7 in the Energy Chapter

Chapter 1
Energy

Introduction

1.1   This chapter presents figures on overall energy production and consumption. Figures showing the flow of energy from production, transformation and energy industry use through to final consumption are presented in the format of an energy balance based on the individual commodity balances presented in Chapters 2 to 5 and 7.

1.2   The chapter begins with aggregate energy balances covering the last three years (Tables 1.1 to 1.3) starting with the latest year, 2002. Energy value balances then follow this for the same years (Tables 1.4 to 1.6) and Table 1.7 shows sales of electricity and gas by sector. Table 1.8 covers final energy consumption by the main industrial sectors over the last five years followed by Table 1.9 which shows the fuels used for electricity generation by these industrial sectors. The explanation of the principles behind the energy balance and commodity balance presentations is set out in Annex A. Long term trends commentary and tables (1.1.1 to 1.1.8) for energy production, consumption and expenditure on energy, temperatures as well as analyses such as the relationship between energy consumption and the economy of the UK appear on DTI's energy statistics web site only at:

(www.dti.gov.uk/energy/inform/dukes/dukes2003/01longterm.pdf).

1.3   The amount of energy transformed into and sold for consumption as heat has been included in the annual energy balances since 1999. An explanation of the methodology that was used to derive the figures can be found in paragraph 1.33.

The energy industries

1.4   The energy industries in the UK play a central role in the economy by producing, transforming and supplying energy in its various forms to all sectors. They are also major contributors to the UK's Balance of Payments through the exports of crude oil and oil products. The box below summarises the energy industries' contribution to the economy:

- 4.3 per cent of GDP;

- 7.2 per cent of total investment;

- 35.2 per cent of industrial investment;

- 165,000 people directly employed (4 per cent of industrial employment);

- Many others indirectly employed (e.g. an estimated 360,000 in support of UK Continental Shelf activities);

- Trade surplus in fuels of £6.0 billion.

Aggregate energy balance (Tables 1.1, 1.2 and 1.3)

1.5   These tables show the flows of energy in the United Kingdom from production to final consumption through conversion into secondary fuels such as coke, petroleum products, secondary electricity and heat sold. The principles behind the presentation used in the Digest and how this links with the figures presented in other chapters are explained in Annex A. The figures are presented on an energy supplied basis, in tonnes of oil equivalent.

1.6   In 2002, the primary supply of fuels was 239.9 million tonnes of oil equivalent, a reduction of 3 per cent compared to 2001. Indigenous production in 2002 was 1½ per cent lower than in 2001. Chart 1.1 illustrates the figures for the production and consumption of individual primary fuels in 2002. In 2002, as in the previous 9 years, overall primary fuel consumption was fully met by indigenous production, with the trade balances for petroleum and its products and gas offsetting net imports of coal, manufactured fuels and electricity.

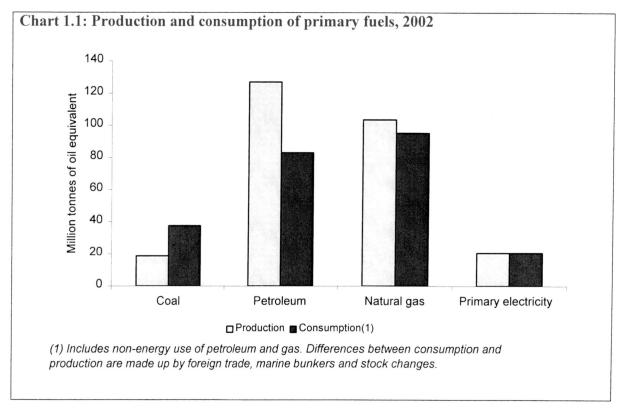

Chart 1.1: Production and consumption of primary fuels, 2002

(1) Includes non-energy use of petroleum and gas. Differences between consumption and production are made up by foreign trade, marine bunkers and stock changes.

1.7   Total primary energy demand was 2½ per cent lower in 2002 than in 2001 at 240.5 million tonnes of oil equivalent. Chart 1.2 shows the composition of primary demand in 2002.

1.8   The transfers row in Tables 1.1 to 1.3 should ideally sum to zero with transfers from primary oils to petroleum products amounting to a net figure of zero. Similarly the manufactured gases and natural gas transfers should sum to zero.

1.9   The transformation section of the energy balance shows, for each fuel, the net inputs for transformation uses. For example, on Table 1.1, 4,336 thousand tonnes of oil equivalent of coal feeds into the production of 4,193 thousand tonnes of oil equivalent of coke, representing a loss of 144 thousand tonnes of oil equivalent in the manufacture of coke in 2002. In 2002, energy losses during the production of electricity and other secondary fuels amounted to 52,394 thousand tonnes of oil equivalent, shown in the transformation row in Table 1.1.

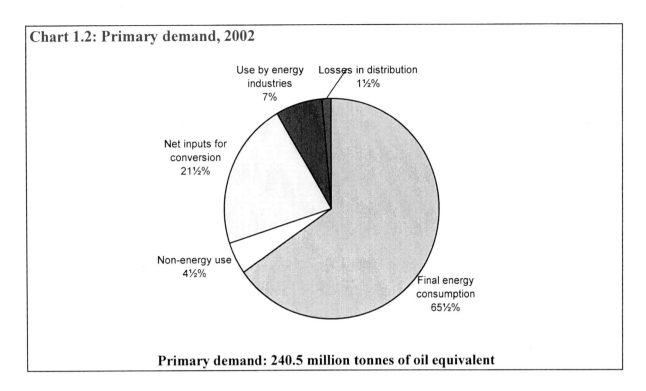

Chart 1.2: Primary demand, 2002

Use by energy industries 7%

Losses in distribution 1½%

Net inputs for conversion 21½%

Non-energy use 4½%

Final energy consumption 65½%

Primary demand: 240.5 million tonnes of oil equivalent

1.10 The next section of the table represents use of fuels by the energy industries themselves. This section also includes consumption by those parts of the iron and steel industry which behave like an energy industry i.e. are involved in transformation processes (see paragraph A.29 of Annex A). In 2002, energy industry use amounted to 16,451 thousand tonnes of oil equivalent of energy, a decrease of 1 per cent on 2001 but a 2½ per cent increase on 2000.

1.11 Losses presented in the energy balance include distribution and transmission losses in the supply of manufactured gases, natural gas, and electricity. Recorded losses fell slightly between 2001 and 2002; this follows a more substantial improvement between 2000 and 2001 due to data collection improvements. Losses in North Sea production of gas are no longer separately identified in a simplified Petroleum Product Reporting System which was introduced in January 2001 and has improved the quality of production data and reduced reported losses. Further details can be found in paragraph 4.29 in Chapter 4.

1.12 Total final consumption, which includes non-energy use of fuels, in 2002 was 168,040 thousand tonnes of oil equivalent, a 2 per cent decrease on 2001. Final energy consumption in 2002 was mainly accounted for by the transport sector (32½ per cent), the domestic sector (28½ per cent), the industrial sector (20½ per cent), the commercial sector (6 per cent) and non-energy use (6½ per cent). These figures are illustrated in Chart 1.3. Recent trends in industrial consumption are shown in Table 1.8 and discussed in paragraphs 1.20 to 1.22.

1.13 The main fuels used by final consumers in 2002 were petroleum products (45½ per cent), natural gas (34 per cent) and electricity (17 per cent). Of the petroleum products consumed by final users 13½ per cent was for non-energy purposes; for natural gas ½ per cent was consumed for non-energy purposes. The amount of heat that was bought for final consumption accounted for ½ per cent of the total.

1.14 Non-energy use of fuels includes use as chemical feedstocks and other uses such as lubricants. Non-energy use of fuels for 2002 are shown in Table 1A. Further details of non-energy use are given in Chapter 3, paragraphs 3.57 to 3.63 and Chapter 4, paragraphs 4.16.

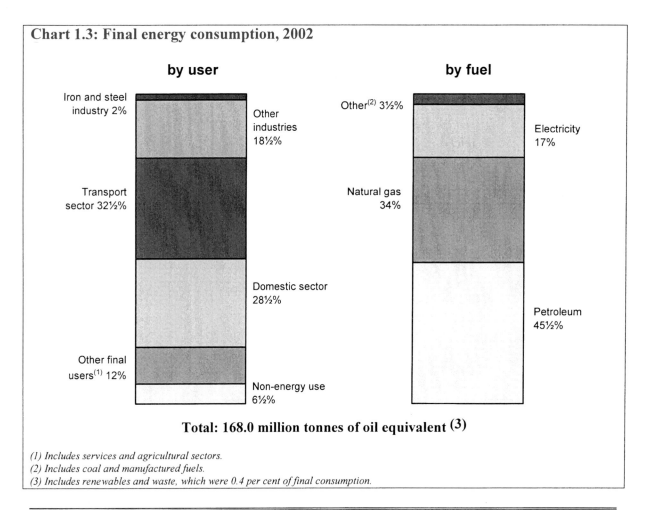

Chart 1.3: Final energy consumption, 2002

by user

Iron and steel industry 2%

Other industries 18½%

Transport sector 32½%

Domestic sector 28½%

Other final users[1] 12%

Non-energy use 6½%

by fuel

Other[2] 3½%

Electricity 17%

Natural gas 34%

Petroleum 45½%

Total: 168.0 million tonnes of oil equivalent [3]

(1) Includes services and agricultural sectors.
(2) Includes coal and manufactured fuels.
(3) Includes renewables and waste, which were 0.4 per cent of final consumption.

Table 1A: Non-energy use of fuels 2002

	Petroleum	Natural gas
		Thousand tonnes of oil equivalent
Petrochemical feedstocks	6,021	384
Other	4,485	-
Total	**10,506**	**384**

Value balance of traded energy (Tables 1.4, 1.5 and 1.6)

1.15 Tables 1.4 to 1.6 present the value of traded energy in a similar format to the energy balances. The balance shows how the value of inland energy supply is made up from the value of indigenous production, trade, tax and margins (profit and distribution costs). The lower half of the table then shows how this value is generated from the final expenditure on energy through transformation processes and other energy sector users as well as from the industrial and domestic sectors. The balances only contain values of energy which is traded i.e. where a transparent market price is applicable. Further technical notes are given in paragraphs 1.24 to 1.59. In keeping with the energy balances, the value balances for 1999 onwards now include data on heat generation and heat sold. Additionally, an estimate of the amount of Climate Change levy paid is included in Tables 1.4 and 1.5. This levy was introduced in April 2001 and is payable by non-domestic final consumers of gas, electricity, coal, coke and LPG.

1.16 Total expenditure by final consumers in 2002 is estimated at £62,130 million, (£61,920 million shown as actual final consumption and £210 million of coal consumed by the iron and steel sector in producing coke for their own consumption).

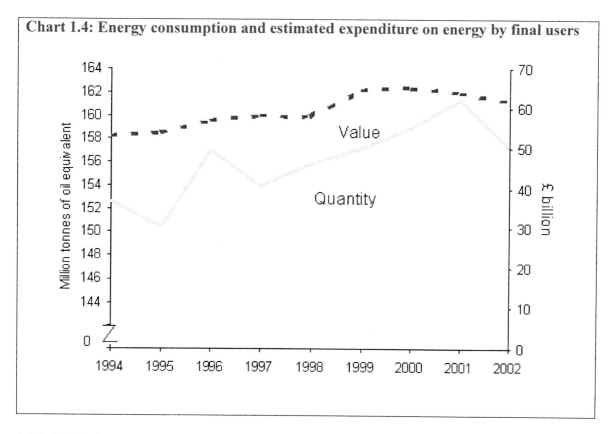

Chart 1.4: Energy consumption and estimated expenditure on energy by final users

1.17 This balance provides a guide on how the value chain works in the production and consumption of energy. For example in 2002, £14,620 million of crude oil were indigenously produced, of which £10,440 million were exported and £6,380 million were imported. Allowing for stock changes this provides a total value of inland crude oil supply of £10,565 million. This fuel was then completely consumed within the petroleum industry in the process of producing £12,830 million of petroleum products. Again some external trade and stock changes took place before arriving at a basic value of petroleum products of £11,650 million. In supplying the fuel to final consumers distribution costs were incurred and some profit was made amounting to £1,920 million whilst duty and tax meant a further £25,910 million was added to the basic price to arrive at the final market value of £39,480 million. This was the value of petroleum products purchased of which industry purchased £1,135 million, domestic consumers for heating purposes purchased £645 million, with the vast majority purchased within the transportation sectors, £35,710 million.

1.18 Of the total final expenditure on energy in 2002 (£62,130 million) the biggest share, 58 per cent fell to the transport sector. Of the remaining 42 per cent industry purchased around a quarter or £5,895 million with the domestic sector purchasing over a half or £14,740 million.

Sales of electricity and gas by sector (Table 1.7)
1.19 Table 1.7 shows broad estimates for the total value of electricity and gas to final consumption. Net selling values provide some indication of typical prices paid in broad sectors and can be of use to supplement more detailed and accurate information contained in the rest of this chapter.

Energy consumption by main industrial groups (Table 1.8)
1.20 This table presents final energy consumption for the main industrial sub-sectors over the last 5 years.

1.21 So far as is practicable, the user categories have been grouped on the basis of the 1992 Standard Industrial Classification (see paragraphs 1.54 to 1.58). However, some data suppliers have difficulty in classifying consumers to this level of detail and the breakdown presented in these tables must therefore be treated with caution. The groupings used are consistent with those used in Table 1.9 which show industrial sectors' use of fuels for generation of electricity (autogeneration).

1.22 In 2002, 34.8 million tonnes of oil equivalent were consumed by the main industrial groups. The largest consuming groups were chemicals (22 per cent), iron and steel and non-ferrous metals (12½ per cent), metal products, machinery and equipment (12½ per cent), food, beverages and tobacco (11 per cent), and paper, printing and publishing (7 per cent). The remaining groups accounted for 35 per cent of total final energy consumption by industry. The figures are illustrated in Chart 1.5.

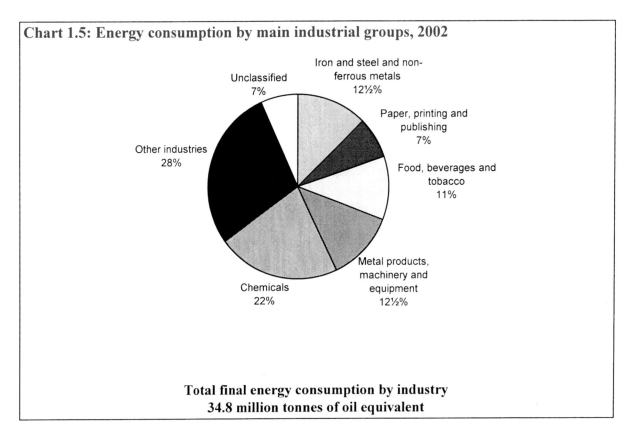

Chart 1.5: Energy consumption by main industrial groups, 2002

Iron and steel and non-ferrous metals 12½%

Unclassified 7%

Paper, printing and publishing 7%

Other industries 28%

Food, beverages and tobacco 11%

Chemicals 22%

Metal products, machinery and equipment 12½%

Total final energy consumption by industry
34.8 million tonnes of oil equivalent

Fuels consumed for electricity generation by main industrial groups (autogeneration) (Table 1.9)

1.23 This table gives details of the amount of each fuel consumed by industries in order to generate electricity for their own use. Fuel consumption is consistent with the figures given for "other generators" in Table 5.4 of Chapter 5. The term autogeneration is explained further in paragraphs 1.29 and 1.30. Electricity produced via autogeneration is included within the figures for electricity consumed by industrial sectors in Table 1.8. Table 1.9 has been produced using the information currently available and shows the same sector detail as Table 1.8, data cannot be given in as much detail as in the individual commodity balances and the energy balance because it could disclose information about individual companies. Table 1.9 allows users to allocate the fuel used for autogeneration to individual industry groups in place of the electricity consumed. Further information on the way Table 1.9 links with the other tables is given in paragraph 1.30.

Technical notes and definitions

I Units and measurement of energy

Units of measurement

1.24 The original units of measurement appropriate to each fuel are used in the individual fuel chapters. A common unit of measurement, the tonne of oil equivalent (toe), which enables different fuels to be compared and aggregated, is used in Chapter 1. For consistency with the International Energy Agency and with the Statistical Office of the European Communities, the tonne of oil equivalent is defined as follows:

1 tonne of oil equivalent
$= 10^7$ kilocalories
$= 396.83$ therms
$= 41.868$ Gigajoules (GJ)
$= 11,630$ kWh

1.25 This unit should be regarded as a measure of energy content rather than a physical quantity. There is no intention to represent an actual physical tonne of oil, and indeed actual tonnes of oil will normally have measurements in tonnes of oil equivalent which differ from unity.

Thermal content - energy supplied basis of measurement

1.26 Tables 1.1 to 1.3, 1.8 and 1.1.1 to 1.1.5 (available on DTI's energy statistics site at www.dti.gov.uk/energy/inform/energy_stats/total_energy/) are compiled on an energy-supplied basis. Detailed data for individual fuels are converted from original units to tonnes of oil equivalent using gross calorific values and conversion factors appropriate to each category of fuel. The results are then aggregated according to the categories used in the tables. Gross calorific values represent the total energy content of the fuel, including the energy needed to evaporate the water present in the fuel (see also paragraph 1.52).

1.27 Estimated gross calorific values for 2002 are given on page 203. Calorific values are reviewed each year in collaboration with the fuel industries, and figures for earlier years can be found in Table A.2 on page 204. To construct energy balances on an energy supplied basis; calorific values are required for production, trade, and stocks, as follows:

Coal The weighted average gross calorific value of all indigenous coal consumed is used to derive the thermal content of coal production and undistributed stocks. Thermal contents of imports and exports allow for the quality of coal. Thermal contents of changes in coal stocks at secondary fuel producers are the average calorific values of indigenous coal consumed.

Petroleum Work was carried out in 1997 to revise calorific values for petroleum products. It has not been possible to find any recent work on the subject. In the absence of such work, the gross calorific values, included in Annex A, and used in the construction of these energy balances from 1990 onwards have been calculated using a formula derived by the US Bureau of Standards. This formula estimates the gross calorific value of products according to their density. This formula is as follows:

$Gj = 51.83 - 8.78 \times d^2$, where d is the density of the product in terms of kilograms per litre.

For crude petroleum and refinery losses, the weighted average calorific value for all petroleum products from UK refineries is used. A notional figure of 42.7 GJ per tonne is used for non-energy petroleum products (industrial and white spirits, lubricants, bitumen, petroleum coke, waxes and miscellaneous products).

Gases Although the original unit for gases is the cubic metre, figures for gases are generally presented in the fuel sections of this Digest in gigawatt hours (GWh), having been converted from cubic metres using gross calorific values provided by the industries concerned. Conversion factors between units of energy are given on the flap inside the back cover.

Electricity and heat Unlike other fuels, the original unit used to measure electricity and heat is a measure of energy. The figures for electricity and heat can therefore be converted directly to toe using the conversion factors on the flap inside the back cover.

Primary electricity Hydro electricity and net imports of electricity are presented in terms of the energy content of the electricity produced (the energy supplied basis). This is consistent with international practice. Primary inputs for nuclear electricity assume the thermal efficiencies at nuclear stations given in Chapter 5, Table 5.9 (37.25 per cent in 2002). (See Chapter 5, paragraphs 5.26 and 5.53.)

Non-energy uses of fuel

1.28 Energy use of fuel mainly comprises use for lighting, heating, motive power and power for appliances. Non-energy use includes use as chemical feedstocks, solvents, lubricants and road making material. The non-energy use of natural gas as a chemical feedstock was separately identified for the first time in the 1994 edition of the Digest. It should be noted that the estimated amounts of non-energy use of natural gas included in the Digest are very approximate. Non-energy uses of petroleum and gas are now included in the figures for final energy consumption following the move over to the presentation of energy data in the format of commodity and energy balances. Further discussion of non-energy uses of lubricating oils and petroleum coke appears in Chapter 3, paragraphs 3.57 to 3.63.

Autogeneration of electricity

1.29 Autogeneration is defined as the generation of electricity by companies whose main business is not electricity generation, the electricity being produced mainly for that company's own use. Estimated amounts of fuel used for thermal generation of electricity by such companies, the output of electricity and the thermal losses incurred in generation are included within the Transformation sector in the energy balances shown in Tables 1.1 to 1.3. Electricity used in the power generation process by autogenerators is shown within the Energy Industry Use section. Electricity consumed by industry and commerce from its own generation is included as part of Final consumption. This treatment is in line with the practice in international energy statistics.

1.30 Figures on total amount of fuel used and electricity generated by autogenerators, and the amount of electricity for own consumption are shown in Tables 1.9, 5.1, 5.3 to 5.6. Table 1.9 summarises the figures by broad industrial groups. Much of the power generated is from combined heat and power (CHP) plants and data from Chapter 6 are included within Table 1.9. Differences will occur where CHP plants are classified to major power producers, and this mainly affects the chemicals sector. The method of allocating fuel used in CHP plants between electricity production and heat production is described in paragraphs 6.35 to 6.37 of Chapter 6. This method can give rise to high implied conversion efficiencies in some sectors, most notably in the iron and steel sector.

Final consumption, deliveries, stock changes

1.31 Figures for final consumption relate to deliveries, if fuels can be stored by users and data on actual consumption are not available. Final consumption of petroleum and solid fuels is on deliveries basis throughout, except for the use of solid fuels by the iron and steel industry. Figures for domestic use of coal are based on deliveries to merchants. Figures for stock changes in Tables 1.1 to 1.3 cover stocks held by primary and secondary fuel producers, major distributors of petroleum products, and stocks of coke and breeze held by the iron and steel industry. Figures for stock changes in natural gas represent the net amount put into storage by gas companies operating pipelines.

1.32 Figures for final consumption of electricity include sales by the public distribution system and consumption of electricity produced by generators other than the major electricity producing companies. Thus electricity consumption includes that produced by industry and figures for deliveries of other fuels to industry exclude amounts used to generate electricity (except for years prior to 1987).

Heat sold

1.33 Heat sold is defined as heat that is produced and sold under the provision of a contract. The heat sold figures have been derived from two sources covering CHP plants and community heating schemes without CHP plants. Data for heat sold were supplied by CHP plants to the Combined Heat and Power Quality Assurance Programme and were processed by Future Energy Solutions (part of AEA Technology Environment). Data for heat consumption from community heating schemes were derived from the Building Research Establishment's (BRE) 'Nationwide Survey of Community Heating' that was carried out in 1997, a database of community heating schemes in social housing in 2000, and a Community Heating Sales Survey undertaken in early 2003. The estimates from these sources have been used to derive heat sold figures since 1999. When information about where the heat was generated was not available from the BRE sources, it was assumed that domestic sector heat consumption was provided by the commercial sector, public sector heat consumption was provided by the public administration and industrial sectors (using proportions derived from CHP statistics) and that industrial sector heat consumption was provided by the industrial sector. The introduction of heat sold into the energy balances has not affected the individual fuel totals, since the energy used to generate the heat has been deducted from the final consumption section of the energy balance and transferred to the transformation section. The figures that are included in the balances should be treated as indicative of the amount of heat sold.

Valuation of energy purchases (Tables 1.4, 1.5, 1.6, 1.1.6)

1.34 In common with the rest of the chapter, these tables covering energy expenditure follow a balance format. Whilst a user may derive data on a similar basis as that previously published, the balance table allows for more varied use and interpretation of traded energy value data. That said the table continues to only show values for energy that has to be purchased and therefore does not include estimated values of a sector's internal consumption, such as coal used in the process of coal extraction.

The balance

1.35 The table balances around **market value of inland consumption** with the lower half of the table showing the total value of consumption by end users, sub divided into energy sector users and final users both for energy and non energy use. The top half of the table shows the supply components that go to make up the final market value of inland consumption, namely upstream cost of production, imports, taxes and the margins and costs of delivering and packaging the fuel for the final consumer. The total final consumers value of energy consumption is represented by the lines 'total non energy sector use' and iron and steel sectors purchases of coal for use in solid fuel manufacture.

Fuel definitions in value balances

1.36 **Crude oil** includes NGLs and refinery feedstocks. **Natural gas** does not include colliery methane. **Electricity** only includes electricity delivered via the public distribution system and therefore does not value electricity produced and consumed by autogenerators, but the input fuels are included in transformation. **Manufactured solid fuels** includes coke, breeze and other solid manufactured fuels, mainly products from patent fuel and carbonisation plants. **Other fuels** includes all other fuels not listed, where they can be clearly considered as traded and some reasonable valuation can be made. Fuels mainly contributing to this year's values are wood, coke oven and colliery methane gases sold on to other industrial users and some use of waste products such as poultry litter.

Valuation

1.37 All figures are estimates and have been rounded to the nearest £5 million.

Energy end use

1.38 Values represent the cost to the final user including transportation of the fuel. They are derived, except where actual values are available, from the traded element of the volumes presented in aggregate energy balance and end user prices collected from information supplied by users or energy suppliers. The **energy sector** consists of those industries engaged in the production and sale of energy products, but values are not given for consumption of self generated fuels e.g. coke oven gas used by coke producers. Many of the processes in the **iron and steel** industry are considered to be part of the energy sector in the energy balances, but for the purposes of this economic balance their genuine purchases are treated as those of final consumers, except for purchases of coal directly used in coke manufacture, which is shown separately as part of manufacture of solid fuel. Coal used directly in or to heat blast furnaces is shown as iron and steel final use. **Transformation** are those fuels used directly in producing other fuels e.g. crude oil in petroleum products. **Electricity generators** keep and use significant stocks of coal and the stocks used in consumption each year are shown separately. The value and margins for these being assumed to be the same as other coal purchased in the year. **Road transport** includes all motor spirit and DERV use. **Commercial and other users** includes public administration and miscellaneous uses not classified to the industrial sector.

Supply

1.39 The supply side money chain is derived using various methods. **Indigenous production** represents the estimated basic value of in year sales by the upstream producers. This value is gross of any taxes or cost they must meet. The valuation problems in attributing network losses in gas and electricity between upstream and downstream within this value chain, means any costs borne are included in the production value. **Imports and exports** are valued in accordance with Annex G (which can be found on the internet). However crude oil is treated differently where the value is formed from price data taken from a census survey of refiners and volume data taken from Tables 3.1 to 3.3. These values are considered to reflect the complete money chain more accurately than Tables G.1 to G.4. **Stock changes** are those for undistributed stocks except for coal where coke oven and generators stocks are included. A stock increase takes money out of the money chain and is therefore represented as a negative. **Distribution costs** are arrived at by removing an estimate of producers value along with any taxes from the end user values shown. For most fuel the estimate of producer value is derived from the consumption used for end use and the producer price taken from survey of producers. For electricity the Pool Purchase Price is used to value public distribution supply. No sector breakdown is given for gas and electricity margins because it is not possible to accurately measure delivery costs for each sector. **Taxes** include VAT where not refundable and duties paid on downstream sales. Excluded are the gas and fossil fuel levies, petroleum revenue tax and production royalties and licence fees. The proceeds from the fossil fuel levy are redistributed across the electricity industry, whilst the rest are treated as part of the production costs.

Sales of electricity and gas by sector (Table 1.7)

1.40 This table provides data on the total value of gas and electricity sold to final consumers. The data are collected from the energy supply companies. The data are useful in indicating relative total expenditure between sectors, but the quality of data provided in terms of industrial classification has been worsening in recent years.

II Energy balances (Tables 1.1, 1.2 and 1.3)

1.41 Tables 1.1, 1.2 and 1.3 show the energy flows as the primary fuels are processed (or used) and as the consequent secondary fuels are used. The net inputs to transformation are shown in the transformation rows and hence outputs from transformation processes into which primary fuels are input (such as electricity generation, heat generation or petroleum refining) appear as positive figures under the secondary product's heading in the tables. Similarly the net inputs are shown as negative figures under the primary fuel headings.

1.42 Readers should note that the energy and commodity balances presentation changed from the 1999 edition of the Digest following the consultation undertaken on the 1998 edition. Annex A explains in detail the principles behind the presentation.

1.43 The amount of heat sold in the UK was included in the energy balances from 1999. As discussed in paragraph 1.33 above, there are two main sources of heat data in the UK: from CHP plants and from district heating (community heating schemes).

III Measurement of energy consumption
Primary fuel input basis

1.44 Energy consumption is usually measured in one of three different ways. The first, known as the primary fuel input basis, assesses the total input of primary fuels and their equivalents. This measure includes energy used or lost in the conversion of primary fuels to secondary fuels (for example in power stations and oil refineries), energy lost in the distribution of fuels (for example in transmission lines) and energy conversion losses by final users. Primary demands as in Table 1.1, 1.2 and 1.3 are on this basis.

Final consumption - energy supplied basis

1.45 The second method, known as the energy supplied basis, measures the energy content of the fuels, both primary and secondary, supplied to final users. Thus it is net of fuel industry own use and conversion, transmission and distribution losses, but it includes conversion losses by final users. Table 1B presents shares of final consumption on this basis. The final consumption figures are presented on this basis throughout Chapter 1.

1.46 Although this is the usual and most direct way to measure final energy consumption, it is also possible to present final consumption on a primary fuel input basis. This can be done by allocating the conversion losses, distribution losses and energy industry use to final users. This approach can be used to compare the total primary fuel use which each sector of the economy accounts for. Table 1C presents shares of final consumption on this basis.

Final consumption - useful energy basis

1.47 Thirdly, final consumption may be expressed in the form of useful energy available after deduction of the losses incurred when final users convert energy supplied into space or process heat, motive power or light. Such losses depend on the type and quality of fuel and the equipment used and on the purpose, conditions, duration and intensity of use. Statistics on useful energy are not sufficiently reliable to be given in this Digest; there is a lack of data on utilisation efficiencies and on the purposes for which fuels are used.

Shares of each fuel in energy supply and demand

1.48 The relative importance of the energy consumption of each sector of the economy depends on the method used to measure consumption. Shares of final consumption on an energy supplied basis (that is in terms of the primary and secondary fuels directly consumed) in 2002 are presented in Table 1B. For comparison, Table 1C presents shares of final consumption on a primary fuel input basis.

Table 1B: Primary and secondary fuels consumed by final users in 2002 - energy supplied basis

	Percentage of each fuel						Percentage of each sector				
	Industry	Transport	Domestic	Others	Total		Solid fuels	Petrol-eum	Gas	Secondary electricity	Total
Solid fuels	51	-	48	2	100	Industry	6	20	45	29	100
Petroleum	10	82	5	3	100	Transport	-	99	-	1	100
Gas	27	-	58	16	100	Domestic	4	8	68	20	100
Secondary electricity	34	3	33	30	100	Others	-	9	45	44	100
All fuels	21	35	31	13	100	All users	2	43	36	18	100

Table 1C: Total primary fuel consumption by final users in 2002 - primary input basis

	Percentage of each fuel						Percentage of each sector				
	Industry	Transport	Domestic	Others	Total		Coal	Petrol-eum	Gas	Primary electricity	Total
Coal	36	2	35	27	100	Industry	24	14	49	14	100
Petroleum	10	81	6	3	100	Transport	1	96	1	1	100
Gas	29	1	50	21	100	Domestic	18	6	65	11	100
Primary electricity	34	3	33	30	100	Others	26	6	50	18	100
All fuels	24	27	31	17	100	All users	16	33	41	10	100

1.49 In 2002, every 1 toe of secondary electricity consumed by final users required, on average, 0.9 toe of coal, 0.9 toe of natural gas, 0.6 toe of primary electricity (nuclear, natural flow hydro and imports) and 0.1 toe of oil and renewables combined. The extent of this primary consumption is hidden in Table 1B, which presents final consumption only in terms of the fuels directly consumed. When all such primary consumption is allocated to final users, as in Table 1C, the relative importance of fuels and sectors changes; the transport sector, which uses very little electricity, declines in importance, whilst the true cost of final consumption in terms of coal use can now be seen.

1.50 Another view comes from shares of users' expenditure on each fuel (Table 1D based on Table 1.4). In this case the importance of fuels which require most handling by the user (solids and liquid fuels) is slightly understated, and the importance of uses taxed at higher rates (transport) is overstated in the All users line.

Table 1D: Value of fuels purchased by final users in 2002

					Percentage of each sector	
	Solid fuels	Petroleum	Gas	Secondary electricity	Heat	Total
Industry	2	19	24	51	4	100
Transport	-	99	-	1	-	100
Domestic	3	5	41	51	-	100
Others	-	7	19	71	3	100
All users	1	61	14	23	1	100

Systems of measurement - international statistics

1.51 The systems of energy measurement used in various international statistics differ from the methods of the Digest as follows:

Net calorific values

1.52 Calorific values (thermal contents) used internationally are net rather than gross. The difference between the net and gross thermal content is the amount of energy necessary to evaporate the water present in the fuel or formed during the combustion process. The differences between gross and net values are taken to be 5 per cent for liquid and solid fuels (except for coke and coke breeze where there is no difference), 10 per cent for gases (except for blast furnace gas, 1 per cent), 15 per cent for straw, and 16 per cent for poultry litter. The calorific value of wood is highly dependent on its moisture content. In Annex A the gross calorific value is given as 10 GJ per tonne at 50 per cent moisture content and this rises to 14.5 GJ at 25 per cent moisture content and 19 GJ for dry wood (equivalent to a net calorific value).

IV Definitions of fuels

1.53 The following paragraphs explain what is covered under the terms "primary" and "secondary" fuels.

Primary fuels

Coal - Production comprises all grades of coal, including slurry.

Primary oils - This includes crude oil, natural gas liquids (NGLs) and feedstock.

Natural gas liquids - Natural gas liquids (NGLs) consist of condensates (C_5 or heavier) and petroleum gases other than methane C_1, that is ethane C_2, propane C_3 and butane C_4, obtained from the onshore processing of associated and non-associated gas. These are treated as primary fuels when looking at primary supply but in the consumption data presented in this chapter these fuels are treated as secondary fuels, being transferred from the primary oils column in Tables 1.1, 1.2 and 1.3.

Natural gas - Production relates to associated or non-associated methane C_1 from land and the United Kingdom sector of the Continental Shelf. It includes that used for drilling production and pumping operations, but excludes gas flared or re-injected. It also includes colliery methane piped to the surface and consumed by collieries or others.

Nuclear electricity - Electricity generated by nuclear power stations belonging to the major power producers. See Chapter 5, paragraphs 5.46 and 5.47.

Natural flow hydro-electricity - Electricity generated by public supply and industrial natural flow hydroelectric power stations. Pumped storage stations are not included (see under secondary electricity below).

Renewable energy sources - In this chapter figures are presented for renewables and waste in total. Further details, including a detailed breakdown of the commodities covered are in Chapter 7.

Secondary fuels

Manufactured fuel - This heading includes manufactured solid fuels such as coke and breeze, other manufactured solid fuels, liquids such as benzole and tars and gases such as coke oven gas and blast furnace gas. Further details are given in Chapter 2, Tables 2.4, 2.5 and 2.6.

Coke and breeze - Coke oven coke and hard coke breeze (Chapter 2, Tables 2.4, 2.5 and 2.6).

Other manufactured solid fuels – Manufactured solid fuels produced at low temperature carbonisation plants and other manufactured fuel and briquetting plants (Chapter 2, Tables 2.4, 2.5 and 2.6).

Coke oven gas - Gas produced at coke ovens, excluding low temperature carbonisation plants. Gas bled or burnt to waste is included in production and losses (Chapter 2, Tables 2.4, 2.5 and 2.6).

Blast furnace gas - Blast furnace gas is mainly produced and consumed within the iron and steel industry (Chapter 2, Tables 2.4, 2.5 and 2.6).

Petroleum products - Petroleum products produced mainly at refineries, together with inland deliveries of natural gas liquids.

Secondary electricity - Secondary electricity is that generated by the combustion of another fuel, usually coal, natural gas or oil. The figure for outputs from transformation in the electricity column of

Tables 1.1, 1.2 and 1.3 is the total of primary and secondary electricity, and the subsequent analysis of consumption is based on this total.

Heat sold – Heat sold is heat that is produced and sold under the provision of a contract.

V Classification of consumers

1.54 The Digest has been prepared, as far as is practicable, on the basis of the *Standard Industrial Classification (SIC) 1992* (The Stationery Office 1991) since 1995. However, not all consumption/disposals data are on this basis, and where they are, there are sometimes constraints on the detail available. Between 1986 and 1994 data in the Digest were prepared on the basis of the previous classification, SIC 1980. The exceptions are Chapter 2, Tables 2.8 in the Digest and Chapter 3, long term trends, Table 3.1.1 (available on DTI's energy statistics web site www.dti.gov.uk/energy/inform/energy_stats/oil/ and the corresponding tables in previous editions which have been prepared largely on the basis of SIC 1968. The main differences between the 1968 SIC (which was used as the basis for most data published for years prior to 1984) and the 1980 SIC were described in the 1986 and 1987 issues of the Digest. The differences between SIC 1980 and SIC 1992 are relatively minor. At the time of the change from the 1980 SIC to the 1992 SIC the main difference was that under the former showrooms belonging to the fuel supply industries were classified to the energy sector, whilst in the latter they are in the commercial sector. Since privatisation few gas, coal and electricity companies have retained showrooms and the difference is therefore minimal.

1.55 Table 1E shows the categories of consumers together with their codes in SIC 1992. The coverage varies between tables (e.g. in some instances the 'other' category is split into major constituents, whereas elsewhere it may include transport). This is because the coverage is dictated by what data suppliers can provide. The table also shows the disaggregation available within industry. This disaggregation forms the basis of virtually all the tables that show a disaggregated industrial breakdown. There are a few notable exceptions that are detailed in paragraph 1.54.

Table 1E: SIC 1992 classifications

Fuel producers	10-12, 23, 40
Final consumers:	
Industrial	
Unclassified	See paragraph 1.56 below
Iron and steel	27, *excluding* 27.4, 27.53, 27.54
Non-ferrous metals	27.4, 27.53, 27.54
Mineral products	14, 26
Chemicals	24
Mechanical engineering and metal products	28, 29
Electrical and instrument engineering	30-33
Vehicles	34, 35
Food, beverages & tobacco	15, 16
Textiles, clothing, leather, & footwear	17-19
Paper, printing & publishing	21, 22
Other industries	13, 20, 25, 36, 37, 41
Construction	45
Transport	60-63
Other final users	
Domestic	Not covered by SIC 1992.
Public administration	75, 80, 85
Commercial	50-52, 55, 64-67, 70-74
Agriculture	01, 02, 05
Miscellaneous	90-93, 99

1.56 There is also an 'unclassified' category in the industry sector (see Table 1E). Wherever the data supplier is unable to allocate an amount between categories, but the Department of Trade and Industry has additional information, not readily available to readers, with which to allocate between categories, then this has been done. Where such additional information is not available the data are included in the 'unclassified' category, enabling the reader to decide whether to accept a residual, pro-rate, or otherwise adjust the figures. The 'miscellaneous' category also contains some unallocated figures for the services sector.

1.57 In Tables 6.8 and 6.9 of Chapter 6 the following abbreviated grouping of industries, based on SIC 1992, is used in order to prevent disclosure of information about individual companies:

Table 1F: Abbreviated grouping of Industry

Iron and steel and non-ferrous metal	27
Chemicals	24
Oil refineries	23.2
Paper, printing and publishing	21, 22
Food, beverages and tobacco	15, 16
Metal products, machinery and equipment	28, 29, 30, 31, 32, 34, 35
Mineral products, extraction, mining and agglomeration of solid fuels	10, 11, 14, 26
Sewage Treatment	(parts of 41 and 90)
Electricity supply	40.1
Other industrial branches	12, 13, 17, 18, 19, 20, 23.1, 23.3, 25, 33, 36, 37, 40.2, 41 (remainder) 45
Transport, commerce, and administration	1, 2, 5, 50 to 99 (except 90 and 92)
Other	40.3, 90 (remainder), 92

1.58 In Tables 1.8 and 1.9 the list above is further condensed and includes only manufacturing industry and construction as follows:

Table 1G: Abbreviated grouping of Industry for Tables 1.8 and 1.9

Iron and steel and non-ferrous metals	27
Chemicals	24
Paper, printing and publishing	21, 22
Food, beverages and tobacco	15, 16
Metal products, machinery and equipment	28, 29, 30, 31, 32, 34, 35
Other (including construction)	12, 13, 14, 17, 18, 19, 20, 23.1, 23.3, 25, 26, 33, 36, 37, 45

VI Monthly and quarterly data

1.59 Monthly and quarterly data on energy production and consumption (including on a seasonally adjusted and temperature corrected basis) split by fuel type are provided on the DTI website at www.dti.gov.uk/energy/inform/energy_stats/. Quarterly figures are also published in the DTI's quarterly statistical bulletin *Energy Trends and Quarterly Energy Prices*. See Annex C for more information about these bulletins.

Contact: *Julian Prime (Statistician)*   *Sara Atkins*
             julian.prime@dti.gsi.gov.uk   *Energy Prices*
             020-7215 6178   *sara.atkins@dti.gsi.gov.uk*
                                                020-7215 6532

             Chris Michaels
             chris.michaels@dti.gsi.gov.uk
             020-7215 2710

1.1 Aggregate energy balance 2002

Thousand tonnes of oil equivalent

	Coal	Manu-factured fuels (1)	Primary oils	Petroleum products	Natural gas (2)	Renewable & waste (3)	Primary electricity	Elect-ricity	Heat sold	Total
Supply										
Indigenous production	18,808	-	127,038	-	103,621	2,681	20,663	-	-	272,811
Imports	18,829	181	61,850	14,832	5,201	-	-	790	-	101,682
Exports	-394	-272	-94,896	-24,744	-12,961	-	-	-66	-	-133,334
Marine bunkers	-	-	-	-2,626	-	-	-	-	-	-2,626
Stock change (4)	+279	+190	+159	+1,366	-633	-	-	-	-	+1,362
Primary supply	**37,521**	**99**	**94,151**	**-11,171**	**95,229**	**2,681**	**20,663**	**724**	**-**	**239,897**
Statistical difference (5)	**-131**	**-33**	**-435**	**-219**	**+169**	**-**	**-**	**+79**	**-**	**-569**
Primary demand	**37,652**	**132**	**94,585**	**-10,952**	**95,060**	**2,681**	**20,663**	**644**	**-**	**240,466**
Transfers	-	-102	-1,308	+1,335	-9	-	-519	+519	-	-83
Transformation	**-35,347**	**2,386**	**-93,277**	**91,344**	**-29,749**	**-2,035**	**-20,144**	**32,541**	**1,888**	**-52,394**
Electricity generation	-29,681	-592	-	-731	-28,059	-1,964	-20,144	32,541	-	-48,630
Major power producers	-28,721	-	-	-120	-25,044	-718	-20,144	29,891	-	-44,856
Autogenerators	-959	-592	-	-611	-3,015	-1,247	-	2,650	-	-3,774
Heat generation	-472	-169	-	-254	-1,690	-71	-	-	1,888	-768
Petroleum refineries	-	-	-93,277	92,460	-	-	-	-	-	-817
Coke manufacture	-4,336	4,193	-	-	-	-	-	-	-	-144
Blast furnaces	-542	-1,362	-	-131	-	-	-	-	-	-2,035
Patent fuel manufacture	-316	316	-	-	-	-	-	-	-	-
Other	-	-	-	-	-	-	-	-	-	-
Energy industry use	**6**	**829**	**-**	**5,265**	**7,832**	**-**	**-**	**2,513**	**6**	**16,451**
Electricity generation	-	-	-	-	-	-	-	1,493	6	1,498
Oil and gas extraction	-	-	-	-	6,818	-	-	46	-	6,865
Petroleum refineries	-	-	-	5,140	279	-	-	564	-	5,982
Coal extraction	6	-	-	-	17	-	-	105	-	128
Coke manufacture	-	411	-	-	-	-	-	-	-	411
Blast furnaces	-	399	-	125	19	-	-	70	-	613
Patent fuel manufacture	-	20	-	-	-	-	-	-	-	20
Pumped storage	-	-	-	-	-	-	-	70	-	70
Other	-	-	-	-	699	-	-	165	-	864
Losses	**-**	**89**	**-**	**-**	**831**	**-**	**-**	**2,578**	**-**	**3,498**
Final consumption	**2,299**	**1,497**	**-**	**76,462**	**56,639**	**646**	**-**	**28,614**	**1,883**	**168,040**
Industry	**859**	**1,083**	**-**	**6,686**	**15,186**	**214**	**-**	**9,609**	**1,120**	**34,757**
Unclassified	-	191	-	1,955	8	214	-	-	-	2,368
Iron and steel	-	849	-	120	1,680	-	-	546	-	3,195
Non-ferrous metals	87	42	-	85	425	-	-	542	-	1,181
Mineral products	323	-	-	264	1,087	-	-	602	5	2,280
Chemicals	166	-	-	329	4,104	-	-	1,916	1,107	7,623
Mechanical engineering etc.	10	-	-	280	719	-	-	739	-	1,748
Electrical engineering etc.	3	-	-	54	357	-	-	497	-	911
Vehicles	37	-	-	203	924	-	-	462	-	1,625
Food, beverages, etc.	136	-	-	329	2,339	-	-	1,048	-	3,852
Textiles, leather, etc.	14	-	-	191	633	-	-	294	8	1,140
Paper, printing etc.	52	-	-	115	1,251	-	-	1,010	-	2,429
Other industries	31	-	-	2,286	1,413	-	-	1,815	-	5,546
Construction	-	-	-	476	245	-	-	139	-	860
Transport	**-**	**-**	**-**	**53,819**	**-**	**-**	**-**	**729**	**-**	**54,549**
Air	-	-	-	11,252	-	-	-	-	-	11,252
Rail	-	-	-	377	-	-	-	-	-	377
Road	-	-	-	41,495	-	-	-	-	-	41,495
National navigation	-	-	-	695	-	-	-	-	-	695
Pipelines	-	-	-	-	-	-	-	-	-	-
Other	**1,439**	**414**	**-**	**5,451**	**41,069**	**432**	**-**	**18,276**	**763**	**67,845**
Domestic	1,394	414	-	3,618	32,358	243	-	9,848	12	47,887
Public administration	36	-	-	769	3,759	97	-	1,796	752	7,208
Commercial	-	-	-	399	3,073	-	-	6,274	-	9,746
Agriculture	4	-	-	563	130	72	-	358	-	1,126
Miscellaneous	6	-	-	103	1,749	20	-	-	-	1,877
Non energy use	**-**	**-**	**-**	**10,506**	**384**	**-**	**-**	**-**	**-**	**10,890**

(1) Includes all manufactured solid fuels, benzole, tars, coke oven gas and blast furnace gas.
(2) Includes colliery methane.
(3) Includes geothermal and solar heat.
(4) Stock fall (+), stock rise (-).
(5) Primary supply minus primary demand.

1.2 Aggregate energy balance 2001

Thousand tonnes of oil equivalent

	Coal	Manu-factured fuels (1)	Primary oils	Petroleum products	Natural gas (2)	Renewable & waste (3)	Primary electricity	Elect-ricity	Heat sold	Total
Supply										
Indigenous production	19,968r	-	127,828r	-	105,840r	2,542r	21,227r	-	-	277,405r
Imports	23,431r	111	58,425	18,541r	2,619	-	-	917	-	104,044r
Exports	-412r	-268	-95,035r	-20,633r	-11,894r	-	-	-23	-	-128,264r
Marine bunkers	-	-	-	-2,433r	-	-	-	-	-	-2,433r
Stock change (4)	-1,868r	+115	-666r	-665r	-57	-	-	-	-	-3,141r
Primary supply	**41,119r**	**-42r**	**90,553r**	**-5,190r**	**96,508r**	**2,542r**	**21,227r**	**894**	**-**	**247,611r**
Statistical difference (5)	-88r	-55r	+115r	+299	+229r	-	-	+93r	-	+594r
Primary demand	**41,207r**	**13**	**90,437r**	**-5,489r**	**96,280r**	**2,542r**	**21,227r**	**801r**	**-**	**247,018r**
Transfers	-	-112r	+605r	-480r	-6	-	-432	+432	-	+8r
Transformation	**-38,198r**	**2,878r**	**-91,042r**	**87,971r**	**-28,609r**	**-1,911r**	**-20,795r**	**32,462r**	**2,330r**	**-54,916r**
Electricity generation	-31,435r	-600r	-	-1,023r	-26,639r	-1,840r	-20,795r	32,462r	-	-49,871r
Major power producers	-30,442r	-	-	-363r	-23,797r	-253r	-20,795r	29,873r	-	-45,778r
Autogenerators	-993r	-600r	-	-660r	-2,841r	-1,587r	-	2,589r	-	-4,093r
Heat generation	-469r	-209r	-	-698	-1,971r	-71	-	-	2,330r	-1,088r
Petroleum refineries	-	-	-91,042r	89,824r	-	-	-	-	-	-1,218r
Coke manufacture	-5,372r	5,058	-	-	-	-	-	-	-	-313r
Blast furnaces	-575r	-1,727	-	-132r	-	-	-	-	-	-2,434r
Patent fuel manufacture	-348r	356r	-	-	-	-	-	-	-	8
Other	-	-	-	-	-	-	-	-	-	-
Energy industry use	**7**	**957**	**-**	**5,416r**	**7,864r**	**-**	**-**	**2,405r**	**3r**	**16,651r**
Electricity generation	-	-	-	-	-	-	-	1,491r	3r	1,494r
Oil and gas extraction	-	-	-	-	6,746r	-	-	58	-	6,804r
Petroleum refineries	-	-	-	5,276r	360	-	-	450r	-	6,087r
Coal extraction	7	-	-	-	18	-	-	105	-	130
Coke manufacture	-	462	-	-	1	-	-	-	-	462
Blast furnaces	-	464	-	139	32	-	-	76	-	711
Patent fuel manufacture	-	32	-	-	-	-	-	-	-	32
Pumped storage	-	-	-	-	-	-	-	73	-	73
Other	-	-	-	-	706	-	-	152r	-	858r
Losses	**-**	**103**	**-**	**-**	**839r**	**-**	**-**	**2,657**	**-**	**3,599r**
Final consumption	**3,001r**	**1,719r**	**-**	**76,586r**	**58,962r**	**631**	**-**	**28,632r**	**2,327r**	**171,860r**
Industry	**1,130r**	**1,343r**	**-**	**6,628r**	**15,726r**	**214**	**-**	**9,605r**	**1,001r**	**35,647r**
Unclassified	-	240r	-	2,137r	9	214	-	-	-	2,600r
Iron and steel	1	1,014r	-	105r	1,803	-	-	725r	-	3,648r
Non-ferrous metals	131r	89	-	79	449r	-	-	617r	-	1,364r
Mineral products	325r	-	-	291r	1,186r	-	-	618r	2	2,422r
Chemicals	264r	-	-	335r	4,171r	-	-	1,791r	988r	7,549r
Mechanical engineering etc.	10	-	-	244r	738r	-	-	707r	-	1,700r
Electrical engineering etc.	3	-	-	51r	380r	-	-	470r	-	903r
Vehicles	48	-	-	175	959r	-	-	479r	-	1,662r
Food, beverages, etc.	152r	-	-	276	2,359r	-	-	956r	-	3,744r
Textiles, leather, etc.	34r	-	-	216r	642r	-	-	276r	10	1,178r
Paper, printing etc.	115r	-	-	83r	1,351r	-	-	964r	-	2,514r
Other industries	46r	-	-	2,121r	1,426r	-	-	1,868r	-	5,461r
Construction	-	-	-	514r	253r	-	-	134r	-	901r
Transport	**-**	**-**	**-**	**54,196r**	**-**	**-**	**-**	**760**	**-**	**54,955r**
Air	-	-	-	11,424	-	-	-	-	-	11,424
Rail	-	-	-	451r	-	-	-	-	-	451r
Road	-	-	-	41,479r	-	-	-	-	-	41,479r
National navigation	-	-	-	841r	-	-	-	-	-	841r
Pipelines	-	-	-	-	-	-	-	-	-	-
Other	**1,872r**	**376r**	**-**	**6,067r**	**42,300r**	**417**	**-**	**18,268r**	**1,326**	**70,626r**
Domestic	1,821r	376r	-	3,553r	32,602	241	-	9,917	32	48,542r
Public administration	41r	-	-	777r	3,966r	93	-	1,775r	1,287	7,938r
Commercial	-	-	-	948r	3,184	-	-	6,192r	-	10,324r
Agriculture	3	-	-	658r	140r	72	-	383r	7	1,263r
Miscellaneous	7	-	-	132r	2,409r	11	-	-	-	2,559r
Non energy use	**-**	**-**	**-**	**9,695r**	**936r**	**-**	**-**	**-**	**-**	**10,631r**

(1) Includes all manufactured solid fuels, benzole, tars, coke oven gas and blast furnace gas.
(2) Includes colliery methane.
(3) Includes geothermal and solar heat.
(4) Stock fall (+), stock rise (-).
(5) Primary supply minus primary demand.

1.3 Aggregate energy balance 2000

Thousand tonnes of oil equivalent

	Coal	Manu-factured fuels (1)	Primary oils	Petroleum products	Natural gas (2)	Renewable & waste (3)	Primary electricity	Elect-ricity	Heat sold	Total
Supply										
Indigenous production	19,553	-	138,282	-	108,395r	2,312r	20,153	-	-	288,695r
Imports	15,732r	346r	59,341r	15,471	2,238	-	-	1,230	-	94,359
Exports	-497r	-316r	-101,585	-22,338	-12,583	-	-	-12	-	-137,331r
Marine bunkers	-	-	-	-2,207	-	-	-	-	-	-2,207
Stock change (4)	+3,080	-112r	+1,196	-389	-952r	-	-	-	-	+2,823r
Primary supply	**37,867r**	**-82r**	**97,235r**	**-9,464**	**97,099r**	**2,312r**	**20,153**	**1,219**	**-**	**246,338r**
Statistical difference (5)	-74r	-207	+542r	+46r	+289r	-	-	+128r	-	+725r
Primary demand	**37,941r**	**125r**	**96,693**	**-9,510r**	**96,810r**	**2,312r**	**20,153**	**1,090r**	**-**	**245,614r**
Transfers	-	-61r	-196r	+307	-38r	-	-519	+519	-	+13
Transformation	**-35,922r**	**2,996r**	**-96,140r**	**92,341r**	**-30,048r**	**-1,690r**	**-19,634**	**31,674r**	**2,515**	**-53,908r**
Electricity generation	-28,626r	-899	-	-1,049r	-27,907r	-1,585r	-19,634	31,674r	-	-48,027r
Major power producers	-27,748	-	-	-392r	-24,401	-251r	-19,634	28,786r	-	-43,640r
Autogenerators	-878r	-899	-	-657r	-3,506r	-1,334r	-	2,888r	-	-4,386r
Heat generation	-443r	-209r	-	-733r	-2,140r	-105	-	-	2,515	-1,115r
Petroleum refineries	-	-	-96,140r	94,323	-	-	-	-	-	-1,817r
Coke manufacture	-6,131	5,686r	-	-	-	-	-	-	-	-446r
Blast furnaces	-340	-1,977r	-	-200	-	-	-	-	-	-2,517r
Patent fuel manufacture	-382r	395	-	-	-	-	-	-	-	13
Other	-	-	-	-	-	-	-	-	-	-
Energy industry use	**9r**	**1,134r**	**357**	**5,411r**	**6,702r**	**-**	**-**	**2,408r**	**-**	**16,020r**
Electricity generation	-	-	-	-	-	-	-	1,404	-	1,404
Oil and gas extraction	-	-	357	-	5,637r	-	-	45	-	6,039r
Petroleum refineries	-	-	-	5,246r	313	-	-	547	-	6,106r
Coal extraction	9r	-	-	-	19	-	-	110	-	138
Coke manufacture	-	569r	-	-	1	-	-	-	-	570r
Blast furnaces	-	531r	-	118	61	-	-	75	-	785r
Patent fuel manufacture	-	35	-	-	-	-	-	-	-	35
Pumped storage	-	-	-	-	-	-	-	69	-	69
Other	-	-	-	47	670r	-	-	157	-	874r
Losses	**-**	**165r**	**-**	**-**	**1,761r**	**-**	**-**	**2,549**	**-**	**4,475r**
Final consumption	**2,010r**	**1,762r**	**-**	**77,727r**	**58,261r**	**622**	**-**	**28,325r**	**2,515**	**171,223r**
Industry	**485r**	**1,294r**	**-**	**6,077r**	**15,773r**	**213**	**-**	**9,812r**	**1,099**	**34,754r**
Unclassified	-	248r	-	2,399r	10	213	-	-	-	2,870r
Iron and steel	1	932r	-	150r	1,939r	-	-	794r	-	3,816r
Non-ferrous metals	49r	114	-	41	470r	-	-	516r	-	1,190r
Mineral products	130r	-	-	261	1,195r	-	-	676r	2	2,263r
Chemicals	57r	-	-	217r	4,003r	-	-	1,998r	1,087	7,363r
Mechanical engineering etc.	6	-	-	199r	840r	-	-	782r	-	1,828r
Electrical engineering etc.	2r	-	-	36	404r	-	-	515r	-	956r
Vehicles	30r	-	-	136	931r	-	-	524r	-	1,620r
Food, beverages, etc.	77r	-	-	224r	2,372r	-	-	974r	-	3,647r
Textiles, leather, etc.	25r	-	-	149	667r	-	-	298r	10	1,150r
Paper, printing etc.	37r	-	-	45	1,383r	-	-	958r	-	2,423r
Other industries	71r	-	-	1,754	1,303r	-	-	1,640r	-	4,768r
Construction	-	-	-	467	256r	-	-	136	-	859r
Transport	**-**	**-**	**-**	**55,058r**	**-**	**-**	**-**	**741r**	**-**	**55,800r**
Air	-	-	-	11,978	-	-	-	-	-	11,978
Rail	-	-	-	477r	-	-	-	-	-	477r
Road	-	-	-	41,567	-	-	-	-	-	41,567
National navigation	-	-	-	1,037r	-	-	-	-	-	1,037r
Pipelines	-	-	-	-	-	-	-	-	-	-
Other	**1,525r**	**468**	**-**	**5,532r**	**41,304r**	**409**	**-**	**17,772r**	**1,416**	**68,426r**
Domestic	1,468r	468	-	3,239	31,806	237	-	9,617	44	46,880r
Public administration	47r	-	-	1,042r	3,831r	89	-	1,798r	1,287	8,093r
Commercial	-	-	-	469r	3,114r	-	-	5,982r	-	9,565r
Agriculture	5r	-	-	633r	131r	72	-	375r	-	1,216r
Miscellaneous	6r	-	-	149r	2,422r	12	-	-	84	2,672r
Non energy use	**-**	**-**	**-**	**11,059**	**1,184r**	**-**	**-**	**-**	**-**	**12,243r**

(1) Includes all manufactured solid fuels, benzole, tars, coke oven gas and blast furnace gas.
(2) Includes colliery methane.
(3) Includes geothermal and solar heat.
(4) Stock fall (+), stock rise (-).
(5) Primary supply minus primary demand.

1.4 Value balance of traded energy in 2002[1]

£million

	Coal	Manufactured solid fuels	Crude oil	Petroleum products	Natural gas	Electricity	Heat sold	Other fuels	Total
Supply									
Indigenous production	900	180	14,620	12,830	6,460	7,540	360	50	42,940
Imports	850	20	6,380	3,070	270	190			10,780
Exports	-30	-25	-10,440	-4,120	-865				-15,480
Marine bunkers				-320					-320
Stock change	-10		5	190	-5				180
Basic value of inland consumption	1,710	175	10,565	11,650	5,860	7,725	360	50	38,100
Tax and margins									
Distribution costs and margins	325	25		1,920	4,245	5,995			12,510
Electricity generation	50			5					55
Solid fuel manufacture	5								5
of which iron & steel sector	5								5
Iron & steel final use		5		5					10
Other industry	10	10		240					260
Air transport				45					45
Rail and national navigation				5					5
Road transport				1,185					1,185
Domestic	250	10		85					345
Agriculture				15					15
Commercial and other services				30					35
Non energy use				300	35				335
VAT and duties	15	5		25,910	290	360			26,580
Electricity generation				15					15
Iron & steel final use				10					10
Other industry				185					185
Air transport				20					20
Rail and national navigation				45					45
Road transport				25,525					25,525
Domestic	15	5		40	290	360			710
Agriculture				20					20
Commercial and other services				50					50
Climate Change Levy	5				205	625			835
Total tax and margins	345	30		27,835	4,740	6,980			39,925
Market value of inland consumption	2,055	205	10,565	39,480	10,600	14,705	360	55	78,025
Energy end use									
Total energy sector	1,630		10,565	130	2,070	150		15	14,565
Transformation	1,630		10,565	130	2,000			15	14,345
Electricity generation	1,365			100	1,985			15	3,465
of which from stocks	35								35
Heat Generation	25			30	10				65
Petroleum refineries			10,565						10,565
Solid fuel manufacture	245								245
of which iron & steel sector	210								210
Other energy sector use					70	150			220
Oil & gas extraction						15			15
Petroleum refineries					20	95			115
Coal extraction						40			40
Other energy sector					50				50
Total non energy sector use	420	205		37,845	8,495	14,550	360	40	61,920
Industry	75	85		1,135	1,380	2,995	215	10	5,895
Iron & steel final use	30	55		60	145	120			410
Other industry	45	30		1,075	1,235	2,870	215	10	5,485
Transport				35,710		220			35,930
Air				1,730					1,730
Rail and national navigation				190		220			410
Road				33,790					33,790
Other final users	345	120		995	7,120	11,340	145	30	20,095
Domestic	345	120		645	6,085	7,510		30	14,740
Agriculture				105	20	215			340
Commercial and other services	5			245	1,015	3,615	145		5,020
Total value of energy end use	2,055	205	10,565	37,975	10,565	14,705	360	55	76,485
Value of non energy end use				1,505	35				1,540
Market value of inland consumption	2,055	205	10,565	39,480	10,600	14,705	360	55	78,025

(1) For further information see paragraphs 1.34 to 1.38.

1.5 Value balance of traded energy in 2001[(1)]

£million

	Coal	Manufactured solid fuels	Crude oil	Petroleum products	Natural gas	Electricity	Heat sold	Other fuels	Total
Supply									
Indigenous production	965	190	14,910r	13,215r	6,985r	7,805r	405	55	44,530r
Imports	1,180	10	6,235	3,520r	185r	180r	-	-	11,310r
Exports	-30	-25	-10,840r	-3,755r	-745r	-	-	-	-15,400r
Marine bunkers	-	-	-	-325	-	-	-	-	-325
Stock change	-110r	-	-130	-115r	-	-	-	-	-355r
Basic value of inland consumption	**2,005r**	**180**	**10,175r**	**12,540r**	**6,425r**	**7,980r**	**405**	**55**	**39,765r**
Tax and margins									
Distribution costs and margins	**410r**	**30**	**-**	**1,820r**	**3,755r**	**6,450r**	**-**	**-**	**12,470r**
Electricity generation	85	-	-	5	-	-	-	-	90
Solid fuel manufacture	10	-	-	-	-	-	-	-	10
of which iron & steel sector	5	-	-	-	-	-	-	-	5
Iron & steel final use	-	5	-	5	-	-	-	-	10
Other industry	10	15	-	235r	-	-	-	-	260r
Air transport	-	-	-	125	-	-	-	-	125
Rail and national navigation	-	-	-	15	-	-	-	-	15
Road transport	-	-	-	950	-	-	-	-	950
Domestic	305r	10	-	125r	-	-	-	-	440r
Agriculture	-	-	-	20	-	-	-	-	20
Commercial and other services	-	-	-	60r	-	-	-	-	65
Non energy use	-	-	-	280	90r	-	-	-	370r
VAT and duties	**20**	**5**	**-**	**26,560**	**275**	**360**	**-**	**-**	**27,220**
Electricity generation	-	-	-	20	-	-	-	-	20
Iron & steel final use	-	-	-	10	-	-	-	-	10
Other industry	-	-	-	140	-	-	-	-	140
Air transport	-	-	-	20	-	-	-	-	20
Rail and national navigation	-	-	-	45	-	-	-	-	45
Road transport	-	-	-	26,220	-	360	-	-	26,220
Domestic	20	5	-	40	275	-	-	-	700
Agriculture	-	-	-	15	-	-	-	-	15
Commercial and other services	-	-	-	45	-	-	-	-	45
Climate Change Levy	-	-	-	-	120	400	-	-	520
Total tax and margins	**430r**	**35**	**-**	**28,380r**	**4,150r**	**7,210r**	**-**	**-**	**40,210r**
Market value of inland consumption	**2,435r**	**215**	**10,175r**	**40,920r**	**10,575**	**15,195r**	**405**	**55**	**79,975r**
Energy end use									
Total energy sector	**1,910**	**-**	**10,175r**	**200r**	**2,155r**	**175**	**-**	**15**	**14,630r**
Transformation	**1,910**	**-**	**10,175r**	**20r**	**2,070r**	**-**	**-**	**15**	**14,370r**
Electricity generation	1,595	-	-	120r	2,055r	-	-	15	3,790
of which from stocks	40	-	-	-	-	-	-	-	40
Heat Generation	25	-	-	80	15	-	-	-	120
Petroleum refineries	-	-	10,175r	-	-	-	-	-	10,175r
Solid fuel manufacture	290	-	-	-	-	-	-	-	290
of which iron & steel sector	245	-	-	-	-	-	-	-	245
Other energy sector use	**-**	**-**	**-**	**-**	**80**	**175**	**-**	**-**	**260**
Oil & gas extraction	-	-	-	-	-	25	-	-	25
Petroleum refineries	-	-	-	-	30	110	-	-	140
Coal extraction	-	-	-	-	-	40	-	-	40
Other energy sector	-	-	-	-	55	-	-	-	55
Total non energy sector use	**525r**	**215**	**-**	**39,335r**	**8,335r**	**15,020r**	**405**	**40**	**63,875r**
Industry	**95**	**105**	**-**	**1,200r**	**1,495r**	**3,145r**	**175r**	**15**	**6,225r**
Iron & steel final use	30	65	-	60	165	195r	-	-	515r
Other industry	65	40	-	1,140r	1,325r	2,950r	175r	15	5,710r
Transport	**-**	**-**	**-**	**36,930r**	**-**	**240r**	**-**	**-**	**37,175r**
Air	-	-	-	2,075	-	-	-	-	2,075
Rail and national navigation	-	-	-	240	-	240r	-	-	485r
Road	-	-	-	34,615r	-	-	-	-	34,615r
Other final users	**435r**	**105**	**-**	**1,205**	**6,840r**	**11,630r**	**230**	**30**	**20,475r**
Domestic	430r	105	-	720r	5,735	7,540	5	30	14,565r
Agriculture	-	-	-	130r	20r	225	-	-	375r
Commercial and other services	5	-	-	355r	1,085r	3,865r	225	-	5,535r
Total value of energy end use	**2,435r**	**215**	**10,175r**	**39,535r**	**10,485r**	**15,195r**	**405**	**55**	**78,500r**
Value of non energy end use	**-**	**-**	**-**	**1,385**	**90r**	**-**	**-**	**-**	**1,470r**
Market value of inland consumption	**2,435r**	**215**	**10,175r**	**40,920r**	**10,575**	**15,195r**	**405**	**55**	**79,975r**

(1) For further information see paragraphs 1.34 to 1.38.

31

1.6 Value balance of traded energy in 2000[1]

£million

	Coal	Manufactured solid fuels	Crude oil	Petroleum products	Natural gas	Electricity	Heat Sold	Other fuels	Total
Supply									
Indigenous production	970	205	17,175r	15,570r	5,890r	7,840	440	60r	48,145r
Imports	665	25	6,875	3,250r	135	375	-	-	11,320r
Exports	-30	-30	12,215r	-4,435r	-575	-	-	-	-17,290r
Marine bunkers	-	-	-	-285	-	-	-	-	-285
Stock change	105	5	165	-35	-5	-	-	-	235
Basic value of inland consumption	**1,710**	**205**	**12,000r**	**14,065r**	**5,440r**	**8,215**	**440**	**60r**	**42,125r**
Tax and margins									
Distribution costs and margins	295	35	-	1,910r	3,840r	7,455	-	-	13,540r
Electricity generation	20	-	-	10	-	-	-	-	30r
Solid fuel manufacture	40	-	-	-	-	-	-	-	40
of which iron & steel sector	35	-	-	-	-	-	-	-	35
Iron & steel final use	-	5	-	10r	-	-	-	-	20r
Other industry	5	15	-	240r	-	-	-	-	260r
Air transport	-	-	-	215	-	-	-	-	215
Rail and national navigation	-	-	-	25	-	-	-	-	25
Road transport	-	-	-	875	-	-	-	-	875
Domestic	225	15	-	130	-	-	-	-	365
Agriculture	-	-	-	25	-	-	-	-	25
Commercial and other services	-	-	-	60	-	-	-	-	60
Non energy use	-	-	-	330	85	-	-	-	415r
VAT and duties	**15**	**5**	**-**	**26,675r**	**260**	**355**	**-**	**-**	**27,315r**
Electricity generation	-	-	-	25	-	-	-	-	25
Iron & steel final use	-	-	-	5r	-	-	-	-	5r
Other industry	-	-	-	115	-	-	-	-	115
Air transport	-	-	-	20	-	-	-	-	20
Rail and national navigation	-	-	-	50	-	-	-	-	50
Road transport	-	-	-	26,345	-	-	-	-	26,345
Domestic	15	5	-	40	260	355	-	-	680
Agriculture	-	-	-	20	-	-	-	-	20
Commercial and other services	-	-	-	55	-	-	-	-	55
Total tax and margins	**310**	**40**	**-**	**28,590r**	**4,105r**	**7,810**	**-**	**-**	**40,855r**
Market value of inland consumption	**2,020**	**245**	**12,000r**	**42,650r**	**9,545r**	**16,025**	**440**	**60r**	**82,980r**
Energy end use									
Total energy sector	**1,640**	**-**	**12,000r**	**235r**	**2,015r**	**165**	**-**	**15**	**16,070r**
Transformation	1,640	-	12,000r	230r	1,945r	-	-	15	15,830r
Electricity generation	1,315	-	-	140r	1,930	-	-	10	3,400r
of which from stocks	30r	-	-	-	-	-	-	-	30r
Heat Generation	20	-	-	90	15	-	-	5	125
Petroleum refineries	-	-	12,000r	-	-	-	-	-	12,000r
Solid fuel manufacture	305	-	-	-	-	-	-	-	305
of which iron & steel sector	270	-	-	-	-	-	-	-	270
Other energy sector use	-	-	-	10	70r	165	-	-	240r
Oil & gas extraction	-	-	-	-	-	20	-	-	20
Petroleum refineries	-	-	-	-	20	100	-	-	125
Coal extraction	-	-	-	-	-	45	-	-	45
Other energy sector	-	-	-	10	45r	-	-	-	55r
Total non energy sector use	**375r**	**245**	**-**	**40,740**	**7,445r**	**15,860**	**440**	**45r**	**65,155r**
Industry	40	120	-	1,145	1,115r	3,435r	190	15r	6,065r
Iron & steel final use	15	75	-	70r	135r	125r	-	-	420
Other industry	25	45	-	1,080	980	3,310r	190	15r	5,645r
Transport	-	-	-	38,395	-	285	-	-	38,685
Air	-	-	-	2,485	-	-	-	-	2,485
Rail and national navigation	-	-	-	280	-	285	-	-	565
Road	-	-	-	35,635	-	-	-	-	35,635
Other final users	**335r**	**130**	**-**	**1,200r**	**6,330r**	**12,135r**	**245**	**30**	**20,405r**
Domestic	335r	130	-	735	5,485	7,475	10	30	14,195r
Agriculture	-	-	-	130	15r	230	-	-	370
Commercial and other services	5	-	-	335r	835r	4,435	240	-	5,840r
Total value of energy end use	**2,020**	**245**	**12,000r**	**40,980r**	**9,460r**	**16,025**	**440**	**60r**	**81,225r**
Value of non energy end use	**-**	**-**	**-**	**1,670**	**85r**	**-**	**-**	**-**	**1,755r**
Market value of inland consumption	**2,020**	**245**	**12,000r**	**42,650r**	**9,545r**	**16,025**	**440**	**60r**	**82,980r**

1.7 Sales of electricity and gas by sector

United Kingdom

	1998	1999	2000	2001	2002
Total selling value (£ million)[1]					
Electricity generation - Gas	1,756	1,934	2,005r	2,065r	1,987
Industrial - Gas	1,095	1,131	1,243r	1,749r	1,592
- Electricity	3,699	3,872	3,601r	3,319r	3,146
of which:					
Fuel industries	162	141	166	175	152
Industrial sector	3,537	3,731	3,435r	3,144r	2,994
Domestic sector - Gas	5,225	5,343	5,222	5,460	5,797
- Electricity	7,232	7,240	7,120	7,182	7,154
Other - Gas	906	927	1,004r	1,413r	1,288
- Electricity	5,203	4,995	4,951	4,327	4,046
of which:					
Agricultural sector	230	222	228	227	213
Commercial sector	3,506	3,378	3,433r	3,072r	2,895
Transport sector	301	306	287	242	218
Public lighting	121	110	99	86	75
Public admin. and other services	1,045	979	901r	706r	645
Total, all consumers	**25,116**	**25,442**	**25,146r**	**25,515r**	**25,010**
of which gas	**8,982**	**9,335**	**9,474r**	**10,687r**	**10,664**
of which electricity	**16,134**	**16,107**	**15,672r**	**14,828r**	**14,346**
Average net selling value per kWh sold (pence)[1]					
Electricity generation - Gas	0.656	0.613	0.618r	0.667r	0.609
Industrial - Gas	0.565	0.548	0.583r	0.838	0.819
- Electricity	3.900	3.902	3.530	3.247r	3.096
of which:					
Fuel industries	3.576	3.429	3.524	3.362r	3.194
Industrial sector	3.805	3.923	3.530r	3.241r	3.092
Domestic sector - Gas	1.468	1.492	1.412	1.440	1.540
- Electricity	6.610	6.564	6.366	6.227	6.246
Other - Gas	0.770	0.757	0.805r	1.114	1.146
- Electricity	5.386	5.054	4.912r	4.180	3.903
of which:					
Agricultural sector	5.940	5.788	6.033r	5.537r	5.149
Commercial sector	5.399	5.061	4.935	4.266	3.967
Transport sector	4.430	4.466	4.018r	3.247r	3.085
Public lighting	5.566	5.086	4.985r	4.207r	3.913
Public admin. and other services	5.551	5.092	4.918r	3.945r	3.669
Average, all consumers	**2.028**	**1.939**	**1.867r**	**1.896r**	**1.882**
of which gas	**0.961**	**0.928**	**0.918r**	**1.043r**	**1.057**
of which electricity	**5.316**	**5.223**	**4.981r**	**4.618r**	**4.486**

(1) Excludes VAT where payable - see paragraph 1.40 for a definition of average net selling value.

1.8 Final energy consumption by main industrial groups[(1)]

Thousand tonnes of oil equivalent

	1998	1999	2000	2001	2002
Iron and steel and non-ferrous metals					
Coal	128	216	50r	131r	87
Manufactured solid fuels *(2)*	764	791	751r	710	592
Blast furnace gas	278	139	96r	272r	227
Coke oven gas	375	199	199r	121r	72
Natural gas	2,204	2,336	2,409r	2,252r	2,105
Petroleum	130	105	191r	185r	204
Electricity	1,313	1,348	1,310	1,341r	1,089
Total iron and steel and non-ferrous metals	**5,193**	**5,134**	**5,006r**	**5,012r**	**4,376**
Chemicals					
Coal	444	297	57r	264r	166
Natural gas	3,988	4,023	4,003r	4,171r	4,104
Petroleum	605	168	217r	335r	329
Electricity	1,798	1,864	1,998r	1,791r	1,916
Heat sold	..	1,074	1,087	988r	1,107
Total chemicals	**6,837**	**7,427**	**7,363r**	**7,549r**	**7,623**
Metal products, machinery and equipment					
Coal	54	78r	38r	61	49
Natural gas	2,047	2,126	2,175r	2,077r	2,000
Petroleum	441	357	371r	471r	537
Electricity	1,728	1,758	1,821r	1,656r	1,697
Total metal products, machinery and equipment	**4,270**	**4,319**	**4,405r**	**4,266r**	**4,284**
Food, beverages and tobacco					
Coal	204	151	77r	152r	136
Natural gas	2,345	2,399	2,372r	2,359r	2,339
Petroleum	418	281	224r	276	329
Electricity	1,019	1,077	974r	956r	1,048
Total food, beverages and tobacco	**3,986**	**3,908**	**3,647r**	**3,744r**	**3,852**

(1) Industrial categories used are described in Table 1G. Data from 1999 onwards excludes energy used to generate heat for all fuels except manufactured solid fuels and electricity.

(2) Includes tars, benzole, coke and breeze and other manufactured solid fuels.

1.8 Final energy consumption by main industrial groups[1] (continued)

Thousand tonnes of oil equivalent

	1998	1999	2000	2001	2002
Paper, printing and publishing					
Coal	75	83	37r	115r	52
Natural gas	1,225	1,078	1,383r	1,351r	1,251
Petroleum	125	65	45r	83r	115
Electricity	919	945	958r	964r	1,010
Total paper, printing and publishing	**2,343**	**2,170**	**2,423r**	**2,514r**	**2,429**
Other industries					
Coal	702	551	226r	405r	368
Natural gas	3,316	3,228	3,421r	3,507r	3,379
Petroleum	2,679	2,567	2,631	3,141r	3,217
Electricity	2,438	2,551	2,751r	2,896r	2,849
Heat sold	..	12	12	13	12
Total other industries	**9,135**	**8,909**	**9,040r**	**9,962r**	**9,826**
Unclassified					
Manufactured solid fuels (2)	282	244	231	209	189
Coke oven gas	10	6	17r	31r	3
Natural gas	15	13	10	9	8
Petroleum	1,929	2,328	2,399r	2,137r	1,955
Renewables & waste	461	283	213	214	214
Total unclassified	**2,697**	**2,875**	**2,870r**	**2,600r**	**2,368**
Total					
Coal	1,605	1,375	485r	1,130r	859
Manufactured solid fuels (2)	1,046	1,035	982	919	781
Blast furnace gas	278	139	96r	272r	227
Coke oven gas	385	205	216r	153r	75
Natural gas	15,140	15,203	15,773r	15,726r	15,186
Petroleum	6,328	5,871	6,077r	6,628r	6,686
Renewables & waste	461	283	213	214	214
Electricity	9,216	9,542	9,812r	9,605r	9,609
Heat sold	..	1,086	1,099	1,001r	1,120
Total	**34,459**	**34,741**	**34,754r**	**35,647r**	**34,757**

1.9 Fuels consumed for electricity generation (autogeneration) by main industrial groups[1]

Thousand tonnes of oil equivalent
(except where shown otherwise)

	1998	1999	2000	2001	2002
Iron and steel and non-ferrous metals					
Coal	852	726	703	769r	750
Blast furnace gas	732	729	728r	472r	465
Coke oven gas	162	165	166r	123r	122
Natural gas	52	53	75r	63r	61
Petroleum	57	57	34r	19r	18
Other (including renewables) *(2)*	88	72	58r	55r	57
Total fuel input *(3)*	**1,943**	**1,801**	**1,764**	**1,501r**	**1,472**
Electricity generated by iron & steel and non-ferrous	**536**	**545**	**459**	**504r**	**413**
metals *(4)* *(in GWh)*	6,231	6,338	5,338	5,863	4,802
Electricity consumed by iron and steel and non-ferrous	**387**	**400**	**378**	**412r**	**329**
metals from own generation *(5)* *(in GWh)*	4,504	4,656	4,395	4,795	3,826
Chemicals					
Coal	195	119	71	155	145
Natural gas	974	869	1,079r	771r	623
Petroleum	174	132	56	54r	34
Other (including renewables) *(2)*	351	364	352	291r	325
Total fuel input *(3)*	**1,694**	**1,485**	**1,558r**	**1,271r**	**1,127**
Electricity generated by chemicals *(4)*	**669**	**694**	**940r**	**799r**	**767**
(in GWh)	7,783	8,075	10,931	9,288	8,919
Electricity consumed by chemicals from own generation *(5)*	**551**	**585**	**687**	**552r**	**628**
(in GWh)	6,402	6,803	7,993	6,420	7,300
Metal products, machinery and equipment					
Coal	-	-	-	-	-
Natural gas	21	23	137r	47r	82
Petroleum	8	11	11	7	6
Other (including renewables) *(2)*	-	-	-	-	-
Total fuel input *(3)*	**29**	**34**	**147r**	**55r**	**88**
Electricity generated by metal products, machinery	**13**	**15**	**66r**	**24r**	**38**
and equipment *(4)* *(in GWh)*	150	177	765	274	445
Electricity consumed by metal products, machinery	**12**	**15**	**55r**	**21r**	**20**
and equipment from own generation *(5)* *(in GWh)*	143	169	636	241	235
Food, beverages and tobacco					
Coal	33	31	27r	20r	20
Natural gas	237	368	345r	269r	309
Petroleum	12	10	5	5	4
Other (including renewables) *(2)*	-	-	-	-	-
Total fuel input *(3)*	**281**	**409**	**377r**	**294r**	**333**
Electricity generated by food, beverages and tobacco *(4)*	**120**	**191**	**183r**	**145r**	**166**
(in GWh)	1,397	2,220	2,122	1,680	1,929
Electricity consumed by food, beverages and tobacco	**103**	**172**	**86r**	**78r**	**141**
from own generation *(5)* *(in GWh)*	1,200	2,005	1,005	904	1,645

(1) Industrial categories used are described in Table 1G.

(2) Includes hydro electricity, solid and gaseous renewables and waste.

(3) Total fuels used for generation of electricity. Consistent with figures for fuels used by other generators in Table 5.4.

1.9 Fuels consumed for electricity generation (autogeneration) by main industrial groups[(1)] (continued)

Thousand tonnes of oil equivalent

(except where shown otherwise)

	1998	1999	2000	2001	2002
Paper, printing and publishing					
Coal	82	74	52	44r	29
Natural gas	430	498	629r	578r	620
Petroleum	10	15	12	12	9
Other (including renewables) (2)	-	-	9	-	-
Total fuel input (3)	**522**	**586**	**701r**	**634r**	**658**
Electricity generated by paper, printing and publishing (4)	**229**	**267**	**337r**	**296r**	**316**
(in GWh)	2,658	3,103	3,920	3,446	3,680
Electricity consumed by paper, printing and publishing	**211**	**239**	**258r**	**227r**	**202**
from own generation (5) (in GWh)	2,454	2,774	3,002	2,644	2,353
Other industries					
Coal	22	22	24	21r	18
Coke oven gas	7	7	5	5	5
Natural gas	94	91	144r	111r	110
Petroleum	6	6	5	5	5
Other (including renewables) (2)	515	693	838	941	1,009
Total fuel input (3)	**645**	**819**	**1,016r**	**1,083r**	**1,147**
Electricity generated by other industries (4)	**100**	**102**	**131r**	**115r**	**105**
(in GWh)	1,165	1,189	1,528	1,334	1,220
Electricity consumed by other industries from own	**67**	**67**	**94r**	**69r**	**60**
generation (5) (in GWh)	779	776	1,090	804	692
Total					
Coal	1,185	972	877r	1,009r	962
Blast furnace gas	732	729	728r	472r	465
Coke oven gas	169	172	171r	128r	127
Natural gas	1,807	1,902	2,409r	1,840r	1,804
Petroleum	268	229	123r	103r	76
Other (including renewables) (2)	954	1,129	1,257	1,287r	1,391
Total fuel input (3)	**5,114**	**5,133**	**5,564r**	**4,838r**	**4,825**
Electricity generated (4)	**1,667**	**1,814**	**2,116**	**1,882r**	**1,805**
(in GWh)	19,382	21,102	24,604	21,886	20,994
Electricity consumed from own generation (5)	**1,331**	**1,478**	**1,558r**	**1,359r**	**1,380**
(in GWh)	15,483	17,183	18,121	15,808	16,051

(4) Combined heat and power (CHP) generation (i.e. electrical output from Table 6.8) plus non-chp generation, so that the total electricity generated is consistent with the "other generators" figures in Table 5.6.

(5) This is the electricity consumed by the industrial sector from its own generation and is consistent with the other generators final users figures used within the electricity balances (Tables 5.1 and 5.2). These figures are less than the total generated because some of the electricity is sold to the public distribution system and other users.

(6) The figures presented here are consistent with other figures presented elsewhere in this publication as detailed at (3), (4), and (5) above but are further dissaggregated. Overall totals covering all autogenerators can be derived by adding in figures for transport, services and the fuel industries. These can be summarised as follows:

Fuel input	1998	1999	2000	2001	2002
			Thousand tonnes of oil equivalent		
All industry	5,114	5,133	5,564	4,838	4,825
Fuel industries	921	892	1,159	1,097	1,386
Transport, Commerce and Administration	455	463	440	466	478
Services	568	841	859	815	871
Total fuel input	**7,058**	**7,329**	**8,023**	**7,217**	**7,560**
Electricity generated	**2,488**	**2,712**	**3,034**	**2,744**	**2,832**
Electricity consumed	**1,889**	**2,046**	**2,211**	**1,872**	**2,072**
					GWh
Electricity generated	**28,938**	**31,544**	**35,285**	**31,913**	**32,934**
Electricity consumed	**21,971**	**23,979**	**25,714**	**21,769**	**24,096**

Chapter 2
Solid fuels and derived gases

Introduction

2.1   This chapter presents figures on the supply and demand for coal and solid fuels derived from coal, and on the production and consumption of gases derived from the processing of solid fuels.

2.2   Balances for coal and manufactured fuels, covering each of the last three years, form the first six tables of this chapter (Tables 2.1 to 2.6). These are followed by a 5 year table showing the supply and consumption of coal as a time series (Table 2.7). Comparable 5 year tables bring together data for coke oven coke, coke breeze and manufactured solid fuels (Table 2.8) and coke oven gas, blast furnace gas, benzole and tars (Table 2.9). As in previous years, tables showing deep mines in production (Table 2.10) and opencast sites in production (Table 2.11) complete the chapter. The long term trends commentary and tables on coal production and stocks, and on coal consumption are on the DTI energy statistics web site: www.dti.gov.uk/energy/inform/dukes/dukes2003/03longterm.pdf.

2.3   Detailed statistics of imports and exports of solid fuels are in Annex G, available on the DTI energy statistics web site: www.dti.gov.uk/energy/inform/dukes/dukes2003/annnexg.pdf.

2.4   Figures for actual consumption of coal are available for all fuel producers and for final use by the iron and steel industry. The remaining final users consumption figures are based on information on disposals by producers and on imports. For further details see the technical notes and definitions section which begins at paragraph 2.32 of this chapter.

Structure of the coal industry

2.5   When the coal industry was privatised at the end of 1994 there were four main coal producers: RJB Mining, Mining Scotland, Celtic Energy and Coal Investments. The last mentioned went into receivership in June 1996 and only two of their mines remained as going concerns under the company name of Midlands Mining. One of these two mines closed at the end of 1998 and the other at the beginning of 2000. The other four collieries reverted to the Coal Authority and were subsequently closed. RJB mining changed its name to UK Coal in 2001.

2.6   There are also a number of independent deep mines, which are listed in Table 2.10. Independent opencast coal producers are similarly listed in Table 2.11. Further coal and slurry are supplied from recovery operations.

Commodity balances for coal (Tables 2.1, 2.2 and 2.3)

2.7   These balance tables separately identify the three main types of coal, namely steam coal, coking coal, and anthracite, and show the variation both in the sources of supply and where the various types of coal are mainly used.

2.8   In 2002, 84 per cent of coal demand was for steam coal, 11 per cent was for coking coal and 5 per cent was for anthracite. Electricity generation accounted for 94 per cent of demand for steam coal and 56 per cent of demand for anthracite. Coking coal was nearly all used in coke ovens (89 per cent), but 11 per cent was directly injected into blast furnaces.

2.9   Only 5 per cent of the total demand for coal was for final consumption, where it was used for steam raising, space or hot water heating or heat for processing. Steam coal accounted for 74 per cent of this final consumption, just over half of which was by industry, where mineral products (eg cement, glass and bricks) and chemicals were the largest users. Domestic sector accounted for 56½ per cent of the final demand for coal, with just over half of this demand being for steam coal and the remainder for anthracite.

2.10   Chart 2.1, below, compares the sources of coal supplies in the UK in 2002, along with a breakdown of consumption by user and serves to illustrate some of the features brought out below.

2.11   In 2002, 28 per cent of supply was met from deep-mined production, 23 per cent from opencast operations, 48 per cent from net imports and 1 per cent from other sources such as slurry. Supply from all these sources was not quite enough to meet demand and so 0.4 million tonnes (equivalent to under 1 per cent of total supply) were drawn down from coal stocks.

2.12   Recent trends in coal production and consumption are described in paragraphs 2.20 to 2.26.

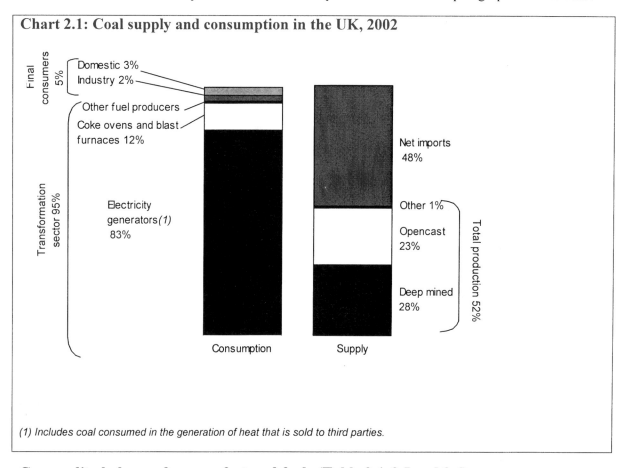

Chart 2.1: Coal supply and consumption in the UK, 2002

(1) Includes coal consumed in the generation of heat that is sold to third parties.

Commodity balances for manufactured fuels (Table 2.4, 2.5 and 2.6)

2.13   The balance tables for manufactured fuels cover fuels manufactured from coal, and gases produced when coal is used in coke ovens and blast furnaces. Definitions of terms associated with coke, breeze and other manufactured solid fuels are set out in paragraphs 2.44 to 2.47.

2.14   The majority of **coke oven coke**, is home produced with the volume of imports equivalent to just 6 per cent of the home produced volume in 2002. About 7 per cent of home production was exported. The amount screened out by producers as breeze and fines amounted to about 21 per cent of production plus imports in 2002, and this appears as transfers in the coke breeze column of the balance. Transfers out of coke oven coke may not always be equal to transfers into coke oven breeze, due to differences arising from the timing, location of measurement and the practise adopted by the Iron and Steel works but over the last three years, the Iron and Steel Statistics Bureau have been able to reconcile the data. In 2002, 88 per cent of the demand for coke was at blast furnaces (part of the transformation sector) with most of the remainder going into final consumption in the non-ferrous metals sector (eg foundry coke).

2.15   Most of the supply of **coke breeze** is from re-screened coke oven coke with direct production accounting for only 20 per cent of total supply. Some breeze is re-used in coke manufacture or in blast furnaces, but the majority is boiler fuel.

2.16   Patent fuels are manufactured smokeless fuels, produced mainly for the domestic market, as the balances show. A small amount of these fuels (only 4½ per cent of total supply in 2002) is imported, but exports generally exceed imports. Imports and exports of manufactured fuels can contain small quantities of non-smokeless fuels.

2.17   Chart 2.2 below shows the sources of coke, breeze and other manufactured solid fuels and a breakdown of their consumption.

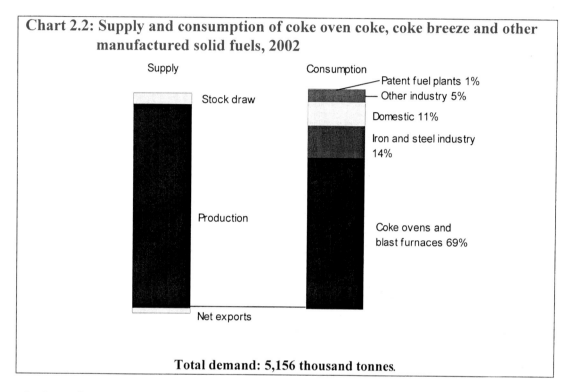

Chart 2.2: Supply and consumption of coke oven coke, coke breeze and other manufactured solid fuels, 2002

Total demand: 5,156 thousand tonnes.

2.18   The carbonisation and gasification of solid fuels at coke ovens produces **coke oven gas** as a by-product. Some of this (44½ per cent in 2002) is used to fuel the coke ovens themselves while at steel works some is piped to blast furnaces and used in the production of steel (11 per cent in 2002). Elsewhere at steel works, the gas is used for electricity generation (15½ per cent) or for heat production and for other iron and steel making processes (16 per cent).

2.19   **Blast furnace gas** is a by-product of iron making in a blast furnace. A similar product is obtained when steel is made in basic oxygen steel converters, and "BOS" gas is included in this category. Most of this gas is used in other parts of integrated steel works with 41 per cent being used for electricity generation in 2002, 31 per cent being used in coke ovens and blast furnaces themselves, and 3 per cent being used for general heat production. The remaining 25 per cent is lost or burned as waste.

Supply and consumption of coal (Table 2.7)

2.20   **Production** - Figures for 2002 show that coal production (including slurry) fell by 6 per cent compared to production in 2001. Deep-mined production fell by 5½ per cent compared to 2001 while opencast production fell by 7 per cent. Overall demand for coal was down by 8½ per cent on 2001 and this resulted in a 19 per cent fall in the volume of net imports. Longer term trends in production are illustrated in Chart 2.3 below.

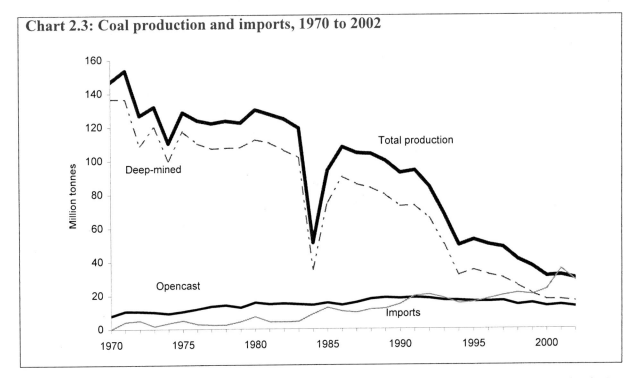

Chart 2.3: Coal production and imports, 1970 to 2002

2.21   Table 2A shows how production of coal is divided between England, Wales and Scotland. In 2002/03 69 per cent of the coal output was in England, 25 per cent in Scotland, and 6 per cent in Wales.

2.22   Table 2A also shows how numbers employed in the production of coal have changed over the last three years. During 2002/2003 employment, including contractors, was lower by 17 per cent. At 31 March 2003, 78 per cent of the 9,289 people employed in UK coal mining worked in England, while 13 per cent were employed in Scotland and 9 per cent in Wales. The closure of Longannet mine in 2002 brought employment in deep mining for coal in Scotland to an end.

Table 2A: Output from UK coal mines and employment in UK coal mines *(1)(2)*

	Million tonnes				**Number**		
	Output				Employment		
	April 2000 to March 2001	April 2001 to March 2002	April 2002 to March 2003		end March 2001	end March 2002	end March 2003
Deep-mined							
England	15.9	16.6	15.0		7,316	7,605	6,100
Scotland	0.7	0.8	-		771	367	-
Wales	0.7	0.7	0.8		552	596	577
Total	17.3	18.1	15.8		8,639	8,568	6,677
Opencast							
England	4.8	4.9	5.0		1,068	1,117	1,113
Scotland	7.1	8.1	7.1		1,267	1,250	1,202
Wales	1.4	1.2	1.0		456	306	297
Total	13.3	14.2	13.1		2,791	2,673	2,612
Total							
England	20.7	21.5	20.0		8,384	8,722	7,213
Scotland	7.8	8.9	7.1		2,038	1,617	1,202
Wales	2.1	1.9	1.8		1,008	902	874
Total	30.6	32.3	28.9		11,430	11,241	9,289

Source: The Coal Authority
(1) Output is the tonnage declared by operators to the Coal Authority, including estimated tonnages. It excludes estimates of slurry recovered from dumps, ponds, rivers, etc.
(2) Employment includes contractors and is as declared by licensees to the Coal Authority at 31 March each year.

2.23   **Foreign trade** - Imports of coal and other solid fuel in 2002 amounted to 28.7 million tonnes, 19 per cent lower than 2001's record level. Within the total, imports of steam coal fell by 19 per cent – largely due to sharp falls in imports from Colombia (nearly halved), Australia (down 70 per cent) and to a lesser extent South Africa (down 4 per cent). As Table 2B shows, in 2002, 67 per cent of the United Kingdom's imports of coal and other solid fuel came from just three countries: Australia, Russia and South Africa. A further 26 per cent of coal imports came from four additional countries, Colombia (steam coal), USA (mainly coking coal), Poland (mainly steam coal) and Canada (coking coal). Steam coal imports came mainly from South Africa (45 per cent), Colombia and Russia (16 per cent each). All but 1 per cent of UK coking coal imports came from just three countries, Australia (67 per cent), the USA (20 per cent) and Canada (12 per cent). For more details of imports and exports of solid fuels by country of origin see Annex G on the DTI energy statistics web site – see paragraph 2.3 above.

2.24   Major power producers have sourced an increasing proportion of their coal from imports over the last four years. In 1999 only 20.4 per cent of the coal they consumed was imported. This rose to a record level of 46.9 per cent (23.2 million tonnes) in 2001 but fell slightly to 42.0 per cent in 2002.

Table 2B: Imports of coal and other solid fuel in 2002[1]

Thousand tonnes

	Steam coal	Coking coal	Anthracite	Other solid fuel	Total
European Union [2]	307	-	59	210	576
Australia	864	4,229	-	-	5,094
Canada	-	750	-	-	750
Colombia	3,518	-	29	-	3,547
Indonesia	45	-	-	-	45
Norway	163	-	1	-	164
People's Republic of China	208	-	80	41	329
Poland	1,558	-	38	-	1,597
Republic of South Africa	9,769	-	107	-	9,876
Russia	4,294	48	26	3	4,371
United States of America	252	1,286	29	-	1,567
Vietnam	-	-	86	-	86
Other countries	917	-	23	-	939
Total all countries	**21,895**	**6,315**	**477**	**255**	**28,941**

Source: H M Customs and Excise

(1) Country of origin basis.
(2) Includes extra-EU coal routed through the Netherlands.

2.25   **Transformation** - The 8½ per cent fall in coal consumption during 2002 compared to 2001 mainly results from a 6½ per cent fall in consumption by major power producers. This 3.1 million tonnes decrease in coal consumption at power stations resulted from increased use of gas fired stations mainly because of a fall in gas prices in 2002 from their very high 2001 levels. In addition, reductions in UK steel making capacity led to a decline of 17 per cent in the use of coal for coke making and at blast furnaces.

2.26   **Consumption** - Consumption by final consumers in 2002 showed a 23 per cent fall compared to 2001, but was still 17½ per cent higher than in 2000. Consumption in 2001 was higher than in 2000 partly because consumers appear to have replenished their stocks during 2001. Domestic sector consumption was 23½ per cent down largely due to the very mild 2002 winter temperatures. Industrial consumption was 23 per cent lower than in 2001 at 1.3 million tonnes.

2.27   Long term trends commentary and tables on the consumption of coal in the UK since 1970 onwards can be found on the DTI energy statistics web site – see paragraph 2.2 above.

2.28   **Stocks** – Production and net imports together in 2002 were 13 per cent lower than in 2001, while demand for coal fell by only 8½ per cent. This led to stocks of coal falling slightly by 0.4 million tonnes (2 per cent). This contrasts with 2.9 million tonnes being added to stocks in 2001. Total stocks at the end of 2002 were therefore equivalent to 27½ per cent of the year's coal consumption, the proportion having risen for the second consecutive year, but were still lower than the peak proportion of 33 per cent in 1999. Stocks held at collieries and opencast sites at the end of 2002 were 0.9 million tonnes higher than a year earlier but stocks held by the major power producers were 1.3 million tonnes lower. The recent changes in coal stocks are illustrated in Chart 2.4 below.

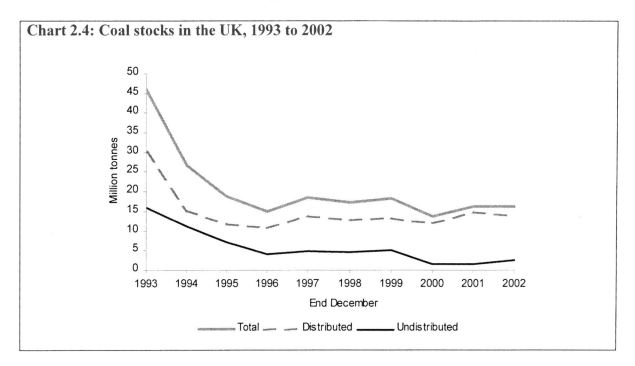

Chart 2.4: Coal stocks in the UK, 1993 to 2002

Supply and consumption of coke oven coke, coke breeze and other manufactured fuels (Table 2.8)
2.29   This table presents figures for the most recent five years on the same basis as the balance tables. Figures for stocks are also included. Coal used to produce these manufactured fuels is shown in Table 2.7. For **coke oven coke,** 2002 saw a decrease in demand of 17 per cent while production fell by 18½ per cent. However, imports were more than double the level recorded in 2001, whilst exports rose by 43 per cent so that the UK became a net exporter of coke oven coke, although by only a small amount compared with production. The net result of these changes was that stocks of coke were 261 thousand tonnes lower than in 2001.

2.30   In 2002, the demand for **coke breeze** fell by 4 per cent but production rose by 6½ per cent so there was a 7 per cent increase in stock. There was a 14½ per cent decline in the demand for **other manufactured solid fuels**, mainly because of a 12½ per cent fall in domestic sector demand. UK production was down 11½ per cent on 2001 levels.

Supply and consumption of coke oven gas, blast furnace gas, benzole and tars (Table 2.9)
2.31   This table presents figures for the most recent five years on the same basis as the balance tables. In 2002, production of and demand for **coke oven gas** fell by around 16 per cent each. Demand fell in all sectors, but the sharpest fall was in iron and steel making processes other than coke manufacture and blast furnaces, largely due to the closure of one large steel plant. Both production and demand for **blast furnace gas** were lower in 2002 than in 2001 by around 11 per cent. Similarly, this decline cuts across all areas of use.

Technical notes and definitions

2.32   These notes and definitions are in addition to the technical notes and definitions covering all fuels and energy as a whole in Chapter 1, paragraphs 1.24 to 1.58. For notes on the commodity balances and definitions of the terms used in the row headings see Annex A, paragraphs A.7 to A.42.

Steam coal, coking coal, and anthracite

2.33   **Steam coal** is coal classified as such by UK coal producers and by importers of coal. It tends to have calorific values at the lower end of the range.

2.34   **Coking coal** is coal sold by producers for use in coke ovens and similar carbonising processes. The definition is not therefore determined by the calorific value or caking qualities of each batch of coal sold, although calorific values tend to be higher than for steam coal.

2.35   **Anthracite** is coal classified as such by UK coal producers and importers of coal. Typically it has a high heat content making it particularly suitable for certain industrial processes and for use as a domestic fuel. Some UK anthracite producers have found a market for their lower calorific value output at power stations.

Coal production

2.36   **Deep-mined** - The statistics cover saleable output from deep mines including coal obtained from working on both revenue and capital accounts. All licensed collieries (and British Coal collieries prior to 1995) are included, even where coal is only a subsidiary product.

2.37   **Opencast** - The figures cover saleable output and include the output of sites worked by operators under agency agreements and licences, as well as the output of sites licensed for the production of coal as a subsidiary to the production of other minerals.

2.38   **Other** - Estimates of slurry etc recovered and disposed of from dumps, ponds, rivers, etc.

Imports and exports of coal and other solid fuels

2.39   Figures are derived from returns made to HM Customs and Excise and are broken down in greater detail in Annex G on the DTI energy statistics web site.

2.40   However, in Tables 2.4, 2.5, 2.6 and 2.8, the export figures used for hard coke, coke breeze and other manufactured solid fuels for the years before 1998 are quantities of fuel exported as reported to DTI by the companies concerned, rather than quantities recorded by HM Customs and Excise in their Trade Statistics.

Allocation of imported coal

2.41   Although data are available on consumption of home produced coal, and also on consumption of imported coal by secondary fuel producers there is only very limited direct information on consumption of imported coal by final users. The DTI carries out surveys of the destination of steam coal imports (excluding those used by electricity generators) from time to time. The most recent was in 1998 and concluded that it was appropriate to allocate 60 per cent of such imports each year to industry, 15 per cent to the public administration sector, and 25 per cent to the domestic sector. This was revised in 2002 to 70, 25 and 5 per cent to industry, domestic and public adminstration respectively. In addition, 10 per cent of anthracite imports, excluding cleaned smalls, are allocated to industry, with 90 per cent to the domestic sector in all years shown in the tables. All imports of coking coal and cleaned anthracite smalls are allocated to coke and other solid fuel producers.

Stocks of coal

2.42   Undistributed stocks are those held at collieries and opencast sites. It is not possible to distinguish these two locations in the stock figures. Distributed stocks are those held at power stations and stocking grounds of the major power producing companies (as defined in Chapter 5, paragraph 5.47), coke ovens and low temperature carbonisation plants, and patent fuel plants.

Transformation, energy industry use and consumption of solid fuels

2.43   Annex A of this Digest outlines the principles of energy and commodity balances and defines the activities that fall within these parts of the balances. However, the following additional notes relevant to solid fuels are given below:

Transformation: Blast furnaces - Coking coal injected into blast furnaces is shown separately within the balance tables.

Transformation: Low temperature carbonisation plants and patent fuel plants - Coal used at these plants for the manufacture of domestic coke such as Coalite and of briquetted fuels such as Phurnacite and Homefire.

Consumption: Industry - The statistics comprise sales of coal by the nine main coal producers to the iron and steel industry (excluding that used at coke ovens and blast furnaces) and to other industrial sectors and estimated proportions of anthracite and steam coal imports. The figures exclude coal used for industries' own generation of electricity, which appear separately under transformation.

Consumption: Domestic - Coal supplied free of charge or at reduced prices to current and retired miners, officials, etc in the coalfields. The concessionary fuel provided to miners in 2002 is estimated at 207 thousand tonnes. This estimate is included in the domestic steam coal and domestic anthracite figures.

Consumption of coke and other manufactured solid fuels - These are disposals from coke ovens to merchants. The figures also include estimated proportions of coke imports.

Coke oven coke (hard coke) and hard coke breeze

2.44   The statistics cover coke produced at coke ovens owned by Corus plc (formerly British Steel), Coal Products Ltd and other producers. Low temperature carbonisation plants are not included (see paragraph 2.47, below). Breeze (as defined in paragraph 2.45) is excluded from the figures for coke oven coke.

2.45   Breeze can generally be described as coke screened below 19 mm (¾ inch) with no fines removed, but the screen size may vary in different areas and to meet the requirements of particular markets. Coke that has been transported from one location to another is usually re-screened before use to remove smaller sizes, giving rise to further breeze.

2.46   In 1998, an assessment using industry data showed that on average over the last five years 91 per cent of imports have been coke and 9 per cent breeze and it is these proportions that have been used for 1998 and subsequent years in Tables 2.4, 2.5, 2.6 and 2.8.

2.47   Other manufactured solid fuels are mainly solid smokeless fuels for the domestic market for use in both open fires and in boilers. A smaller quantity is exported (although exports are largely offset by similar quantities of imports in most years). Manufacture takes place in patented fuel plants and low temperature carbonisation plants. The brand names used for these fuels include Homefire, Phurnacite, Ancit and Coalite.

Blast furnace gas, coke oven gas, benzole and tars

2.48   The following definitions are used in the tables that include these fuels:

Blast furnace gas - includes basic oxygen steel furnace (BOS) gas. Blast furnace gas is the gas produced during iron ore smelting when hot air passes over coke within the blast ovens. It contains carbon monoxide, carbon dioxide, hydrogen and nitrogen. In a basic oxygen steel furnace the aim is not to introduce nitrogen or hydrogen into the steel making process, so pure oxygen gas and suitable fluxes are used to remove the carbon and phosphorous from the molten pig iron and steel scrap. A similar fuel gas is thus produced.

Coke oven gas - is a gas produced during the carbonisation of coal to form coke at coke ovens.

Synthetic coke oven gas - is mainly natural gas that is mixed with smaller amounts of blast furnace and BOS gas to produce a gas with almost the same quantities as coke oven gas. The transfers row of Tables 2.4, 2.5 and 2.6 show the quantities of blast furnace gas used for this purpose and the total input of gases to the synthetic coke oven gas process. There is a corresponding outward transfer from natural gas in Chapter 4, Table 4.1.

Benzole - a colourless, liquid, flammable, aromatic hydrocarbon by-product of the iron and steel making process. It is used as a solvent in the manufacture of styrenes and phenols but can also be used as a motor fuel.

Tars - viscous materials usually derived from the destructive distillation of coal, which are by-products of the coke and iron making processes.

Periods covered

2.49   Figures in this chapter (and figures for earlier years given in the tables on the DTI website) generally relate to periods of 52 weeks or 53 weeks as follows:

Year	52 weeks ended
1997	27 December 1997
1998	26 December 1998
1999	25 December 1999
	53 weeks ended
2000	30 December 2000
	52 weeks ended
2001	29 December 2001
2002	28 December 2002

The 53 week data for 2000 have been adjusted to 52 weeks by omitting data for an average week based on information provided by the largest companies for the first week in April 2000.

2.50   Data for coal used for electricity generation by major power producers follow the electricity industry calendar (see Chapter 5, paragraph 5.55) and coal use by other generators is for the 12 months ending 31 December each year. HM Customs and Excise data on imports and exports are also for the 12 months ended 31 December each year. Data for coal and coke use in the iron and steel industry, and for gases, benzole and tars produced by the iron and steel industry follow the iron and steel industry calendar (see Chapter 5, paragraph 5.56).

Data collection

2.51   In 2002, aggregate data on coal production were obtained from the Coal Authority. In addition the largest producers (Betws Anthracite, Celtic Energy, Coalpower Ltd, Goitre Tower

Anthracite, H J Banks, Hall Construction Services Ltd (formerly known as Coal Contractors Limited), J D Flack & Sons Ltd, Scottish Coal Company Ltd and UK Coal plc) have provided data in response to an annual DTI inquiry covering production (deep-mined and opencast), trade, stocks, and disposals. The Iron and Steel Statistics Bureau (ISSB) provides DTI with an annual statement of coke and breeze production and use of coal, coke and breeze within that industry. The ISSB is also the source of data on gases produced by the iron and steel industry (coke oven gas, blast furnace gas and basic oxygen steel furnace gas). DTI directly surveys producers of manufactured fuels other than coke or breeze.

2.52   Trade in solid fuels is also covered by using data from HM Customs and Excise (see Annex G on DTI energy statistics web site). Consumption of coal for electricity generation is covered by data collected by DTI from electricity generators as described in Chapter 5, paragraphs 5.58 to 5.60.

Monthly and quarterly data

2.53   Monthly data on coal production, foreign trade, consumption and stocks are available on DTI's Energy Statistics web site www.dti.gov.uk/energy/inform/energy_stats/ in monthly tables 2.4, 2.5, and 2.6. Quarterly commodity balances for coal; coke oven coke, coke breeze and other manufactured solid fuels; and coke oven gas, blast furnace gas, benzole and tars are published in DTI's quarterly statistical bulletin *Energy Trends* and these balances are also available on DTI's Energy Statistics web site. See Annex C for more information about *Energy Trends* and the DTI energy statistics web site.

Statistical differences

2.54   Tables 2.1 to 2.9 each contain a statistical difference term covering the difference between recorded supply and recorded demand. These statistical differences arise for a number of reasons. First, the data within each table are taken from varied sources, as described above, such as producers, intermediate consumers (such as electricity generators), final consumers (such as the iron and steel industry), and HM Customs and Excise. Second, some of these industries work to different statistical calendars (see paragraphs 2.49 and 2.50, above), and third, some of the figures are estimated either because data in the required detail are not readily available within the industry or because the methods of collecting the data do not cover the smallest members of the industry.

Contact: James Achur
*   Energy Markets Information and Analysis*
*   james.achur@dti.gsi.gov.uk*
*   020-7215 2717*

*   John Castle*
*   Energy Information Systems*
*   john.castle@dti.gsi.gov.uk*
*   020-7215 2718*

2.1 Commodity balances 2002
Coal

Thousand tonnes

	Steam coal	Coking coal	Anthracite	Total
Supply				
Production	..	373	..	29,539
Other sources	..	-	..	450
Imports	21,895	6,315	477	28,687
Exports	-342	-3	-192	-537
Marine bunkers	-	-	-	-
Stock change (1)	..	+162	..	+350
Transfers	-	-	-	-
Total supply	..	6,847	..	58,489
Statistical difference (2)	..	+314	..	-153
Total demand	49,199	6,533	2,910	58,642
Transformation	46,832	6,533	2,075	55,440
Electricity generation	46,073	-	1,639	47,712
Major power producers	44,506	-	1,639	46,145
Autogenerators	1,567	-	-	1,567
Heat generation	759	-	-	759
Petroleum refineries	-	-	-	-
Coke manufacture	-	5,807	-	5,807
Blast furnaces	-	726	-	726
Patent fuel manufacture and low temperature carbonisation	-	-	436	436
Energy industry use	..	-	..	9
Electricity generation	-	-	-	-
Oil and gas extraction	-	-	-	-
Petroleum refineries	-	-	-	-
Coal extraction	..	-	..	9
Coke manufacture	-	-	-	-
Blast furnaces	-	-	-	-
Patent fuel manufacture	-	-	-	-
Pumped storage	-	-	-	-
Other	-	-	-	-
Losses	-	-	-	-
Final consumption	2,359	-	834	3,193
Industry	1,294	-	31	1,325
Unclassified	-	-	-	-
Iron and steel	-	-	-	-
Non-ferrous metals	..	-	..	146
Mineral products	..	-	..	500
Chemicals	..	-	..	278
Mechanical engineering etc	..	-	..	14
Electrical engineering etc	..	-	..	4
Vehicles	..	-	..	53
Food, beverages etc	..	-	..	189
Textiles, leather, etc	..	-	..	20
Paper, printing etc	..	-	..	76
Other industries	..	-	..	45
Construction	-	-	-	-
Transport	-	-	-	-
Air	-	-	-	-
Rail	-	-	-	-
Road	-	-	-	-
National navigation	-	-	-	-
Pipelines	-	-	-	-
Other	..	-	..	1,868
Domestic	1,001	-	803	1,804
Public administration	..	-	..	45
Commercial	-	-	-	5
Agriculture	..	-	..	6
Miscellaneous	..	-	..	8
Non energy use	-	-	-	-

(1) Stock fall (+), stock rise (-).
(2) Total supply minus total demand.

2.2 Commodity balances 2001
Coal

	Steam coal	Coking coal	Anthracite	Total
Supply				
Production	..	312	..	31,513
Other sources	..	-	..	417
Imports	27,041	7,723	778	35,542
Exports	-302	-4	-244	-550
Marine bunkers	-	-	-	-
Stock change (1)	..	-366	..	-2,886r
Transfers	-	-	-	-
Total supply	..	**7,665**	..	**64,037r**
Statistical difference (2)	..	-231	..	-208r
Total demand	**53,316r**	**7,896**	**3,032r**	**64,245r**
Transformation	**50,309r**	**7,896**	**1,874r**	**60,079r**
Electricity generation	49,550r	-	1,378r	50,928r
Major power producers	47,913r	-	1,378r	49,291r
Autogenerators	1,637r	-	-	1,637r
Heat generation	759r	-	-	759r
Petroleum refineries	-	-	-	-
Coke manufacture	-	7,132	-	7,132
Blast furnaces	-	764	-	764
Patent fuel manufacture and low temperature carbonisation	-	-	496	496
Energy industry use	..	-	..	**10**
Electricity generation	-	-	-	-
Oil and gas extraction	-	-	-	-
Petroleum refineries	-	-	-	-
Coal extraction	..	-	..	10
Coke manufacture	-	-	-	-
Blast furnaces	-	-	-	-
Patent fuel manufacture	-	-	-	-
Pumped storage	-	-	-	-
Other	-	-	-	-
Losses	-	-	-	-
Final consumption	**2,998r**	**-**	**1,158r**	**4,156r**
Industry	**1,674r**	**-**	**48r**	**1,722r**
Unclassified	-	-	-	-
Iron and steel	1	-	-	1
Non-ferrous metals	..	-	..	219r
Mineral products	..	-	..	504r
Chemicals	..	-	..	409r
Mechanical engineering etc	..	-	..	14
Electrical engineering etc	..	-	..	4
Vehicles	..	-	..	70r
Food, beverages etc	..	-	..	217r
Textiles, leather, etc	..	-	..	48
Paper, printing etc	..	-	..	168r
Other industries	..	-	..	68r
Construction	-	-	-	-
Transport	-	-	-	-
Air	-	-	-	-
Rail	-	-	-	-
Road	-	-	-	-
National navigation	-	-	-	-
Pipelines	-	-	-	-
Other	..	-	..	**2,434r**
Domestic	1,251	-	1,110	2,361r
Public administration	..	-	..	52r
Commercial	-	-	-	6
Agriculture	..	-	..	5
Miscellaneous	..	-	..	10
Non energy use	-	-	-	-

(1) Stock fall (+), stock rise (-).

(2) Total supply minus total demand.

2.3 Commodity balances 2000
Coal

Thousand tonnes

	Steam coal	Coking coal	Anthracite	Total
Supply				
Production	..	255	..	30,600
Other sources	..	-	..	598
Imports	14,425	8,462	558	23,446
Exports	-351	-4	-306	-661
Marine bunkers	-	-	-	-
Stock change (1)	..	+111	..	+4,681
Transfers	-	-	-	-
Total supply	..	8,824	..	58,663
Statistical difference (2)	..	+139	..	-199r
Total demand	47,268r	8,685	2,908	58,862r
Transformation	45,539r	8,685	1,913	56,136r
Electricity generation	44,825r	-	1,373	46,198r
Major power producers	43,389	-	1,373	44,762
Autogenerators	1,436r	-	-	1,436r
Heat generation	714r	-	-	714r
Petroleum refineries	-	-	-	-
Coke manufacture	-	8,229	-	8,229
Blast furnaces	-	456	-	456
Patent fuel manufacture and low temperature carbonisation	-	-	540	540
Energy industry use	..	-	..	12
Electricity generation	-	-	-	-
Oil and gas extraction	-	-	-	-
Petroleum refineries	-	-	-	-
Coal extraction	..	-	..	12
Coke manufacture	-	-	-	-
Blast furnaces	-	-	-	-
Patent fuel manufacture	-	-	-	-
Pumped storage	-	-	-	-
Other	-	-	-	-
Losses	-	-	-	-
Final consumption	1,720r	-	992	2,713r
Industry	648r	-	75	724r
Unclassified	-	-	-	-
Iron and steel	2	-	-	2
Non-ferrous metals	..	-	..	82r
Mineral products	..	-	..	202r
Chemicals	..	-	..	83r
Mechanical engineering etc	..	-	..	8
Electrical engineering etc	..	-	..	2
Vehicles	..	-	..	44r
Food, beverages etc	..	-	..	110r
Textiles, leather, etc	..	-	..	34r
Paper, printing etc	..	-	..	54r
Other industries	..	-	..	103r
Construction	-	-	-	-
Transport	-	-	-	-
Air	-	-	-	-
Rail	-	-	-	-
Road	-	-	-	-
National navigation	-	-	-	-
Pipelines	-	-	-	-
Other	..	-	..	1,990r
Domestic	990	-	917	1,908r
Public administration	..	-	..	60r
Commercial	-	-	-	7
Agriculture	..	-	..	7
Miscellaneous	..	-	..	8
Non energy use	-	-	-	-

(1) Stock fall (+), stock rise (-).
(2) Total supply minus total demand.

2.4 Commodity balances 2002

Manufactured fuels

	Thousand tonnes					GWh	
	Coke oven coke	Coke breeze	Other manuf. solid fuel	Total manuf. solid fuel	Benzole and tars (4)	Coke oven gas	Blast furnace gas
Supply							
Production	4,335	224	430	4,989	1,880	9,549	13,130
Other sources	-	-	-	-			-
Imports	226	12	18	256	-	-	-
Exports	-272	-46	-67	-385	-	-	-
Marine bunkers	-	-	-	-	-	-	-
Stock change (1)	+261	-14	+17	+264	-	-	-
Transfers (2)	-927	+927	-	-	-	+104	-4
Total supply	3,624	1,102	398	5,124	1,880	9,653	13,126
Statistical difference (3)	-34	+27	-25	-32	-	+62	-93
Total demand	3,658	1,075	423	5,156	1,880	9,591	13,219
Transformation	3,224	331	-	3,555	-	3,011	5,836
Electricity generation	-	-	-	-	-	1,480	5,402
Major power producers	-	-	-	-	-	-	-
Autogenerators	-	-	-	-	-	1,480	5,402
Heat generation	-	-	-	-	-	1,531	434
Petroleum refineries	-	-	-	-	-	-	-
Coke manufacture	-	-	-	-		-	-
Blast furnaces	3,224	331	-	3,555	-	-	-
Patent fuel manufacture	-	-	-	-		-	-
Low temperature carbonisation	-	-	-	-		-	-
Energy industry use	17	-	10	27	-	5,321	4,095
Electricity generation	-	-	-	-	-	-	-
Oil and gas extraction	-	-	-	-	-	-	-
Petroleum refineries	-	-	-	-	-	-	-
Coal extraction	-	-	-	-	-	-	-
Coke manufacture	-	-	-	-	-	4,270	510
Blast furnaces	-	-	-	-	-	1,051	3,585
Patent fuel manufacture	17	-	10	27	-	-	-
Pumped storage	-	-	-	-	-	-	-
Other	-	-	-	-	-	387	648
Losses	-	-	-	-	-	387	648
Final consumption	417	744	413	1,574	1,880	872	2,640
Industry	239	744	22	1,005	1,880	872	2,640
Unclassified	151	44	22	217	469	32	
Iron and steel	29	700	-	729	1,411	840	2,640
Non-ferrous metals	59	-	-	59	-	-	-
Mineral products	-	-	-	-	-	-	-
Chemicals	-	-	-	-	-	-	-
Mechanical engineering, etc	-	-	-	-	-	-	-
Electrical engineering, etc	-	-	-	-	-	-	-
Vehicles	-	-	-	-	-	-	-
Food, beverages, etc	-	-	-	-	-	-	-
Textiles, leather, etc	-	-	-	-	-	-	-
Paper, printing, etc	-	-	-	-	-	-	-
Other industries	-	-	-	-	-	-	-
Construction	-	-	-	-	-	-	-
Transport	-	-	-	-	-	-	-
Air	-	-	-	-	-	-	-
Rail	-	-	-	-	-	-	-
Road	-	-	-	-	-	-	-
National navigation	-	-	-	-	-	-	-
Pipelines	-	-	-	-	-	-	-
Other	178	-	391	569	-	-	-
Domestic	178	-	391	569	-	-	-
Public administration	-	-	-	-	-	-	-
Commercial	-	-	-	-	-	-	-
Agriculture	-	-	-	-	-	-	-
Miscellaneous	-	-	-	-	-	-	-
Non energy use	-	-	-	-	-	-	-

(1) Stock fall (+), stock rise (-).

(2) Coke oven gas and blast furnace gas transfers are for synthetic coke oven gas, see paragraph 2.48.

(3) Total supply minus total demand.

(4) Because of the small number of benzole suppliers, figures for benzole and tars cannot be given separately.

2.5 Commodity balances 2001
Manufactured fuels

	Thousand tonnes				GWh		
	Coke oven coke	Coke breeze	Other manuf. solid fuel	Total manuf. solid fuel	Benzole and tars (4)	Coke oven gas	Blast furnace gas
Supply							
Production	5,306	210	487	6,003	2,115	11,516r	14,767r
Other sources	-	-	-	-	-	-	-
Imports	101	56	8	165	-	-	-
Exports	-176	-143	-75	-394	-	-	-
Marine bunkers	-	-	-	-	-	-	-
Stock change (1)	+116	+8	+37	+161	-	-	-
Transfers (2)	-982	+982	-	-	-	+68r	-3r
Total supply	**4,365**	**1,112r**	**457**	**5,935**	**2,115**	**11,584**	**14,764**
Statistical difference (3)	-29	-7	-38	-74	-	+142r	-100
Total demand	**4,394**	**1,120**	**495**	**6,009**	**2,115**	**11,442r**	**14,864**
Transformation	**3,957**	**313**	**-**	**4,270**	**-**	**3,383r**	**6,030r**
Electricity generation	-	-			-	1,490r	5,493r
Major power producers	-	-	-	-	-	-	-
Autogenerators	-	-	-	-	-	1,490r	5,493r
Heat generation	-	-	-	-	-	1,893r	537r
Petroleum refineries	-	-	-	-	-	-	-
Coke manufacture	-	9	-	9	-	-	-
Blast furnaces	3,957	304	-	4,261	-	-	-
Patent fuel manufacture	-	-	-	-	-	-	-
Low temperature carbonisation	-	-	-	-	-	-	-
Energy industry use	**32**	**-**	**12**	**44**	**-**	**6,053**	**4,709**
Electricity generation	-	-	-	-	-	-	-
Oil and gas extraction	-	-	-	-	-	-	-
Petroleum refineries	-	-	-	-	-	-	-
Coal extraction	-	-	-	-	-	-	-
Coke manufacture	-	-	-	-	-	4,720	649
Blast furnaces	-	-	-	-	-	1,333	4,060
Patent fuel manufacture	32	-	12	44	-	-	-
Pumped storage	-	-	-	-	-	-	-
Other	-	-	-	-	-	-	-
Losses	**-**	**-**	**-**	**-**	**-**	**231**	**965**
Final consumption	**405**	**807**	**483**	**1,695**	**2,115**	**1,775r**	**3,160r**
Industry	**338**	**807**	**37**	**1,182**	**2,115**	**1,775r**	**3,160r**
Unclassified	181	16	37	234	522	363r	-
Iron and steel	32	791	-	823	1,593	1,412r	3,160r
Non-ferrous metals	125	-	-	125	-	-	-
Mineral products	-	-	-	-	-	-	-
Chemicals	-	-	-	-	-	-	-
Mechanical engineering, etc	-	-	-	-	-	-	-
Electrical engineering, etc	-	-	-	-	-	-	-
Vehicles	-	-	-	-	-	-	-
Food, beverages, etc	-	-	-	-	-	-	-
Textiles, leather, etc	-	-	-	-	-	-	-
Paper, printing, etc	-	-	-	-	-	-	-
Other industries	-	-	-	-	-	-	-
Construction	-	-	-	-	-	-	-
Transport	**-**	**-**	**-**	**-**	**-**	**-**	**-**
Air	-	-	-	-	-	-	-
Rail	-	-	-	-	-	-	-
Road	-	-	-	-	-	-	-
National navigation	-	-	-	-	-	-	-
Pipelines	-	-	-	-	-	-	-
Other	**67**	**-**	**446**	**513**	**-**	**-**	**-**
Domestic	67	-	446	513	-	-	-
Public administration	-	-	-	-	-	-	-
Commercial	-	-	-	-	-	-	-
Agriculture	-	-	-	-	-	-	-
Miscellaneous	-	-	-	-	-	-	-
Non energy use	**-**	**-**	**-**	**-**	**-**	**-**	**-**

(1) Stock fall (+), stock rise (-).
(2) Coke oven gas and blast furnace gas transfers are for synthetic coke oven gas, see paragraph 2.48.
(3) Total supply minus total demand.
(4) Because of the small number of benzole suppliers, figures for benzole and tars cannot be given separately.

2.6 Commodity balances 2000
Manufactured fuels

	Thousand tonnes					GWh	
	Coke oven coke	Coke breeze	Other manuf. solid fuel	Total manuf. solid fuel	Benzole and tars (4)	Coke oven gas	Blast furnace gas
Supply							
Production	6,058	148	537	6,743	2,393	12,661r	17,743r
Other sources	-	-	-	-	-	-	-
Imports	421	62	14	497	-	-	-
Exports	-243	-138	-79	-460	-	-	-
Marine bunkers	-	-	-	-	-	-	-
Stock change (1)	-216	+22r	+38	-156r	-		
Transfers (2)	-827	+827	-	-	-	+460r	-17r
Total supply	**5,193**	**921r**	**510**	**6,624r**	**2,393**	**13,121r**	**17,726r**
Statistical difference (3)	-123	-115r	-22	-260r	-	-264	-103r
Total demand	**5,316**	**1,036**	**532**	**6,884**	**2,393**	**13,385r**	**17,829r**
Transformation	**4,764**	**202**	**-**	**4,966**	**-**	**3,797r**	**9,089r**
Electricity generation	-	-	-	-	-	1,987r	8,470r
Major power producers	-	-	-	-	-	-	-
Autogenerators	-	-	-	-	-	1,987r	8,470r
Heat generation	-	-	-	-	-	1,810r	619r
Petroleum refineries	-	-	-	-	-	-	-
Coke manufacture	-	14	-	14	-	-	-
Blast furnaces	4,764	188	-	4,952	-	-	-
Patent fuel manufacture	-	-	-	-	-	-	-
Low temperature carbonisation	-	-	-	-	-	-	-
Energy industry use	**37**	**-**	**11**	**48**	**-**	**6,748**	**6,034r**
Electricity generation	-	-	-	-	-	-	-
Oil and gas extraction	-	-	-	-	-	-	-
Petroleum refineries	-	-	-	-	-	-	-
Coal extraction	-	-	-	-	-	-	-
Coke manufacture	-	-	-	-	-	5,555	1,057r
Blast furnaces	-	-	-	-	-	1,193	4,977r
Patent fuel manufacture	37	-	11	48	-	-	-
Pumped storage	-	-	-	-	-	-	-
Other	-	-	-	-	-	-	-
Losses	-	-	-	-	-	325	1,592r
Final consumption	**515**	**834**	**521**	**1,870**	**2,393**	**2,515r**	**1,114r**
Industry	**370**	**834**	**25**	**1,229**	**2,393**	**2,515r**	**1,114r**
Unclassified	191	41	25	257	597	200r	-
Iron and steel	19	793	-	812	1,796	2,315r	1,114r
Non-ferrous metals	160	-	-	160	-	-	-
Mineral products	-	-	-	-	-	-	-
Chemicals	-	-	-	-	-	-	-
Mechanical engineering, etc	-	-	-	-	-	-	-
Electrical engineering, etc	-	-	-	-	-	-	-
Vehicles	-	-	-	-	-	-	-
Food, beverages, etc	-	-	-	-	-	-	-
Textiles, leather, etc	-	-	-	-	-	-	-
Paper, printing, etc	-	-	-	-	-	-	-
Other industries	-	-	-	-	-	-	-
Construction	-	-	-	-	-	-	-
Transport	-	-	-	-	-	-	-
Air	-	-	-	-	-	-	-
Rail	-	-	-	-	-	-	-
Road	-	-	-	-	-	-	-
National navigation	-	-	-	-	-	-	-
Pipelines	-	-	-	-	-	-	-
Other	**145**	**-**	**496**	**641**	**-**	**-**	**-**
Domestic	145	-	496	641	-	-	-
Public administration	-	-	-	-	-	-	-
Commercial	-	-	-	-	-	-	-
Agriculture	-	-	-	-	-	-	-
Miscellaneous	-	-	-	-	-	-	-
Non energy use	-	-	-	-	-	-	-

(1) Stock fall (+), stock rise (-).
(2) Coke oven gas and blast furnace gas transfers are for synthetic coke oven gas, see paragraph 2.48.
(3) Total supply minus total demand.
(4) Because of the small number of benzole suppliers, figures for benzole and tars cannot be given separately.

2.7 Supply and consumption of coal

Thousand tonnes

	1998	1999	2000	2001	2002
Supply					
Production	40,046	36,163	30,600	31,513	29,539
Deep-mined	25,731	20,888	17,187	17,347	16,391
Opencast	14,315	15,275	13,412	14,166	13,148
Other sources *(3)*	1,131	914	598	417	450
Imports	21,244	20,293	23,446	35,542	28,687
Exports	-971	-761	-661	-550	-537
Stock change *(1)*	+1,421	-1,164	+4,681	-2,886r	+350
Total supply	**62,871**	**55,445**	**58,663**	**64,037r**	**58,489**
Statistical difference *(2)*	-281	-279	-199r	-208r	-153
Total demand	**63,152**	**55,724**	**58,862r**	**64,245r**	**58,642**
Transformation	**57,951**	**50,886**	**56,136r**	**60,079r**	**55,440**
Electricity generation	48,588	41,178	46,198r	50,928r	47,712
Major power producers	46,627	39,583	44,762	49,291r	46,145
Autogenerators	1,961	1,595	1,436r	1,637r	1,567
Heat generation *(5)*	-	649	714r	759r	759
Coke manufacture	8,169	7,919	8,229	7,132	5,807
Blast furnaces	559	494	456	764	726
Patent fuel manufacture and low temperature carbonisation	635	646	540	496	436
Energy industry use	**5**	**10**	**12**	**10**	**9**
Coal extraction	5	10	12	10	9
Final consumption	**5,196**	**4,828**	**2,713r**	**4,156r**	**3,193**
Industry	**2,414**	**2,040**	**724r**	**1,722r**	**1,325**
Unclassified	-	-			
Iron and steel	9	12	2	1	-
Non-ferrous metals	208	346	82r	219r	146
Mineral products	763	586	202r	504r	500
Chemicals	643	434	83r	409r	278
Mechanical engineering etc	28	25	8	14	14
Electrical engineering etc	3	7	2	4	4
Vehicles	46	79	44r	70r	53
Food, beverages etc	288	215	110r	217r	189
Textiles, clothing, leather, etc	69	58	34r	48r	20
Pulp, paper, printing etc	108	121	54r	168r	76
Other industries	249	157	103r	68r	45
Construction	-	-			
Transport	-	-			
Other	**2,782**	**2,788**	**1,990r**	**2,434r**	**1,868**
Domestic	2,366	2,517	1,908r	2,361	1,804
Public administration	312	229	60r	52r	45
Commercial	4	4	7	6	5
Agriculture	9	7	7	5	6
Miscellaneous	91	31	8	10	8
Non energy use	-	-	-	-	-
Stocks at end of year *(4)*					
Distributed stocks	12,602	13,174	12,005	14,953r	13,704
Of which:					
Major power producers	11,270	12,097	11,034	13,620r	12,542
Coke ovens	1,312	1,054	943	1,309	1,148
Undistributed stocks	4,565	5,157	1,646	1,583	2,482
Total stocks	**17,167**	**18,331**	**13,651**	**16,536r**	**16,186**

(1) Stock fall (+), stock rise (-).

(2) Total supply minus total demand.

(3) Estimates of slurry etc. recovered from ponds, dumps, rivers, etc.

(4) Excludes distributed stocks held in merchants' yards, etc., mainly for the domestic market, and stocks held by the industrial sector.

(5) Heat generation data are not available before 1999. For earlier years coal used to generate heat for sale is allocated to final consumption by the industry sector making the sale.

2.8 Supply and consumption of coke oven coke, coke breeze and other manufactured solid fuels

Thousand tonnes

	1998	1999	2000	2001	2002
Coke oven coke					
Supply					
Production	6,178	5,837	6,058	5,306	4,335
Imports	753	389	421	101	226
Exports	-93	-79	-243	-176	-272
Stock change (1)	-314	+290	-216	+116	+261
Transfers	-1,223	-951	-827	-982	-927
Total supply	**5,301**	**5,486**	**5,193**	**4,365**	**3,624**
Statistical difference (2)	-131	-154	-123	-29	-34
Total demand	**5,432**	**5,640**	**5,316**	**4,394**	**3,658**
Transformation	**4,908**	**5,113**	**4,764**	**3,957**	**3,224**
Blast furnaces	4,908	5,113	4,764	3,957	3,224
Energy industry use	**27**	**20**	**37**	**32**	**17**
Final consumption	**497**	**507**	**515**	**405**	**417**
Industry	**377**	**386**	**370**	**338**	**239**
Unclassified	220	226	191	181	151
Iron and steel	23	17	19	32	29
Non-ferrous metals	134	143	160	125	59
Other	**120**	**121**	**145**	**67**	**178**
Domestic	120	121	145	67	178
Stocks at end of year (3)	**623**	**333**	**548**	**432**	**171**
Coke breeze					
Supply					
Production	37	33	148	210	224
Imports	78	40	62	56	12
Exports	-196	-165	-138	-143	-46
Stock change (1)	+42	-40	+22r	+8	-14
Transfers	+1,163	+1,035	+827	+982	+927
Total supply	**1,124**	**903**	**921r**	**1,112r**	**1,102**
Statistical difference (2)	-66	-206	-115r	-7	+27
Total demand	**1,190**	**1,109**	**1,036**	**1,120**	**1,075**
Transformation	**287**	**189**	**202**	**313**	**331**
Coke manufacture	50	24	14	9	-
Blast furnaces	237	165	188	304	331
Energy industry use	**-**	**-**	**-**	**-**	**-**
Final consumption	**903**	**920**	**834**	**807**	**744**
Industry	**903**	**920**	**834**	**807**	**744**
Unclassified	81	33	41	16	44
Iron and steel	822	887	793	791	700
Stocks at end of year (3)	**189**	**229**	**207**	**199**	**213**
Other manufactured solid fuels					
Supply					
Production	616	635	537	487	430
Imports	10	6	14	8	18
Exports	-56	-54	-79	-75	-67
Stock change (1)	+87	-7	+38	+37	+17
Total supply	**657**	**580**	**510**	**457**	**398**
Statistical difference (2)	+13	-5	-22	-38	-25
Total demand	**644**	**585**	**532**	**495**	**423**
Transformation	**-**	**-**	**-**	**-**	**-**
Energy industry use	**14**	**13**	**11**	**12**	**10**
Patent fuel manufacture	14	13	11	12	10
Final consumption	**630**	**572**	**521**	**483**	**413**
Industry	**32**	**18**	**25**	**37**	**22**
Unclassified	32	18	25	37	22
Other	**598**	**554**	**496**	**446**	**391**
Domestic	598	554	496	446	391
Stocks at end of year (3)	**134**	**141**	**103**	**66**	**49**

(1) Stock fall (+), stock rise (-).
(2) Total supply minus total demand.
(3) Producers stocks and distributed stocks.

2.9 Supply and consumption of coke oven gas, blast furnace gas, benzole and tars

GWh

	1998	1999	2000	2001	2002
Coke oven gas					
Supply					
Production	13,126	12,090	12,661r	11,516r	9,549
Imports	-	-	-	-	-
Exports	-	-	-	-	-
Transfers (1)	+630	+528	+460r	+68r	+104
Total supply	**13,756**	**12,618**	**13,121r**	**11,584**	**9,653**
Statistical difference (2)	+127	-210	-264	+142r	+62
Total demand	**13,629**	**12,828**	**13,385r**	**11,442r**	**9,591**
Transformation	**1,963**	**3,748**	**3,797r**	**3,383r**	**3,011**
Electricity generation	1,963	1,999	1,987r	1,490r	1,480
Heat generation (4)	-	1,749	1,810r	1,893r	1,531
Other	-	-	-	-	-
Energy industry use	**6,855**	**6,522**	**6,748**	**6,053**	**5,321**
Coke manufacture	5,690	5,283	5,555	4,720	4,270
Blast furnaces	1,165	1,239	1,193	1,333	1,051
Other	-	-	-	-	-
Losses	**335**	**173**	**325**	**231**	**387**
Final consumption	**4,476**	**2,385**	**2,515r**	**1,775r**	**872**
Industry	**4,476**	**2,385**	**2,515r**	**1,775r**	**872**
Unclassified	116	72	200r	363r	32
Iron and steel	4,360	2,313	2,315r	1,412r	840
Blast furnace gas					
Supply					
Production	20,114	19,023	17,743r	14,767r	13,130
Imports	-	-	-	-	-
Exports	-	-	-	-	-
Transfers (1)	-22	-22	-17r	-3r	-4
Total supply	**20,092**	**19,001**	**17,726r**	**14,764**	**13,126**
Statistical difference (2)	+291	-142	-103r	-100	-93
Total demand	**19,801**	**19,143**	**17,829r**	**14,864**	**13,219**
Transformation	**8,512**	**9,585**	**9,089r**	**6,030r**	**5,836**
Electricity generation	8,512	8,476	8,470r	5,493r	5,402
Heat generation (4)	-	1,109	619r	537r	434
Other	-	-	-	-	-
Energy industry use	**6,578**	**6,219**	**6,034r**	**4,709**	**4,095**
Coke manufacture	1,085	1,083	1,057r	649	510
Blast furnaces	5,493	5,136	4,977r	4,060	3,585
Other	-	-	-	-	-
Losses	**1,474**	**1,723**	**1,592r**	**965**	**648**
Final consumption	**3,237**	**1,616**	**1,114r**	**3,160r**	**2,640**
Industry	**3,237**	**1,616**	**1,114r**	**3,160r**	**2,640**
Unclassified	-	-	-	-	-
Iron and steel	3,237	1,616	1,114r	3,160r	2,640
Benzole and tars (3)					
Supply					
Production	2,542	2,343	2,393	2,115	1,880
Final consumption	**2,542**	**2,343**	**2,393**	**2,115**	**1,880**
Unclassified	617	580	597	522	469
Iron and steel	1,925	1,763	1,796	1,593	1,411

(1) To and from synthetic coke oven gas, see paragraph 2.48.
(2) Total supply minus total demand.
(3) Because of the small number of benzole suppliers, figures for benzole and tars cannot be given separately.
(4) Heat generation data are not available before 1999. For earlier years coke oven gas and blast furnace gas used to generate heat for sale are allocated to final consumption by the iron and steel sector.

2.10 Major deep mines in production at 22 April 2003[1]

Licensee	Site	Location
Betws Anthracite Ltd	Betws Colliery	Carmarthenshire
Coalpower Ltd	Hatfield Colliery	Yorkshire
J Flack & Sons Ltd	Hay Royds Colliery	Yorkshire
Goitre Tower Anthracite Ltd	Tower Colliery	Rhondda, Cynon Taff
UK Coal plc	Clipstone Colliery	Nottinghamshire
	Daw Mill Colliery	Warwickshire
	Ellington Colliery	Northumberland
	Harworth Colliery	Nottinghamshire
	Kellingley Colliery	Yorkshire
	Maltby Colliery	Yorkshire
	Riccall (Selby Complex)	Yorkshire
	Rossington Colliery	Yorkshire
	Stillingfleet (Selby Complex)	Yorkshire
	Thoresby Colliery	Nottinghamshire
	Welbeck Colliery	Nottinghamshire
	Wistow Colliery (Selby Complex)	Yorkshire

(1) In addition there were 8 smaller deep mines in production at 22 April 2003.

Notes:

Clipstone Colliery, owned by UK Coal, ceased production in April 2003.

UK Coal plc has announced that the Selby Complex (consisting of Riccall, Stillingfleet and Wistow mines) is due to close by spring 2004.

Source: The Coal Authority

2.11 Opencast sites in production at 22 April 2003[1]

Licensee	Site Name	Location
Aardvark TMV Ltd (trading as ATH Resources)	Skares Road, Nr Cumnock	East Ayrshire
C Rees & Sons Plant Hire Ltd	Lletty'r Crudd	Carmarthenshire
Celtic Energy Ltd	Brynhenllys Revised	Powys
	Margam Opencast (Parc Slip West)	Neath & Port Talbot
	Nant Helen Extension (Nant Gyrlais)	Powys
	Selar	Neath & Port Talbot
Faldane Ltd	Oxenfoord West	Midlothian
G M Mining Ltd	Boglea Site	North Lanarkshire
	Drumshangie	North Lanarkshire
George Raeburn	Edge Farm Extension	South Lanarkshire
Gordon Harrison Ltd	St John's 2	Wakefield
H J Banks & Company Ltd	Delhi Site	Northumberland
	Lewden	Barnsley
	Moss Carr Site	Leeds
	Pegswood Moor Extension 2	Northumberland
	Pegswood Moor Farm	Northumberland
	Pegswood Moor Farm Extension	Northumberland
	Watsonhead (HJB)	North Lanarkshire
	Woodhead Site	Barnsley
Hall Construction Services Ltd	New Albion Revised	Leicestershire
	Ravenswood Grange	Gateshead
I & H Brown Ltd	Begg Farm	Fife
	Colton Remainder	Fife
J Fenton & Sons (Contractors) Ltd	Meadowhill Farm Gartknowie Extension	Clackmannanshire
Law Mining Ltd	Garleffan Extension	East Ayrshire
LEM Resources Ltd	Crock Hey Site	St Helens
Scottish Coal Company Ltd	Broken Cross & Extension	South Lanarkshire
	Glentaggart	South Lanarkshire
	Greenbank (St Ninians)	Fife
	House of Water	East Ayrshire
	Pennyvenie	East Ayrshire
	Pennyvenie Area L North	East Ayrshire
	Rigghead Farm Prospect Extension	East Ayrshire
	Spireslack Revised	East Ayrshire
	Wilsontown *	South Lanarkshire
UK Coal Mining Ltd	Arkwright Colliery Reclamation	Derbyshire
	Arkwright Extension	Derbyshire
	Ashby Woulds (Hicks Lodge)	Leicestershire
	Burnfoot Moor Extension 2	East Ayrshire
	Ferry Moor Revised-Two Gates Area	Barnsley
	Forge & Monument Restoration	Derbyshire
	Hilltop Group-Southfield Site	Durham
	Maiden's Hall	Northumberland
	Moorhouse (Anglers East)	Wakefield
	Orgreave Reclamation	Rotherham
	Park Brook Reclamation (High Moor)	Derbyshire
	Stobswood	Northumberland

(1) There were 46 opencast sites in production as at 22 April 2003.

Source: The Coal Authority

Note: The site marked * is currently developing and not yet in production.

Chapter 3
Petroleum

Introduction

3.1   This chapter contains commodity balances covering the supply and disposal of primary oils (crude oil and natural gas liquids), feedstocks (including partly processed oils) and petroleum products in the UK in the period 2000 to 2002. These balances are given in Tables 3.1 to 3.6. Additional data have been included in supplementary tables on areas not covered by the format of the balances. This extra information includes details on refinery capacities and aggregates for refinery operations, and extra detail on deliveries into consumption, including breakdowns by country, sector and industry.

3.2   Statistics of imports and exports of crude oil, other refinery feedstocks and petroleum products, refinery receipts, refinery throughput and output and deliveries of petroleum products are obtained from the United Kingdom oil industry and the Department of Trade and Industry's Petroleum Production Reporting System.

3.3   The annual figures relate to calendar years or the ends of calendar years. In the majority of tables the data cover the United Kingdom.

3.4   Information on long-term trends (Tables 3.1.1 and 3.1.2) and the annex on the oil and gas resources of the UK (Annex F) are now only available on DTI's energy statistics web site www.dti.gov.uk/energy/inform/dukes/dukes2003/03longterm.pdf and www.dti.gov.uk/energy/inform/dukes/dukes2003/annexf.pdf. This information is included to provide a more complete picture of the UK oil and gas production sector.

Commodity balances for primary oil (Tables 3.1, 3.2 and 3.3)

3.5   These tables show details of the production, supply and disposals of primary oils (crude oil and natural gas liquids (NGLs)) and feedstocks in 2002, 2001 and 2000. The upper half of the table (Supply) equates to the upstream oil industry, covering the supply chain from the production of oil and NGLs, recorded by individual oil terminals and oil fields, to their disposal to export or to UK refineries (see Annex F, Table F.2 on DTI's energy statistics web site). The lower half of the table covers the use of these primary oils, including the amount used as a fuel during the extraction process (i.e. burned to provide power for drilling and pumping operations) and as inputs into refineries, as recorded by the refineries. The statistical difference in the tables thus represents the differences between data reported by these different sources and the sites of production and consumption.

3.6   Gross production of crude oil and NGLs in 2002 was 116 million tonnes, a decline of less than 1 per cent on 2001 but 15 per cent lower than the peak production level of 137 million tonnes in 1999. About three-quarters of the United Kingdom's primary oil production in 2002 was exported, and imported crude oil accounted for 66 per cent of UK requirements. Feedstocks (including partly processed oils) made up 9 per cent of total imports of oil in 2002. Total oil imports in 2002 were 6 per cent higher than in 2001. Exports of primary oils and feedstocks in 2002 were, at 87 million tonnes, similar to those recorded in 2001 but some 7 per cent lower than the level in 2000. Net exports in 2002 were 53 per cent higher than imports and made a significant contribution to the UK economy (see Annex G on DTI's energy statistics web site). This is down from previous years where exports were 71 per cent higher than imports in 2000 and 62 per cent higher in 2001. Further declines in exports and increases in imports will be seen as indigenous production continues to decline. Chart 3.1 illustrates recent trends in production, imports and exports of crude oil, NGLs and feedstocks.

Chart 3.1: Production, imports and exports of primary oils, 1997 to 2002

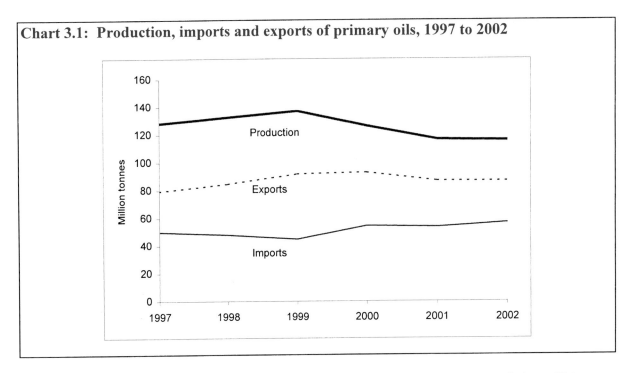

3.7   The UK currently produces more than enough crude oil to meet its own needs but still imports crude oil. Two factors make it financially attractive to export UK produced crude oil rather than use it in the UK, with imports being brought in to make up the difference. Firstly, UK crude oil can command a higher price than other crude oils on the international market as it generally contains lower levels of contaminants such as sulphur (which can make the crude oil difficult to refine). Secondly, UK crude oil contains a higher proportion of the lighter hydrocarbon molecules, resulting in higher yields of products such as motor spirit and other transport fuels. In addition, some crude oils are specifically imported for the heavier hydrocarbons they contain which are needed for the manufacture of various petroleum products, such as bitumen and lubricating oils.

3.8   Chart 3.2 compares the level of imports and exports of crude oil, NGLs and feedstocks with those for petroleum products over the period 1997 to 2002. In the beginning of the period imports of crude oil were lower due to the higher levels of output from the United Kingdom Continental Shelf. Imports of petroleum products increased from 1997 to 2001 while exports of products decreased although the trends switched in 2002 with imports decreasing and exports increasing. The 1997-2001 trends resulted from reductions in refinery processing capacity in the UK following the closures of the Gulf Oil refinery in Milford Haven in December 1997 and the Shell Haven refinery in Essex at the end of November 1999. The reduction in capacity has led to reductions in the levels of exports of petroleum products along with a corresponding increase in the level of imports of products to ensure UK demand for petroleum products continues to be met. At the same time imports of crude oil and feedstocks declined until 1999. From 2000 this trend reversed due to the beginning of a decline in crude oil production. Imports of crude oil and feedstocks were marginally lower in 2001 than in 2000 although this probably reflects the increased number of prolonged shutdowns and slowdowns at a number of refineries in the first half of 2001 for upgrade work for the introduction of ultra low sulphur petrol. As noted above, imports of crude oil and feedstocks have increased in 2002. Additional analysis of the exports and imports of oil products is given in paragraphs 3.11 to 3.19 and the long term trend internet section (3.1.2-3.1.9) and additional details about trends in UK oil production are given in Annex F on DTI's energy statistics web site.

Chart 3.2: Imports and exports of crude oil and petroleum products, 1997 to 2002

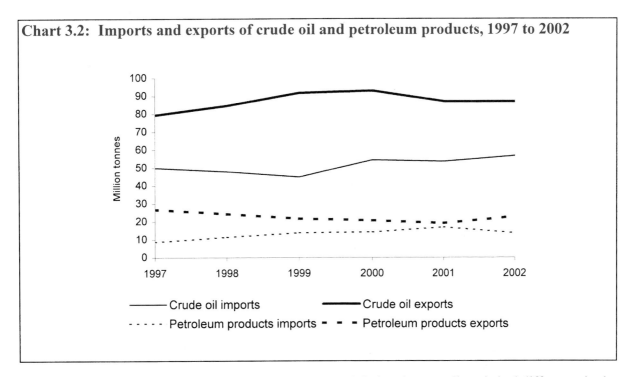

3.9   It will be seen from the balances in Tables 3.1 to 3.3 that the overall statistical difference in the primary oil balance for 2002 is minus 337 thousand tonnes. This means that the total quantities of crude oil and NGLs reported as being produced by the individual UK production fields are 337 thousand tonnes less than the totals reported by UK oil companies as being received by refineries or going for export. The reasons for this are discussed later in paragraphs 3.35 to 3.39.

Commodity balances - Petroleum products (Tables 3.4 to 3.6)

3.10 These tables show details of the production, supply and disposals of petroleum products into the UK market in 2002, 2001 and 2000. The upper half of the table (Supply) covers details of the overall availability of these products in the UK as calculated by observing production at refineries, and adding in the impact of trade (imports and exports), stock changes, product transfers and deliveries to international marine bunkers. The lower half of the table covers the uses made of these products, including the uses made within refineries as fuels in the refining process, and details of the amounts reported by oil companies within the UK as delivered for final consumption.

Supply of petroleum products

3.11 Total petroleum products output from UK refineries in 2002 was 84½ million tonnes, which was 3 per cent higher than in the level in 2001 (but 2 per cent lower than 2000). Prices on international markets for key oil products remained high during 2000, which led to the level of refinery activity in the UK staying at the same level as in 1999 despite the reduction in UK's overall refinery capacity following the closure of the Shell Haven refinery in December 1999. The remaining UK refineries increased both their processing capacities and levels of utilisation to take advantage of the more profitable market conditions of high prices for products on international markets. The first half of 2001 saw the closure of, or slowdowns at, a number of refineries for upgrade work for the introduction of ultra low sulphur petrol. Whilst these refineries were shut down or running slowly for this upgrade work the opportunity was taken to carry out major maintenance overhauls, which in some cases resulted in prolonged shutdowns. The fall in refinery output in 2001 was due to the extended shutdowns in this period while the increase in 2002 reflects the refineries operating normally following the upgrade work in the previous year.

3.12 In terms of output of individual products, production of aviation turbine fuel decreased by 5 per cent in 2002 compared to 2001 while production of motor spirit and gas/diesel oil both increased (by 8 and 6½ per cent respectively). This increased production of road transport fuels was a direct result of the upgrading of the UK refineries to produce low sulphur fuels.

3.13 The decrease in production of aviation turbine fuel over the last few years is primarily due to the fact that aviation turbine fuel and gas diesel oil are extracted from the same fraction of crude oil (middle distillates), though to different quality criteria. Therefore, as production of gas/diesel oil has increased, there is less of the middle distillates fraction of the crude oil processed at refineries available for production of aviation turbine fuel. In addition, the closure of the Shell Haven refinery in late 1999 had a significant effect on reducing the output of aviation turbine fuel and motor spirit in 2000, with some 50 per cent of its total production consisting of these two fuels. More information on refinery capacity in the UK and refinery capacity utilisation is given in paragraphs 3.40 and 3.41.

3.14   The UK has been a net exporter of oil products every year since 1974, with the exception of 1984 due to the effects of the industrial action in the coal-mining sector. Exports of petroleum products were 23 million tonnes in 2002, 19½ per cent higher than in 2001 and 10½ per cent higher than in 2000. The increase in exports is mainly due to the refinery upgrade work on low sulphur fuels mentioned above but also due to favourable product prices in overseas markets. In contrast, imports of oil products into the UK were 14 million tonnes in 2002, which were 19½ per cent lower than in 2001 but 3½ per cent higher than in 2000. Overall, the UK net exports increased to 9 million tonnes in 2002, up from the low level of 2 million tonnes reported in 2001 and higher than the 6½ million tonnes in 2000.

3.15 The United States remains one of the key markets for UK exports of oil products, with 3½ million tonnes being exported there in 2002. These exports made up 17 per cent of total UK exports of oil products in 2002, with the main other countries receiving UK exports of petroleum products being Belgium, Ireland, Italy, France, Germany the Netherlands, and Spain. The main sources of the UK's imports of petroleum products in 2002 were France, Kuwait, the Netherlands, Germany, Saudi Arabia and the UAE.

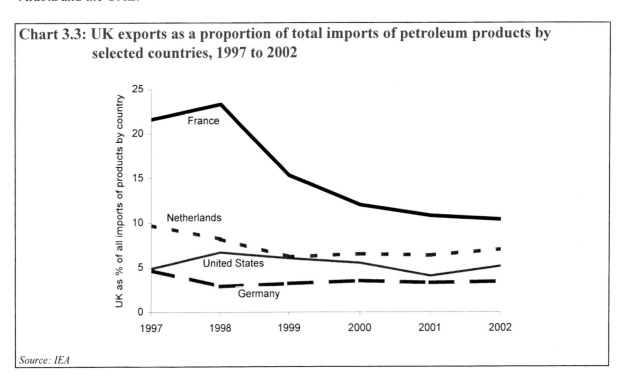

Chart 3.3: UK exports as a proportion of total imports of petroleum products by selected countries, 1997 to 2002

Source: IEA

3.16 Chart 3.3 shows how the UK has penetrated selected overseas markets for its petroleum products. UK products supplied 5 per cent of the total volume of US imports of petroleum products in 2002 (mostly in the form of motor spirit) and 11, 7 and 3½ per cent respectively of the total imports of petroleum products into France, the Netherlands and Germany (mostly as gas oil for heating, motor spirit and fuel oil). The UK regularly supplies the vast majority of total oil products imported into Ireland (mostly motor spirit and DERV fuel for transport and gas/diesel oil and burning oil for heating).

3.17 Differences in product types explain why the UK imports petroleum products when it has a surplus available for export. Exports in 2002 were mainly made up of motor spirit (5½ million tonnes), gas/diesel oil (6½ million tonnes) and fuel oil (5½ million tonnes). Imports were made up of aviation turbine fuel (5 million tonnes), motor spirit (2 million tonnes) and gas/diesel oil (4 million tonnes). The make up of refinery structure in the UK is such that it contains a surplus of capacity for some petroleum products such as motor spirit, leading to a surplus availability within the UK for export. Imports take place to cover specific periods of heavy demand within the UK, such as around the time of the Budget or during the summer, or cover production shortfalls in the refinery shutdowns for maintenance.

3.18 Similarly for gas oil/diesel oil, the exports from the UK tend to be of lower grades of gas/diesel oil for use as heating fuels, while the imports tend to be of higher-grade gas/diesel oil with a low sulphur content. With the introduction of low sulphur DERV fuel and motor spirit into the UK market (see paragraph 3.51 below) and the related increased production capacity at UK refineries for these fuels, UK imports of these products reduced in 2002 to return to broad levels seen in 2000. Aviation turbine fuel is imported simply because the UK cannot make enough of it to meet demand. It is derived from the same sort of hydrocarbons as gas/diesel oil, and as such there is a physical limit to how much can be made from the amount of oil processed in the UK.

3.19 More information on the structure of refineries in the UK and trends in imports and exports of crude oil and oil products is given in the long-term trends section on DTI's energy statistics web site (Table 3.1.1).

3.20 In 2002, 9½ per cent of UK production of fuel oil and 5 per cent of gas oil/diesel oil production went into international marine bunkers, totalling 2½ million tonnes of products, 3 per cent of total UK refinery production in the year. These are sales of fuels that are destined for consumption on ocean going vessels. As such the products cannot be classified as being consumed within the UK, and these quantities are thus treated in a similar way to exports in the commodity balances. It should be noted that these quantities do not include deliveries of fuels for use in UK coastal waters, which are counted as UK consumption and the figures given in the transport section of the commodity balances.

3.21 Details are given in the balances of stocks of products held within the UK either at refineries or oil distribution centres such as coastal oil terminals (undistributed stocks). In addition, some information is available on stocks of oil products held by major electricity generators (distributed stocks). However, these figures exclude any details of stocks held by distributors of fuels or stocks held at retail sites, such as petrol stations. The figures for stocks in the balances also solely relate to those stocks currently present in the UK and as such exclude any stocks that might be held by UK oil companies in other countries under bilateral agreements.

3.22 In order for the UK to be prepared for any oil emergency, the UK Government places an obligation on companies supplying oil products into final consumption in the UK to maintain a certain level of stocks of oil products used as fuels. As part of this, oil companies are allowed to hold stocks abroad under official governmental bilateral agreements that can count towards their stocking obligations. The stocks figures in Table 3.10 take account of these bilateral stocks (see paragraphs 3.65 to 3.68) to give a true picture of the amount of stocks available to the UK.

Consumption of petroleum products

3.23 To help users gain the maximum information from the commodity balances, the text in the following section examines the data given on the consumption of oil products in the period 2000 to 2002. The main sectors of consumers will be looked at first (going down the tables) and then the data for individual products will be looked at (going across the tables).

3.24 Table 3.4 shows how overall deliveries of petroleum products into consumption in the UK in 2002, including those used by the UK refining industry as fuels within the refining process and all other uses, totalled 75 million tonnes. This was 1 per cent lower than in 2001 and 2½ per cent lower than in 2000. Deliveries have been on a declining trend since 1990, barring a slight increase in 1996.

3.25 From the tables, one of the most significant changes in deliveries of products in recent years has been the decline in use for electricity generation. In 2002 only 678 million tonnes of oil products were used for electricity generation by major power producers and autogenerators of electricity, compared with 955 million tonnes in 2001 and much higher levels in earlier years (see long term trends, Table 3.1.2 on DTI's energy statistics web site). This change is primarily a result of the move by major electricity producers away from oil-based fuels towards using natural gas as their fuel of choice for electricity generation. This trend is also reflected in the declining level of usage by auto-producers of electricity over the period, despite the growth in auto-generation of electricity by industry as a whole, and in the significant declining use in heat generation. The data for fuels used in autogeneration of electricity in 2000 and 2001 have been revised in the light of new information that has become available.

3.26 The data included under the blast furnaces heading of the Transformation sector represents fuel oil used in the manufacture of iron and steel which is directly injected into blast furnaces, as opposed to being used as a fuel to heat the blast furnaces. The fuel used for the latter (mostly gas oil/diesel oil) is included under the blast furnaces heading of the Energy Industry Use sector.

3.27 Other figures in the Energy Industry Use sector relate to uses within the UK refining industry in the manufacture of oil products. These are products either used as fuels during refining processes or products used by the refineries themselves as opposed to being sold to other consumers, but excluding any fuels used for the generation of electricity. These amounts are included in the Transformation sector totals. Given the interest in the total amounts of fuels used within refineries, Table 3.7 includes data on total refinery fuel usage (i.e. including that used in the generation of electricity) over the period 1997 to 2002. The data under the other headings of the Energy Industry Use sector represent fuels used by the gas supply industry.

3.28 Final consumption of oil products in 2002, i.e. excluding any uses by the energy industries themselves or for transformation purposes, amounted to 69½ million tonnes, the same as in 2001 and 1 million tonnes lower than in 2000. Chart 3.4 shows the breakdown of consumption for energy uses by each sector in 2002.

3.29 The total amount of oil products used by industry was in decline in the middle-1990s due to industry moving away from the use of oil products as an energy source. In the three-year period 1998 to 2000 oil use by industry was fairly constant. In 2001 industrial use of oil products increased by ½ million tonnes to 6 million tonnes on 2000 and has remained at this level in 2002.

Chart 3.4: Petroleum products used for energy (shares by main sector), 2002

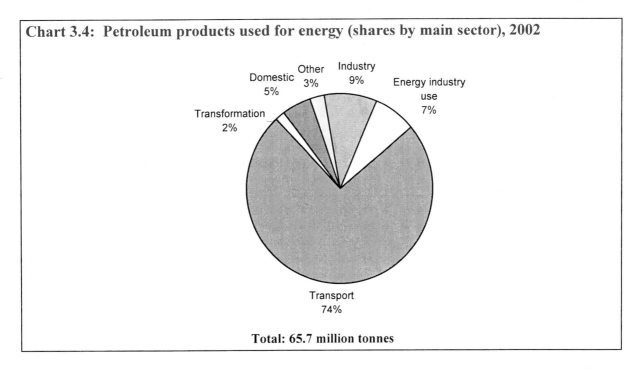

Total: 65.7 million tonnes

3.30 Transport sector consumption in 2002 was ½ a per cent lower than in 2001 and 2 per cent lower than in 2000. Lower usage for air transport in 2002 compared to 2001 (down 1½ per cent) with lower consumption of motor spirit (down 5½ per cent) being partly offset by an increase in use of DERV fuel (up 7½ per cent). In 2002, transport usage totalled 48½ million tonnes and accounted for 70 per cent of total final consumption of oil products. Consumption by other sectors decreased by 7½ per cent in 2002 compared with 2001.

3.31 Consumption of non-energy products increased to 9½ million tonnes in 2002, up by 8 per cent when compared to 2001. In 2002, non-energy products made up 14 per cent of final consumption of oil products, compared with 13 per cent in 2001. More detail on the non-energy uses of oil products, by product and by type of use where such information is available, is given in Table 3D and paragraphs 3.57 to 3.63 later in this text.

3.32 Looking at the final consumption of individual products, 77½ per cent of total final consumption in 2002 was made up of consumption of just three products; aviation turbine fuel, motor spirit and gas/diesel oil, ie transport products. Consumption of aviation turbine fuel decreased by 1½ per cent in 2002 to 10½ million tonnes due to the decline in air travel following the 11th September 2001 terrorist attacks. Changes in the consumption of aviation fuel are discussed in more detail in paragraphs 3.54 to 3.56 below. For motor spirit, consumption decreased by 5½ per cent in 2002. Total consumption of gas/diesel oil increased by 3 per cent in 2002 and, within this, that part of the total consumed as road fuel (ie as DERV) increased by 7½ per cent. More detailed information on consumption of motor spirit and gas oil/diesel oil over the period 1998 to 2002 is given in Table 3.8 and discussed in paragraphs 3.42 to 3.53.

3.33 As mentioned above, fuel oil consumption by electricity generators in the UK has declined in recent years. In 2002 total final consumption of fuel oil was 3¾ million tonnes compared with 4 million tonnes in 2001, down by 8½ per cent. This is due to decreased use by major power producers (down by 75 per cent) and in heat generation (down by 64 per cent). These large decreases were partially offset by a 30 per cent increase in industry usage of fuel oil. Further detail on the consumption of fuel oil broken down by grade is given in Table 3.8.

3.34 Tables 3.4 to 3.6 include estimates for the use of gas for road vehicles. These estimates were based on information on the amounts of duty received by HM Customs and Excise from the tax on gas used as a road fuel. It is estimated that some 86 thousand tonnes of gas (mostly butane or propane) was used in road vehicles in the UK in 2002. While a very small use when compared to overall consumption of these fuels and the consumption of fuels for road transport as a whole, the consumption of these gases for road transport in 2002 has risen four-fold since 2000.

Supply and disposal of products (Table 3.7)
3.35 This table brings together the commodity balances for primary oils and for petroleum products into a single overall balance table.

3.36 The statistical difference for primary oils in the table includes own use in onshore terminals and gas separation plants, losses, platform and other field stock changes. Another factor is the time lag that can exist between production and loading onto tankers being reported at an offshore field and the arrival of these tankers at onshore refineries and oil terminals. This gap is usually minimal and works such that any effect of this at the start of a month is balanced by a similar counterpart effect at the end of a month. However, there can be instances where the length of this interval can be significant and, if it happens at the end of a year, significant effects on the statistical differences seen for the years involved can result.

3.37 With the downstream sector, the statistical differences can similarly be used to assess the validity and consistency of the data. From the tables, these differences are generally a very small proportion of the totals involved.

3.38 Paragraphs 3.72 to 3.83 provide details on the reasons why statistical differences occur for the upstream and downstream sectors.

3.39 The downstream oil data reporting system was reviewed in late 2001 and early 2002 after some discrepancies in the reporting of refinery production data were identified. It was noticed that potential losses within the refining system could be incorrectly reported elsewhere. Given the impact of these factors on the statistical differences, corrections have been incorporated in the "Losses in refining process" line in Table 3.7 for the years affected, ie 1999 to 2002. Further work is planned to improve the quality of the downstream oil data over the next year.

Refinery capacity
3.40 Data for refinery capacity as at the end of 2002 are presented in Table 3A, with the location of these refineries illustrated in Map 3A. These figures are collected annually by the Department of Trade and Industry from individual oil companies. Capacity per annum for each refinery is derived by applying the rated capacity of the plant per day when on-stream by the number of days the plant was on stream during the year. Fluctuations in the number of days the refinery is active are usually the main reasons for annual changes in the level of capacity. Reforming capacity covers catalytic reforming, and cracking/conversion capacity covers processes for upgrading residual oils to lighter products, eg catalytic, thermal or hydro-cracking, visbreaking and coking.

Table 3A: UK refinery processing capacity as at end 2002 [(1)]

| (symbols relates to Map 3A) | Distillation | Million tonnes per annum | |
		Reforming	Cracking and Conversion
Shell UK Ltd			
❶ Stanlow	11.5	1.5	3.8
ExxonMobil Co. Ltd			
❷ Fawley	15.6	2.8	4.5
BP Ltd			
❸ Coryton	8.8	1.8	3.6
❹ Grangemouth	10.0	1.9	3.4
Total (BP)	18.8	3.7	7.1
TotalFinaElf Ltd.			
❺ Lindsey Oil Refinery Ltd South Killingholme	10.0	1.4	4.1
Texaco Refining Co. Ltd			
❻ Pembroke	10.1	1.5	6.1
Conoco Ltd			
❼ Killingholme	10.2	2.2	10.0
TotalFinaElf / Murco Pet. Ltd			
❽ Milford Haven	5.3	0.8	1.9
Petroplus International Ltd			
❾ North Tees	5.0	-	-
Petrochem Carless Ltd			
① Harwich	0.7	-	-
Eastham Refinery Ltd			
② Eastham	1.0	-	-
Nynas UK AB			
③ Dundee (Camperdown)	0.7	-	-
Total all refineries	88.9	13.8	37.5

(1) Rated design capacity per day on stream multiplied by the average number of days on stream.

Map 3A: Distribution of UK refineries active as at end 2002
Symbols relate to refinery details given in Table 3A

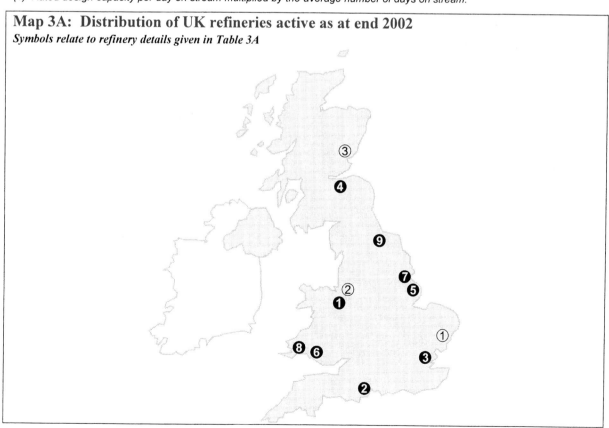

3.41 At the end of 2002 the UK had 9 major refineries operating, with three minor refineries in existence. Distillation capacity in the UK at the end of 2002 was 88.9 million tonnes, 0.8 million tonnes higher than at the end of 2001. Total UK reforming capacity at the end of 2002 was 0.1 million tonnes higher at 13.8 million tonnes and cracking and conversion capacity was 0.6 million tonnes higher at 37.5 million tonnes.

Additional information on inland deliveries of selected products (Table 3.8)
3.42 This table gives details for consumption of motor spirit, gas/diesel oil and fuel oils given in the main commodity balance tables for the period 1998 to 2002. It includes information on retail and commercial deliveries of motor spirit and DERV fuel that cannot be accommodated within the structure of the commodity balances, but which are of interest. The table also includes additional details of the quantities of motor spirit and DERV fuel sold collectively by hypermarket and supermarket companies in the UK.

3.43 Motor spirit deliveries in 2002 were 5½ per cent down compared to 2001, and 8½ per cent lower than in 2000. In contrast, deliveries of DERV fuel were 7½ per cent higher in 2002 compared to 2001 and 13 per cent higher than in 2000.

3.44 Several factors are behind the differing trends seen for motor spirit and DERV fuel. For a number of years, there has been a sustained year-on year increase in the number of diesel-engined vehicles in use in the UK. Diesel vehicles are more fuel-efficient than their petrol equivalents. In the National Travel Survey for 1999 to 2001 carried out by the Department for Transport, diesel-engined cars averaged 39 miles per gallon of fuel, compared with 30 miles per gallon for petrol-engined cars. Traditionally the greater fuel-efficiency of diesel vehicles had been at the expense of higher purchase prices and a performance deficit when compared to petrol-engined equivalents. More recently, the purchase prices between diesel and petrol engined vehicles have become more similar and improved technology has substantially reduced the performance deficit.

3.45 The price differential between DERV fuel and motor spirit has affected the relative demands for the two road fuels. In the early 1990s there was a significant price differential that worked in favour of using DERV fuel. For example, the average retail price for a litre of 4-star petrol in 1990 was 44.87 pence compared to 40.48 pence for a litre of DERV fuel, representing a 10 per cent saving. By December 2002, average retail prices for a litre of the most common grade of motor spirit purchased (ultra low sulphur petrol (ULSP)) and DERV fuel were 73.66 and 75.15 pence per litre respectively. In the mid 1990s, the policy on DERV taxation was changed for environmental reasons and the level of tax was increased to remove the favourable price differential. It is thought that the removal of the favourable differential significantly reduced the rate of transfer from petrol to diesel-engined vehicles in recent years that would have otherwise occurred.

3.46 Chart 3.5 shows how the share of total motor spirit deliveries accounted for by unleaded fuel has increased from 72 per cent in 1997 to effectively 100 per cent in 2002. It should be noted that, since 1st January 2000, retails sales of leaded petrol ceased as a result of the implementation of a European strategy to reduce pollution from road traffic (known as the Auto-Oil Directive). Since 2000 effectively all petrol sold has been unleaded. Prior to 2002, super premium unleaded accounted for about 2 per cent of total motor spirit deliveries but this has since grown to 3½ per cent in 2002. It is suspected that the recent increase in the use of this fuel is due the declining availability of lead replacement petrol (LRP).

3.47 Since 1990 there has been an overall trend of a reduction in the consumption of motor spirit in the UK. Consumption in 2002 was 18 per cent lower than the peak of 24 million tonnes of motor spirit in 1990. Chart 3.5 shows the drop in the level of consumption of leaded fuel caused by motorists switching to using unleaded petrol in their vehicles.

Chart 3.5: Motor spirit deliveries, 1997 to 2002

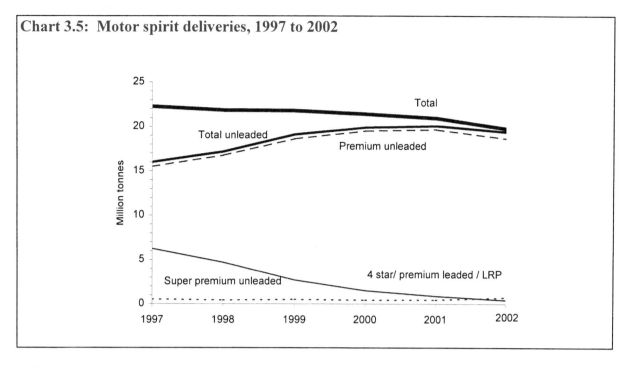

3.48 As mentioned above and as illustrated in Chart 3.6, the large differential between the price of a litre of leaded and unleaded motor spirit helped encourage motorists to switch from leaded to unleaded petrol. In addition, the implementation of the Auto-Oil Directive banned the general sale of leaded petrol (4-star) from 1st January 2000 giving a final push for motorists to switch to unleaded fuels.

3.49 The switch to unleaded petrol provided an impetus for people to change their vehicles to either new ones or those of more recent manufacture. The resultant reduction in the age of the vehicle stock has probably further reduced overall motor spirit consumption, as newer vehicles tend to be more fuel efficient due to improved technology.

Chart 3.6: UK prices of motor spirit and DERV fuel, 1997 to 2002

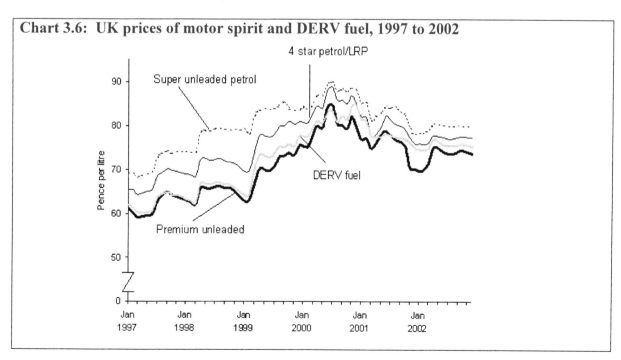

3.50 Chart 3.6 illustrates the large differential that existed between the price of 4-star leaded petrol and DERV fuel, with the latter being priced at similar levels to premium grade unleaded petrol. As with the differential between leaded and unleaded petrol, this price differential also worked to encourage motorists to convert to diesel-engined vehicles. Chart 3.7 contains details of vehicle licence registrations for private cars during each year for the period 1992 to 2002, broken down by type of engine. Whilst the number of petrol-engined vehicles licensed only grew by 8 per cent, the number of diesel-engined vehicles licensed has increased more than four-fold in the same period.

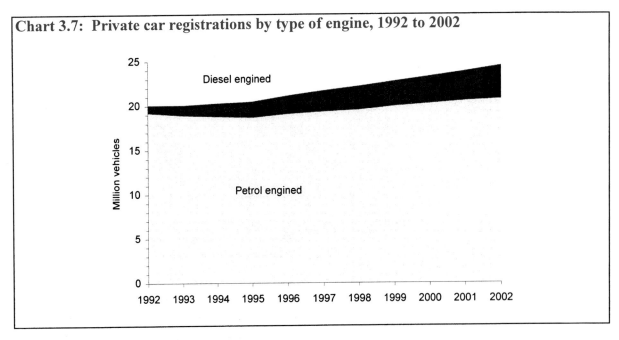

Chart 3.7: Private car registrations by type of engine, 1992 to 2002

3.51 Although not specifically covered by the statistics included in this Digest, differential duty rates have been used to encourage the switch to low sulphur road fuels, specifically Ultra Low Sulphur Diesel fuel (ULSD) and Ultra Low Sulphur Petrol (ULSP). This extra differential has mostly been used to allow producers to cover the additional costs of providing the ULSD and ULSP, initially through covering the extra cost of importing these low sulphur products and then latterly through funding changes in refinery processes. By mid 2002, 100 per cent of UK refinery capacity for the production of premium grade unleaded petrol (the grade replaced by ULSP) had been converted over to produce ULSP. The introduction of duty differentials have had a significant effect on moving consumers over to what are regarded as more environmentally friendly fuels.

3.52 Sales by super/hypermarkets have taken an increasing share of retail deliveries (i.e. deliveries to dealers) of motor spirit and DERV fuel in recent years as Table 3B shows. These figures have been derived from a survey of super/hypermarket companies to collect details of their sales of motor spirit and DERV fuel. The share of total deliveries (ie including deliveries direct to commercial consumers) is shown in brackets.

Table 3B: Super/hypermarkets share of retail deliveries, 1998 to 2002

per cent

	Motor spirit		DERV fuel	
1998	24.0	(23.6r)	17.5	(7.6)
1999	25.6r	(25.2r)	18.7r	(8.6r)
2000	27.0r	(26.3r)	19.3r	(9.2r)
2001	28.2	(27.4)	19.9	(9.9)
2002	30.6	(29.8)	21.3	(10.5)

Figures in brackets are shares of total deliveries.

3.53 The increases seen in recent years represent an increase in sales by super/hypermarket companies although the percentage shares are also affected by the decline in the overall deliveries of motor spirit in the UK seen in these years as mentioned earlier. Hypermarket deliveries of motor spirit in 2002 were 3¾ per cent higher than 2001 while their DERV deliveries increased by 13 per cent. For motor spirit in particular, the hypermarkets are being noticeably successful at increasing their sales as overall consumption declines.

Aviation fuel

3.54 Data are given in Tables 3.4 to 3.6 on the changing amounts of aviation turbine fuel (ATF) kerosene being consumed in the UK. The long-term trends section on the Internet discusses the trend seen since 1970 in the use of ATF kerosene in the UK. Overall, deliveries in the UK in 2002 were 1½ per cent lower than in 2001.

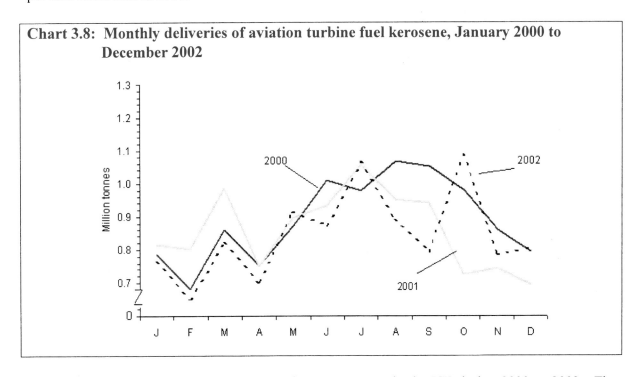

Chart 3.8: Monthly deliveries of aviation turbine fuel kerosene, January 2000 to December 2002

3.55 Chart 3.8 shows monthly deliveries of ATF Kerosene in the UK during 2000 to 2002. The seasonal peak in deliveries in the summer months is clearly evident. In 2000 the deliveries in the summer months were much higher than expected largely as a result of widespread disruptions to the UK rail service that prompted a significant increase in the level of domestic UK passenger movements as travellers turned to air travel as an alternative to rail travel. In 2001 the terrorist attacks on the United States on 11th September had a significant impact on the global aviation industry with many people subsequently reluctant to fly. The chart clearly illustrates the sharp fall in ATF deliveries in the last quarter of 2001. As mentioned above, ATF deliveries fell by 1½ percent in 2002 when compared to 2001 as the impact of the terrorist attacks continued to severely affect the global aviation industry into early 2002. The recovery of the aviation industry has been offset by continued international instability maintaining many people's reluctance to travel on longer distance or international flights. In particular, fear of subsequent terrorist actions in the run up the anniversary of the 11th September attacks suppressed deliveries in September 2002.

3.56 It would, however, be incorrect to assume that all sections of the aviation industry suffered equally. Despite the downturn in long-haul flights that have severely affected the international airlines, domestic air passenger movements within the UK have grown by 9 per cent in 2002 when compared with 2001. It should be noted the domestic passenger movements between 2000 and 2001 had increased by 2 per cent. Chart 3.9 illustrates this with details of passenger numbers on domestic flights operated by UK airlines in 2002 compared with figures for 2001 and 2000. This clearly shows that 11th September events had a more modest impact upon domestic flights. Figures on seat kilometres used (a measure of the total distances passengers flew) from the Department for Transport showed decreases in both 2001 and 2002, reflecting the continued impact on international flights.

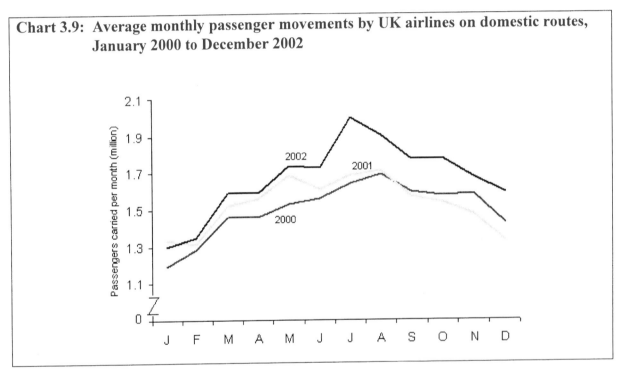

Chart 3.9: Average monthly passenger movements by UK airlines on domestic routes, January 2000 to December 2002

Additional information on inland deliveries for non-energy uses

3.57 Table 3C below summarises additional data on the non–energy uses made of the total deliveries of oil products included as the bottom line in the commodity balances in Tables 3.4 to 3.6. It provides extra information on the uses of lubricating oils and greases by use, and details of products used as petro-chemical feedstocks.

3.58 All inland deliveries of lubricating oils and petroleum coke have been classified as going for non-energy uses only. However, some deliveries are used for energy purposes though it is difficult to estimate energy use figures for these products with any degree of accuracy, hence no such estimates appear in the commodity balance tables.

3.59 For lubricating oils, work done by the International Energy Agency suggests that some 50 per cent of inland deliveries each year are re-used as a fuel, through either being burnt whilst being used as lubricants or by being recycled by being re-refined into fuel oils which are then burnt. The limited available data for the UK suggest a slightly lower figure of 40 per cent (or about 330 thousand tonnes per year) being recycled although this is probably a lower bound.

Table 3C: Additional information on inland deliveries for non-energy uses, 2000 to 2002

Thousand tonnes

	2000	2001	2002
Feedstock for petroleum chemical plants:			
Propane	670	584	883
Butane	259	342	584
Other gases	1,626	1,792	1,881
Total gases	2,555	2,718	3,348
Naphtha (LDF)	2,344	1,594	1,592
Middle Distillate Feedstock (MDF)	945	403	205
Other products	-	-	-
Total feedstock	5,844	4,715	5,145
Lubricating oils and grease:			
Aviation	2	3	3
Industrial	519	509	558
Marine	33	30	32
Motors	239	245	246
Agricultural	11	9	11
Fuel oil sold as lubricant	-	-	-
Total lubricating oils and grease	804	796	850
Other non-energy products:			
Industrial spirit	83	54	41
White spirit	87	96	124
Bitumen	1,975	1,923	1,983
Petroleum wax	32	32	48
Petroleum coke	776	760	893
Miscellaneous products	463	472	464
Total non-energy use	10,062	8,846	9,547

3.60 For petroleum coke, more information is available allowing more accurate estimates to be made. It has been possible to analyse the data available for the imports of petroleum coke to identify which type of company is importing the product. This work has shown that a significant proportion of petroleum coke imports each year are made by energy companies, such as power generators or fuels merchants, with another substantial proportion being imported by cement manufacturers. Whilst it cannot be certain that these imports are being used as a fuel, information on the use of petroleum coke in cement manufacture does suggest that it is being used as a fuel.

3.61 Using imports data, estimates have been constructed which show that around 850 thousand tonnes of petroleum coke were imported for inland deliveries in 2002 compared to around 770 thousand tonnes in 2001. Around 350 thousand tonnes of petroleum coke were estimated to have been imported in 2000 for energy uses (for electricity generation, use as a fuel in the manufacture of cement, sold as a solid fuel or to be used in the manufacture of other solid fuels). In 2001, the level for energy use was 260 thousand tonnes. Estimates of imports for energy uses rose in 2002 to 320 thousand tonnes or 38 per cent of total supplies.

3.62 Analysis of the data on the quantity and value of imports of petroleum coke into the UK from HM Customs and Excise provides some estimates for the cost of imports and gives some indication of the prices being paid. These are only indicative of the prices being paid in the port of importation, and do not include the extra transport costs from the port to the final destination that would be part of more rigorous price estimate. Details of these estimates are included in Annex G on trade in fuels, as part of Table G.3 on the DTI energy statistics website. A breakdown has been made by grade of petroleum coke and type of use for imports into the UK, which is given in Table 3D below. Calcined petroleum coke is virtually pure carbon, and as such is more valuable than non-calcined (otherwise known as "green") petroleum coke, as shown by the higher price per tonne it commands and the fact that it is not used simply as a fuel.

3.63 Petroleum coke is a relatively low energy content fuel, having a calorific value of 35.8 GJ per tonne, compared with an average for petroleum products of 45.9 GJ per tonne, and 43.4 GJ per tonne for fuel oil. It is however higher than coal (27.6 GJ per tonne) and in certain areas is competing with coal as a fuel. It has the advantage of being a very cheap fuel, since it is often regarded as a waste product rather than a specific output from the refining process. Compared to imports of coal, prices of petroleum coke per GJ were about 60 per cent lower in 2002.

Table 3D: Estimated £ per tonne for imports of petroleum coke into the UK				
	Non-calcined ("green") petroleum coke			Calcined petroleum coke
	Energy	Non-energy	Total	Non-energy
2000	21.8	33.4	26.2	146.1
2001	32.9	50.1	41.3	122.4r
2002	18.0	37.9	26.2	130.6

Inland deliveries by country (Table 3.9)

3.64 This table shows deliveries in England and Wales, Scotland, and Northern Ireland for 2000 to 2002. The figures for deliveries for energy use show modest falls in use for Scotland and England and Wales but an increase in use in Northern Ireland. The 14 per cent increase in energy use in Northern Ireland between 2000 and 2003 reflect significant increases in deliveries of road fuels with motor spirit up by 9½ per cent and DERV up by 27 per cent. These increases almost certainly reflect HM Customs and Excise success in tackling illegal cross-border smuggling from the Republic of Ireland into Northern Ireland. Energy deliveries in England and Wales only fell by ½ per cent between 2000 and 2002, with large falls in motor spirit and ATF deliveries (down by 8 per cent and 6 per cent respectively) being countered by a 14 per cent increase in DERV deliveries. The 9 per cent fall in Scotland largely resulted from a 16 per cent decrease in motor spirit deliveries. Scotland and Northern Ireland also experienced significant increases in deliveries of burning oil, up by 34 per cent and 14 per cent respectively. Non-energy use deliveries in England and Wales decreased by 12½ per cent but increased by 14 per cent in Scotland with these changes being driven by demand for feedstock for the petrochemical industry. Non-energy use in Northern Ireland is substantially lower than other parts of the UK since there are no refineries there. Demand for bitumen increased non-energy deliveries in Northern Ireland.

Stocks of oil (Table 3.10)

3.65 This table shows stocks of crude oil, feedstocks (including partly processed oils) and products (in detail) at the end of each year. Stocks of crude oil and feedstocks decreased in 2002, with decreases in stocks held at offshore facilities and oil terminals offsetting an increase in stocks held at refineries.

3.66 The UK holds emergency stocks of oil to help reduce the adverse impact on the UK of any disruptions of supplies of oil arising from domestic or international incidents. These reserves are required under EU legislation (EU Directive 93/98) that requires EU member states to hold strategic oil stocks equivalent to 90 days worth of average daily consumption calculated from the previous calendar year. These stocks are held purely to deal with oil supply emergencies, not to manage or affect prices. Since the UK is currently self-sufficient in oil supplies, it receives a derogation of 25 per cent on it obligation and is only required to hold stocks equivalent to 67½ days of consumption.

3.67 As stated in paragraphs 3.21 and 3.22, the stocks of petroleum products (and crude and process oils) included in Table 3.10 are all owned by UK companies, and thus include details of any stocks owned but held abroad, eg in Rotterdam, under bilateral government agreements. Therefore, the level of stocks in this table represents the full availability of stocks to the UK in case of any oil emergency occurring from a disruption to international supplies.

3.68 Stocks of petroleum products at the end of 2002 were 5½ per cent lower than a year earlier. The total stocks of crude oil and products held by UK companies at the end of 2002 were equivalent to approximately 74 days of UK consumption, in excess of the UK obligation of 67½ days under EU legislation.

Technical notes and definitions

Indigenous production

3.69 The term indigenous is used throughout this chapter and includes oil from the UK Continental Shelf both offshore and onshore.

Deliveries

3.70 These are deliveries into consumption, as opposed to being estimates of actual consumption or use. They are split between inland deliveries and deliveries to marine bunkers. Inland deliveries will not necessarily be consumed in the United Kingdom (eg aviation fuels).

Sources of data

3.71 The majority of the data included in the text and tables of this chapter are derived from the UK Petroleum Industry Association (UKPIA) data collection system. Data relating to the inland operations of the UK oil industry (ie information on the supply, refining and distribution of oil in the UK) are collected from companies. The data format and coverage have been designed to meet most of the needs of both government and the industry itself. Each member of UKPIA provides returns on its refining activities and deliveries of various products to the internal UK market. This information is supplemented whenever necessary to allow for complete coverage within the statistics, with separate exercises carried out on special topics (for example, the work on super/hypermarkets referred to in paragraph 3.52).

Statistical differences

3.72 In Tables 3.1 to 3.7, there are headings titled "statistical differences". These are differences between the separately observed figures for production and delivery of crude oil and products during the path of their movement from the point of production to the point of consumption.

3.73 These headings listed in the primary oil commodity balances (Tables 3.1 to 3.3) are differences between the separately observed and reported figures for production from onshore or offshore fields and supply to the UK market that cannot be accounted for by any specific factors. Primarily they result from inaccuracies in the meters at various points along offshore pipelines. These meters vary slightly in their accuracy within accepted tolerances, giving rise to both losses and gains when the volumes of oil flowing are measured. Errors may also occur when non-standard conditions are used to meter the oil flow.

3.74 Another technical factor that can contribute to the statistical differences relates to the recording of quantities at the producing field (which is the input for the production data) and at oil terminals and refineries, since they are in effect measuring different types of oil. Terminals and refineries are able to measure a standardised, stabilised crude oil, i.e. with its water content and content of NGLs at a standard level and with the amounts being measured at standard conditions. However, at the producing field they are dealing with a "live" crude oil that can have a varying level of water and NGLs within it. Prior to January 2001 producing companies were asked to make adjustments so that production is recorded in terms of stabilised crude oil, but it is known that this estimation is very difficult to carry out. In January 2001 a new simplified crude oil production-reporting system was introduced. This new system allowed companies to report live crude at the field. In order that stabilised crude oil could still be measured the in-house system was redesigned so that stabilised crude oil production became disposals from the oil terminals and offshore loading fields, i.e. sales of crude oil, plus stock change. These data were introduced in the 2002 edition of this Digest.

3.75 Part of the overall statistical difference may also be due to problems with the correct reporting of individual NGLs at the production site and at terminals and refineries. It is known that there is some mixing of condensate and other NGLs in with what might otherwise be stabilised crude oil before it enters the pipeline. This mixing occurs as it removes the need for separate pipeline systems for transporting the NGLs and it also allows the viscosity of the oil passing down the pipeline to be varied as necessary. While the quantity figures recorded by terminals are in terms of stabilised crude oil, with the NGL component removed, there may be situations where what is being reported does not comply with this requirement.

3.76 Refinery data are collated from details of individual shipments received and made by each refinery and terminal operating company. Each year there are thousands of such shipments, which may be reported separately by two or three different companies involved in the movement. Whilst intensive work is carried out to check these returns, it is possible that some double counting of receipts might be occurring.

3.77 Temperature, pressure and natural leakage also contribute to the statistical differences. In addition, small discrepancies can occur between the estimated calorific values used at the field and the more accurate values measured at the onshore terminal where data are shown on an energy basis. The statistical differences can also be affected by rounding or clerical errors or unrecorded losses, such as leakage. Other contributory factors are inaccuracies in the reporting of the amounts being disposed of to the various activities listed, including differences between the quantities reported as going to refineries and the actual amounts passing through refineries.

3.78 Similarly, the data under these headings in Tables 3.4 to 3.6 are the differences between the deliveries of petroleum products to the inland UK market reported by the supplying companies and estimates for such deliveries. These estimates are calculated by taking the output of products reported by refineries and then adjusting it by the relevant factors (such as imports and exports of the products, changes in the levels of stocks etc.).

3.79 It may be thought that such differences should not exist as the data underlying both the observed deliveries into the UK market and the individual components of the estimates (ie production, imports, exports, stocks) come from the same source (the oil companies). While it is true that each oil company provides data on its own activities in each area, there are separate areas of operation within the companies that report their own part of the overall data. Table 3E below illustrates this.

Table 3E: Sources of data within oil companies

Area covered	Source
Refinery production	Refinery
Imports and exports	Refinery, logistics departments, oil traders
Stocks	Refinery, crude and product terminals, major storage and distribution sites
Final deliveries	Sales, marketing and accounts departments

3.80 Each individual reporting source will have direct knowledge of its own data. For example, refineries will know what they produce and how much leaves the refinery gate as part of routine monitoring of the refinery operations. Similarly other such data as sales to final consumers or imports and exports will be closely monitored. Companies will ensure that each component set of data reported is as accurate as possible but their reporting systems may not be integrated, meaning that internal consistency checks across all reported data cannot be made. Each part of a company may also work to different timings as well, which may further add to the degree of differences seen. The main area where there is known to be a problem is with the "Transfers" heading in the commodity balances.

3.81 The data reported under this heading have two components. Firstly there is an allowance for reclassification of products within the refining process. For example, butane can be added to motor spirit to improve the octane rating, aviation turbine fuel could be reclassified as gas diesel oil if its quality deteriorates, and much of the fuel oil imported into the UK is further refined into other petroleum products. Secondly and in addition to these inter-product transfers, the data also include an allowance to cover the receipt of backflows of products from petrochemical plants. Such plants are often very closely integrated with refineries (for example, BP's refinery at Grangemouth is right next to the petrochemical plant). A deduction for these backflows thus needs to be included under the "Transfers" heading so that calculated estimates reflect net output and are thus more comparable with the basis of the observed deliveries data.

3.82 However, there is scope for error in the recording of these two components. With inter-product transfers, the data are recorded within the refinery during the refining and blending processes where the usual units used to record the changes are volume rather than masses. Different factors apply for each product when converting from a volume to mass basis, as shown by the conversion factors given in Annex A of this Digest. Thus, a balanced transfer in volume terms may not be equivalent when converted to a mass basis. This is thought to be the main source of error within the individual product balances.

3.83 With the backflows data, as the observed deliveries data are derived from sales data on a "net" basis and will therefore exclude the element of backflows, it is thought that there is significant scope for error in the recording of the backflows when received at a refinery. For example, these could be seen simply as an input of fuel oils to be used as a feedstock, and thus recorded as an input without their precise nature being recorded – in effect a form of double-counting. It is this relationship between the petrochemical sector and refineries that is thought to be the main source of error in the overall oil commodity balances. As mentioned in paragraph 3.39, work is planned over the next year to review the downstream oil reporting system.

Imports and exports
3.84 The information given under the headings "imports" and "exports" in this chapter are the figures recorded by importers and exporters of oil. They thus differ in some cases from the import and export figures provided by HM Customs and Excise that are given in Annex G on the internet. These differences may arise since whilst the trader's figures are a record of actual movements in the period, for non-EU trade, HM Customs and Excise figures show the trade as declared by exporters on documents received during the period stated. The Customs figures also include re-exports. These are products that may have originally entered the UK as imports from another country and been stored in the UK prior to being exported back out of the UK, as opposed to having been actually produced in the UK.

Marine bunkers
3.85 This covers deliveries to ocean going and coastal vessels under international bunker contracts. Other deliveries to fishing, coastal and inland vessels are excluded.

Crude and process oils
3.86 These are all feedstocks, other than distillation benzene, for refining at refinery plants. Gasoline feedstock is any process oil whether clean or dirty which is used as a refinery feedstock for the manufacture of gasoline or naphtha. Other refinery feedstock is any process oil used for the manufacture of any other petroleum products.

Refineries
3.87 Refineries distilling crude and process oils to obtain petroleum products. This excludes petrochemical plants, plants only engaged in re-distilling products to obtain better grades, crude oil stabilisation plants and gas separation plants.

Products used as fuel (energy use)
3.88 The following paragraphs define the product headings used in the text and tables of this chapter,

which are used for energy in some way, either directly as a fuel or as an input into electricity generation.

Refinery fuel - Petroleum products used as fuel at refineries.

Ethane - An ethane (C_2H_6) rich gas in natural gas and refinery gas streams. Primarily used, or intended to be used, as a chemical feedstock.

Propane - Hydrocarbon containing three carbon atoms, gaseous at normal temperature but generally stored and transported under pressure as a liquid. Used mainly for industrial purposes and some domestic heating and cooking.

Butane - Hydrocarbon containing four carbon atoms, otherwise as for propane. Additionally used as a constituent of motor spirit to increase vapour pressure and as a chemical feedstock.

Other gases for gasworks - Ethane and other refinery gases resulting from the processing of crude petroleum.

Naphtha (Light distillate feedstock) - Petroleum distillate boiling predominantly below $200^{\circ}C$.

Aviation spirit - All light hydrocarbon oils intended for use in aviation piston-engine power units, whether in the air, on land, or on water, including bench testing of aircraft engines.

Motor spirit - Blended light petroleum components used as fuel for spark-ignition internal-combustion engines other than aircraft engines:

(i)   4 star grade - all finished motor spirit with an octane number (research method) not less than 97. This can include leaded petrol or unleaded petrol containing an alternative to lead as an anti-wear additive (lead replacement petrol – LRP).

(ii) Premium unleaded grade - all finished motor spirit, with an octane number (research method) not less than 95.

(iii) Ultra Low Sulphur Petrol - this is finished motor spirit with a specification similar to that for Premium unleaded grade, but with a sulphur content of less that 50 parts per million.

(iv) Super premium unleaded grade - all finished motor spirit, with an octane number (research method) not less than 97.

Aviation turbine fuel (ATF) - All other turbine fuel intended for use in aviation gas-turbine power units, whether in the air, on land or on water, including bench testing of aircraft engines.

Burning oil (kerosene) - Refined petroleum fuel, intermediate in volatility between motor spirit and gas oil, used for lighting and heating. White spirit and kerosene used for lubricant blends are excluded.

Gas oil/automotive diesel - Petroleum fuel having a distillation range immediately between kerosene and light-lubricating oil.

(i)   **DERV (Diesel Engined Road Vehicle) fuel** - automotive diesel fuel for use in high speed, compression ignition engines in vehicles subject to Vehicle Excise Duty.

(ii) **Ultra Low Sulphur Diesel** – A grade of DERV fuel with less than 50 ppm sulphur (below 0.005 per cent).

(iii) **Gas oil** - used as a burner fuel in heating installations, for industrial gas turbines and as for DERV (but in vehicles not subject to Vehicle Excise Duty e.g. Agriculture vehicles, fishing vessels, construction equipment).

(iv) **Marine diesel oil** - heavier type of gas oil suitable for heavy industrial and marine compression-ignition engines.

Fuel oil - Heavy petroleum residue blends used in atomising burners and for heavy duty marine diesel engines (marine bunkers, etc.) normally requiring pre-heating before combustion, but excluding fuel oil for grease making or lubricating oil and fuel oil sold as such for road making.

Orimulsion - An emulsion of bitumen in water used as a fuel primarily in power stations. In the tables Orimulsion is normally excluded from fuel oil, but where it is not shown separately it will be designated as part of fuel oils. From May 1996 Orimulsion has been classified as a type of bitumen for overseas trade purposes (see below). It was last imported in February 1997. Since that time the sole power station in the UK that was using it as a fuel has changed to alternative sources of energy.

Products not used as fuel (non-energy use)
3.89 The following paragraphs define the product headings used in the text and tables of this chapter, which are used for non-energy purposes.

Feedstock for petroleum chemical plants - All petroleum products intended for use in the manufacture of petroleum chemicals. This includes middle distillate feedstock of which there are several grades depending on viscosity. The boiling point ranges between 200°C and 400°C. (A deduction has been made from these figures equal to the quantity of feedstock used in making the conventional petroleum products that are produced during the processing of the feedstock. The output and deliveries of these conventional petroleum products are included elsewhere as appropriate.)

White spirit - A highly refined distillate with a boiling range of about 150°C to 200°C used as a paint solvent and for dry cleaning purposes etc.

Industrial spirit - Refined petroleum fractions with boiling ranges up to 200°C dependent on the use to which they are put - e.g. seed extraction, rubber solvents, perfume etc.

Lubricating oils (and grease) - Refined heavy distillates obtained from the vacuum distillation of petroleum residues. Includes liquid and solid hydrocarbons sold by the lubricating oil trade, either alone or blended with fixed oils, metallic soaps and other organic and/or inorganic bodies. A certain percentage of inland deliveries are re-used as a fuel (see paragraphs 3.57 to 3.63).

Bitumen - The residue left after the production of lubricating oil distillates and vacuum gas oil for upgrading plant feedstock. Used mainly for road making and building construction purposes. Includes other petroleum products, creosote and tar mixed with bitumen for these purposes and fuel oil sold as such for road making. In May 1996 harmonisation of EU trade categories, resulted in Orimulsion being reclassified as a bitumen, but for this chapter Orimulsion is still included under products used as fuel (energy use).

Petroleum wax - Includes paraffin wax, which is a white crystalline hydrocarbon material of low oil content normally obtained during the refining of lubricating oil distillate, paraffin scale, slack wax, microcrystalline wax and wax emulsions. Used for candle manufacture, polishes, food containers, wrappings etc.

Petroleum cokes - Carbonaceous material derived from hydrocarbon oils, uses for which include metallurgical electrode manufacture. Quantities of imports of this product are used as a fuel, primarily in the manufacture of cement (see paragraphs 3.57 to 3.63).

Miscellaneous products - Includes aromatic extracts, defoament solvents and other minor miscellaneous products.

Main classes of consumer

3.90 The following are definitions of the main groupings of users of petroleum products used in the text and tables of this chapter.

Gas works - Deliveries of petroleum products to establishments producing gas for public supply.

Electricity generators - Petroleum products delivered for use by major power producers and other companies for electricity generation including those deliveries to the other industries listed below which are used for autogeneration of electricity (Tables 3.4 to 3.6). This includes petroleum products used to generate electricity at oil refineries and is recorded in the Transformation sector, as opposed to other uses of refinery fuels which are recorded in the Energy Industry Use sector. Because delivered fuel may be put to stock and not used immediately and because generators may consume stocks rather than order new deliveries of petroleum products, these numbers may not necessarily be the same as those reported in Chapter 5 which gives **consumption** of petroleum products by electricity generators.

Agriculture - Deliveries of fuel oil and gas oil/diesel oil for use in agricultural power units, dryers and heaters. Burning oil for farm use.

Iron and steel - Deliveries of petroleum products to steel works and iron foundries.

Other industries - The industries covered correspond to the industrial groups shown in Table 1E excluding Iron and Steel of Chapter 1.

Marine - Fuel oil and gas oil/diesel oil delivered, other than under international bunker contracts, for fishing vessels, UK oil and gas exploration and production, coastal and inland shipping and for use in ports and harbours.

Railways - Deliveries of fuel oil, gas oil/diesel oil and burning oil to railways, excluding deliveries to railway power stations.

Air transport - Total inland deliveries of aviation turbine fuel and aviation spirit. The figures cover deliveries of aviation fuels in the United Kingdom to international and other airlines, British and foreign governments (including armed services) and for private flying. In order to compile the UK Greenhouse Gas Inventory, NETCEN need to estimate how aviation fuel usage splits between domestic and international consumption. Domestic usage is calculated using domestic aircraft kilometres flown (from the Department for Transport) and default fuel consumption factors while international usage is calculated by subtracting domestic and military usage from overall deliveries. NETCEN are currently reviewing this methodology. For further information, see http://www.naei.org.uk/report_link.php?report_id=191.

Road transport - Deliveries of motor spirit and DERV fuel for use in road vehicles of all kinds. The Department for Transport has provided estimates for the consumption of road transport fuels by different vehicle classes, and these are shown in Table 3F. These are based on details of average vehicle mileages and assumed miles per gallon and while these estimates have remained unchanged for some years, they are still thought to be broadly sound.

Table 3F: Estimated consumption of road transport fuels by vehicle class

Motor spirit:	
Cars and taxis	95%
Goods vehicles, mainly light vans	4%
Remainder, mainly motor cycles, mopeds etc	1%
DERV:	
Goods vehicles	68%
Buses and coaches	7%
Remainder, mainly diesel-engined cars and taxis	25%

Source: Department for Transport

Domestic - Fuel oil and gas oil/diesel oil delivered for central heating of private houses and other dwellings and deliveries of kerosene (burning oil) and liquefied petroleum gases for domestic purposes (see Tables 3.4 to 3.6).

Public services - Deliveries to national and local government premises (including educational, medical and welfare establishments and British and foreign armed forces) of fuel oil and gas oil/diesel oil for central heating and of kerosene (burning oil).

Miscellaneous - Deliveries of fuel oil and gas oil/diesel oil for central heating in premises other than those classified as domestic or public.

Monthly and quarterly data

3.91 Monthly or quarterly aggregate data for certain series presented in this chapter are available. This information can be obtained free of charge by following the links given at the Energy Statistics section of the DTI web site, at: www.dti.gov.uk/energy/inform/energy_stats/.

Contact: *Martin Young*
martin.young@dti.gsi.gov.uk
020-7215 5184

Clive Evans
clive.evans@dti.gsi.gov.uk
020-7215 5189

Ian Corrie
ian.corrie@dti.gsi.gov.uk
020-7215 2714

3.1 Commodity balances 2002[1]

Primary oil

Thousand tonnes

	Crude oil	Ethane	Propane	Butane	Condensate	Total NGL	Feedstock	Total primary oil
Supply								
Production (2)	107,430	1,596	2,728	2,071	2,118	8,514	-	115,944
Other sources	-	-	-	-	-	-	-	-
Imports	51,688	-	-	-	-	-	5,001	56,690
Exports	-81,180	-10	-1,703	-727	-869	-3,310	-2,322	-86,812
Marine bunkers	-	-	-	-	-	-	-	-
Stock change (3)	+33	..	..	..	..	+34	+75	+143
Transfers	-	-1,529	-670	-1,046	-	-3,246	+2,333	-913
Total supply	**77,971**	..	..	..	..	**1,993**	**5,087**	**85,051**
Statistical difference (4)(5)	+170	..	..	..	..	+420	-927	-337
Total demand (5)	**77,801**	..	..	..	..	**1,573**	**6,015**	**85,389**
Transformation (5)	**77,801**	..	..	..	..	**1,573**	**6,015**	**85,389**
Electricity generation	-	-	-	-	-	-	-	-
Major power producers	-	-	-	-	-	-	-	-
Autogenerators	-	-	-	-	-	-	-	-
Heat generation	-	-	-	-	-	-	-	-
Petroleum refineries	77,801	..	..	..	..	1,573	6,015	85,389
Coke manufacture	-	-	-	-	-	-	-	-
Blast furnaces	-	-	-	-	-	-	-	-
Patent fuel manufacture	-	-	-	-	-	-	-	-
Other	-	-	-	-	-	-	-	-
Energy industry use	-	-	-	-	-	-	-	-
Electricity generation	-	-	-	-	-	-	-	-
Oil & gas extraction (2) (5)	-	-	-	-	-	-	-	-
Petroleum refineries	-	-	-	-	-	-	-	-
Coal extraction	-	-	-	-	-	-	-	-
Coke manufacture	-	-	-	-	-	-	-	-
Blast furnaces	-	-	-	-	-	-	-	-
Patent fuel manufacture	-	-	-	-	-	-	-	-
Pumped storage	-	-	-	-	-	-	-	-
Other	-	-	-	-	-	-	-	-
Losses	-	-	-	-	-	-	-	-

(1) As there is no use made of primary oils and feedstocks by industries other than the oil and gas extraction and petroleum refining industries, other industry headings have not been included in this table. As such, this table is a summary of the activity of what is known as the Upstream oil industry.

(2) With the introduction of a new Petroleum Production Reporting System in January 2001, the component of the gas used at oil terminals is no longer collected. Thus NGL production in 2002 is net compared to the gross production reported in 2000 and earlier years.

(3) Stock fall (+), stock rise (-).

(4) Total supply minus total demand.

(5) Figures for total demand for the individual NGLs (and thus for the statistical differences as well) are not availble.

3.2 Commodity balances 2001[1]

Primary oil

Thousand tonnes

	Crude oil	Ethane	Propane	Butane	Condensate	Total NGL	Feedstock	Total primary oil
Supply								
Production (2)	108,387	1,599	2,718	1,962	2,012	8,292	-	116,678r
Other sources	-	-	-	-	-	-	-	-
Imports	48,992	-	-	-	-	-	4,559	53,551
Exports	-80,907r	-11	-1,748	-961	-802	-3,522	-2,489	-86,918r
Marine bunkers	-	-	-	-	-	-	-	-
Stock change (3)	-1,045	..	..	..	..	+17r	+414	-614r
Transfers	-	-1,493	-967	-1,020	-	-3,480	+4,328	+847
Total supply	75,427r	..	..	..	..	1,307r	6,811	83,545r
Statistical difference (4)(5)	-483r	..	..	..	..	-227r	+913r	+202r
Total demand (5)	75,910	..	..	..	..	1,534r	5,899r	83,343r
Transformation (5)	75,910	..	..	..	..	1,534r	5,899r	83,343r
Electricity generation	-	-	-	-	-	-	-	-
Major power producers	-	-	-	-	-	-	-	-
Autogenerators	-	-	-	-	-	-	-	-
Heat generation	-	-	-	-	-	-	-	-
Petroleum refineries	75,910	..	..	..	..	1,534r	5,899r	83,343r
Coke manufacture	-	-	-	-	-	-	-	-
Blast furnaces	-	-	-	-	-	-	-	-
Patent fuel manufacture	-	-	-	-	-	-	-	-
Other	-	-	-	-	-	-	-	-
Energy industry use	-	-	-	-	-	-	-	-
Electricity generation	-	-	-	-	-	-	-	-
Oil & gas extraction (2) (5)	-	-	-	-	-	-	-	-
Petroleum refineries	-	-	-	-	-	-	-	-
Coal extraction	-	-	-	-	-	-	-	-
Coke manufacture	-	-	-	-	-	-	-	-
Blast furnaces	-	-	-	-	-	-	-	-
Patent fuel manufacture	-	-	-	-	-	-	-	-
Pumped storage	-	-	-	-	-	-	-	-
Other	-	-	-	-	-	-	-	-
Losses	-	-	-	-	-	-	-	-

(1) As there is no use made of primary oils and feedstocks by industries other than the oil and gas extraction and petroleum refining industries, other industry headings have not been included in this table. As such, this table is a summary of the activity of what is known as the Upstream oil industry.

(2) With the introduction of a new Petroleum Production Reporting System in January 2001, the component of the gas used at oil terminals is no longer collected. Thus NGL production in 2001 is net compared to the gross production reported in 2000 and earlier years.

(3) Stock fall (+), stock rise (-).

(4) Total supply minus total demand.

(5) Figures for total demand for the individual NGLs (and thus for the statistical differences as well) are not availble.

3.3 Commodity balances 2000[(1)]

Primary oil

Thousand tonnes

	Crude oil	Ethane	Propane	Butane	Condensate	Total NGL	Feedstock	Total primary oil
Supply								
Production	117,882	1,884	2,725	1,783	1,971	8,363	-	126,245
Other sources	-	-	-	-	-	-	-	-
Imports	48,868	-	-	-	-	-	5,519	54,387
Exports	-86,533	-18	-1,810	-942	-779	-3,549	-2,836	-92,918
Marine bunkers	-	-	-	-	-	-	-	-
Stock change (2)	+1,171	..	..	..	..	-17	-56	+1,098
Transfers	-	-1,411	-977	-995	-	-3,383	+3,493	+110
Total supply	**81,388**	-	-	-	-	**1,414**	**6,120**	**88,922**
Statistical difference (3)(4)	+697	..	..	..	..	-564	+480	+613
Total demand (4)	**80,691**	..	..	..	..	**1,978**	**5,640**	**88,309**
Transformation (4)	**80,691**	..	..	..	..	**1,683**	**5,640**	**88,014**
Electricity generation	-	-	-	-	-	-	-	-
Major power producers	-	-	-	-	-	-	-	-
Autogenerators	-	-	-	-	-	-	-	-
Heat generation	-	-	-	-	-	-	-	-
Petroleum refineries	80,691	..	..	..	..	1,683	5,640	88,014
Coke manufacture	-	-	-	-	-	-	-	-
Blast furnaces	-	-	-	-	-	-	-	-
Patent fuel manufacture	-	-	-	-	-	-	-	-
Other	-	-	-	-	-	-	-	-
Energy industry use	-	**294**	**1**	-	-	**295**	-	**295**
Electricity generation	-	-	-	-	-	-	-	-
Oil & gas extraction (4)	-	294	1	-	-	295	-	295
Petroleum refineries	-	-	-	-	-	-	-	-
Coal extraction	-	-	-	-	-	-	-	-
Coke manufacture	-	-	-	-	-	-	-	-
Blast furnaces	-	-	-	-	-	-	-	-
Patent fuel manufacture	-	-	-	-	-	-	-	-
Pumped storage	-	-	-	-	-	-	-	-
Other	-	-	-	-	-	-	-	-
Losses	-	-	-	-	-	-	-	-

(1) As there is no use made of primary oils and feedstocks by industries other than the oil and gas extraction and petroleum refining industries, other industry headings have not been included in this table. As such, this table is a summary of the activity of what is known as the Upstream oil industry.

(2) Stock fall (+), stock rise (-).

(3) Total supply minus total demand.

(4) Figures for total demand for the individual NGLs (and thus for the statistical differences as well) are not availble. While separate data are available on the use of individual NGLs in the extraction of oil and gas, details of inputs into refineries of NGLs are only available at aggregate level for total NGLs.

3.4 Commodity balances 2002
Petroleum products

	Ethane	Propane	Butane	Other gases	Naphtha	Aviation spirit	Motor spirit	Industrial spirit	White spirit	Aviation turbine fuel	Burning oil
Supply											
Production	50	1,625	542	2,655	3,117	28	23,178	6	115	5,603	3,344
Other sources	1,529	670	1,046	-	-	-	-	-	-	-	-
Imports	-	111	144	-	96	9	2,017	37	7	5,078	226
Exports	-	-354	-214	-	-1,758	-6	-5,734	-2	-	-639	-420
Marine bunkers	-	-	-	-	-	-	-	-	-	-	-
Stock change (1)	-	+80	-11	-3	+20	-4	+281	+1	+2	+269	-8
Transfers	-53	-159	-458	+43	+145	+3	+669	-	-	-1,299	+135
Total supply (2)	**1,526**	**1,973**	**1,050**	**2,694**	**1,620**	**30**	**20,412**	**42**	**124**	**9,012**	**3,278**
Statistical difference (3)	-191	+151	+319	+119	+1	-23	+660	+1	-	-1,136	-572
Total demand	**1,717**	**1,822**	**731**	**2,575**	**1,619**	**52**	**19,752**	**41**	**124**	**10,148**	**3,851**
Transformation	-	-	-	**218**	-	-	-	-	-	-	-
Electricity generation	-	-	-	218	-	-	-	-	-	-	-
Major power producers	-	-	-	-	-	-	-	-	-	-	-
Autogenerators	-	-	-	218	-	-	-	-	-	-	-
Heat generation	-	-	-	-	-	-	-	-	-	-	-
Petroleum refineries	-	-	-	-	-	-	-	-	-	-	-
Coke manufacture	-	-	-	-	-	-	-	-	-	-	-
Blast furnaces	-	-	-	-	-	-	-	-	-	-	-
Patent fuel manufacture	-	-	-	-	-	-	-	-	-	-	-
Other	-	-	-	-	-	-	-	-	-	-	-
Energy industry use	**49**	**10**	**-**	**2,073**	**27**	**-**	**-**	**-**	**-**	**-**	**-**
Electricity generation	-	-	-	-	-	-	-	-	-	-	-
Oil & gas extraction	-	-	-	-	-	-	-	-	-	-	-
Petroleum refineries	49	10	-	2,073	27	-	-	-	-	-	-
Coal extraction	-	-	-	-	-	-	-	-	-	-	-
Coke manufacture	-	-	-	-	-	-	-	-	-	-	-
Blast furnaces	-	-	-	-	-	-	-	-	-	-	-
Patent fuel manufacture	-	-	-	-	-	-	-	-	-	-	-
Pumped storage	-	-	-	-	-	-	-	-	-	-	-
Other	-	-	-	-	-	-	-	-	-	-	-
Losses	-	-	-	-	-	-	-	-	-	-	-
Final consumption	**1,668**	**1,812**	**731**	**284**	**1,592**	**52**	**19,752**	**41**	**124**	**10,148**	**3,851**
Industry	**72**	**474**	**99**	**-**	**-**	**-**	**-**	**-**	**-**	**-**	**1,080**
Unclassified	72	474	99	-	-	-	-	-	-	-	1,080
Iron & steel	-	-	-	-	-	-	-	-	-	-	-
Non-ferrous metals	-	-	-	-	-	-	-	-	-	-	-
Mineral products	-	-	-	-	-	-	-	-	-	-	-
Chemicals	-	-	-	-	-	-	-	-	-	-	-
Mechanical engineering, etc	-	-	-	-	-	-	-	-	-	-	-
Electrical engineering, etc	-	-	-	-	-	-	-	-	-	-	-
Vehicles	-	-	-	-	-	-	-	-	-	-	-
Food, beverages, etc	-	-	-	-	-	-	-	-	-	-	-
Textiles, leather, etc	-	-	-	-	-	-	-	-	-	-	-
Paper, printing etc	-	-	-	-	-	-	-	-	-	-	-
Other industries	-	-	-	-	-	-	-	-	-	-	-
Construction	-	-	-	-	-	-	-	-	-	-	-
Transport	**-**	**86**	**-**	**-**	**-**	**52**	**19,752**	**-**	**-**	**10,148**	**12**
Air	-	-	-	-	-	52	-	-	-	10,148	-
Rail	-	-	-	-	-	-	-	-	-	-	12
Road	-	86	-	-	-	-	19,752	-	-	-	-
National navigation	-	-	-	-	-	-	-	-	-	-	-
Pipelines	-	-	-	-	-	-	-	-	-	-	-
Other	**-**	**369**	**48**	**-**	**-**	**-**	**-**	**-**	**-**	**-**	**2,759**
Domestic	-	271	48	-	-	-	-	-	-	-	2,735
Public administration	-	-	-	-	-	-	-	-	-	-	12
Commercial	-	-	-	-	-	-	-	-	-	-	-
Agriculture	-	98	-	-	-	-	-	-	-	-	12
Miscellaneous	-	-	-	-	-	-	-	-	-	-	-
Non energy use	**1,597**	**883**	**584**	**284**	**1,592**	**-**	**-**	**41**	**124**	**-**	**-**

(1) Stock fall (+), stock rise (-).
(2) Incorporates an extra adjustment for what are thought to be refinery losses. These data are the subject of ongoing investigations.
(3) Total supply minus total demand.

3.4 Commodity balances 2002 (continued)
Petroleum products

Thousand tonnes

Gas oil	Marine diesel oil	Fuel oils	Lubri-cants	Bitu-men	Petroleum wax	Petroleum coke	Orimul-sion	Misc. products	Total Products	
										Supply
28,529	-	10,426	516	1,909	447	1,544	-	908	84,543	Production
-	-	-	-	-	-	-	-	-	3,246	Other sources
3,778	-	857	297	221	17	790	-	10	13,696	Imports
-6,549	-	-5,269	-521	-264	-59	-541	-	-497	-22,827	Exports
-1,428	-47	-991	-	-	-	-	-	-	-2,466	Marine bunkers
+193	-	-32	-11	+24	-6	+16	-	+427	+1,236	Stock change (1)
-695	-	-833	+466	+45	-324	-1	-	-15	-2,333	Transfers (2)
23,827	-47	4,157	747	1,935	75	1,807	-	833	75,094	**Total supply** (2)
-220	-86	+341	-103	-48	+27	+260	-	+341	-160	**Statistical difference** (3)
24,047	39	3,816	850	1,983	48	1,547	-	492	75,255	**Total demand**
52	-	780	-	-	-	-	-	-	1,050	**Transformation**
30	-	431	-	-	-	-	-	-	678	Electricity generation
10	-	105	-	-	-	-	-	-	116	Major power producers
19	-	326	-	-	-	-	-	-	563	Autogenerators
22	-	221	-	-	-	-	-	-	244	Heat generation
-	-	-	-	-	-	-	-	-	-	Petroleum refineries
-	-	-	-	-	-	-	-	-	-	Coke manufacture
-	-	128	-	-	-	-	-	-	128	Blast furnaces
-	-	-	-	-	-	-	-	-	-	Patent fuel manufacture
-	-	-	-	-	-	-	-	-	-	Other
261	-	1,806	-	-	-	654	-	29	4,908	**Energy industry use**
-	-	-	-	-	-	-	-	-	-	Electricity generation
-	-	-	-	-	-	-	-	-	-	Oil & gas extraction
146	-	1,806	-	-	-	654	-	29	4,793	Petroleum refineries
-	-	-	-	-	-	-	-	-	-	Coal extraction
-	-	-	-	-	-	-	-	-	-	Coke manufacture
115	-	-	-	-	-	-	-	-	115	Blast furnaces
-	-	-	-	-	-	-	-	-	-	Patent fuel manufacture
-	-	-	-	-	-	-	-	-	-	Pumped storage
-	-	-	-	-	-	-	-	-	-	Other
-	-	-	-	-	-	-	-	-	-	**Losses**
23,734	39	1,231	850	1,983	48	893	-	464	69,297	**Final Consumption**
3,377	-	1,024	-	-	-	-	-	-	6,126	**Industry**
-	-	-	-	-	-	-	-	-	1,725	Unclassified
73	-	39	-	-	-	-	-	-	112	Iron & steel
41	-	39	-	-	-	-	-	-	80	Non-ferrous metals
213	-	31	-	-	-	-	-	-	244	Mineral products
129	-	183	-	-	-	-	-	-	312	Chemicals
155	-	109	-	-	-	-	-	-	263	Mechanical engineering etc
21	-	30	-	-	-	-	-	-	51	Electrical engineering etc
151	-	37	-	-	-	-	-	-	188	Vehicles
180	-	129	-	-	-	-	-	-	309	Food, beverages etc
79	-	102	-	-	-	-	-	-	181	Textiles, leather, etc
35	-	74	-	-	-	-	-	-	110	Paper, printing etc
1,864	-	250	-	-	-	-	-	-	2,114	Other industries
435	-	2	-	-	-	-	-	-	437	Construction
18,554	39	36	-	-	-	-	-	-	48,680	**Transport**
-	-	-	-	-	-	-	-	-	10,201	Air
334	-	6	-	-	-	-	-	-	346	Rail
17,654	-	-	-	-	-	-	-	-	37,492	Road
566	39	30	-	-	-	-	-	-	641	National navigation
-	-	-	-	-	-	-	-	-	-	Pipelines
1,598	-	170	-	-	-	-	-	-	4,944	**Other**
202	-	4	-	-	-	-	-	-	3,260	Domestic
602	-	97	-	-	-	-	-	-	712	Public administration
315	-	55	-	-	-	-	-	-	369	Commercial
395	-	3	-	-	-	-	-	-	508	Agriculture
84	-	11	-	-	-	-	-	-	95	Miscellaneous
205	-	-	850	1,983	48	893	-	464	9,547	**Non energy use**

3.5 Commodity balances 2001

Petroleum products

	Ethane	Propane	Butane	Other gases	Naphtha	Aviation spirit	Motor spirit	Industrial spirit	White spirit	Aviation turbine fuel	Burning oil
Supply											
Production	83	1,250	520	2,544	3,463	101	21,455	9	113	5,910	3,088
Other sources	1,493	967	1,020	-	-	-	-	-	-	-	-
Imports	-	245	178	-	345	10	3,608	21	3	6,130	190
Exports	-	-315r	-77	-	-1,078	-6	-4,447	-2	-	-456	-167
Marine bunkers	-	-	-	-	-	-	-	-	-	-	-
Stock change (1)	-	-26r	-17r	2r	4r	6r	-377r	2r	-2r	-291r	122r
Transfers	-101r	-258r	-314r	-	-633r	+5r	1,062r	+1r	-1r	+9r	+261r
Total supply (2)	1,475r	1,864r	1,311r	2,546r	2,102r	115r	21,302r	30r	113r	11,301r	3,494r
Statistical difference (3)	-219r	+233r	+781r	-146r	+449r	+56r	+369r	-23r	+17r	1,004r	-751r
Total demand	1,693	1,631	530	2,692	1,652	59	20,933	54	96	10,297	4,244
Transformation	-	36	-	179r	-	-	-	-	-	-	-
Electricity generation	-	36	-	179r	-	-	-	-	-	-	-
Major power producers	-	-	-	-	-	-	-	-	-	-	-
Autogenerators	-	36	-	179r	-	-	-	-	-	-	-
Heat generation	-	-	-	-	-	-	-	-	-	-	-
Petroleum refineries	-	-	-	-	-	-	-	-	-	-	-
Coke manufacture	-	-	-	-	-	-	-	-	-	-	-
Blast furnaces	-	-	-	-	-	-	-	-	-	-	-
Patent fuel manufacture	-	-	-	-	-	-	-	-	-	-	-
Other	-	-	-	-	-	-	-	-	-	-	-
Energy industry use	83	7	-	2,249r	58	-	-	-	-	-	-
Electricity generation	-	-	-	-	-	-	-	-	-	-	-
Oil & gas extraction	-	-	-	-	-	-	-	-	-	-	-
Petroleum refineries	83	7	-	2,249r	58	-	-	-	-	-	-
Coal extraction	-	-	-	-	-	-	-	-	-	-	-
Coke manufacture	-	-	-	-	-	-	-	-	-	-	-
Blast furnaces	-	-	-	-	-	-	-	-	-	-	-
Patent fuel manufacture	-	-	-	-	-	-	-	-	-	-	-
Pumped storage	-	-	-	-	-	-	-	-	-	-	-
Other	-	-	-	-	-	-	-	-	-	-	-
Losses	-	-	-	-	-	-	-	-	-	-	-
Final consumption	1,610	1,588	530	263	1,594	59	20,933	54	96	10,297	4,244
Industry	82	200r	69r	-	-	-	-	-	-	-	1,561
Unclassified	82	200r	69r	-	-	-	-	-	-	-	1,561
Iron & steel	-	-	-	-	-	-	-	-	-	-	-
Non-ferrous metals	-	-	-	-	-	-	-	-	-	-	-
Mineral products	-	-	-	-	-	-	-	-	-	-	-
Chemicals	-	-	-	-	-	-	-	-	-	-	-
Mechanical engineering, etc	-	-	-	-	-	-	-	-	-	-	-
Electrical engineering, etc	-	-	-	-	-	-	-	-	-	-	-
Vehicles	-	-	-	-	-	-	-	-	-	-	-
Food, beverages, etc	-	-	-	-	-	-	-	-	-	-	-
Textiles, leather, etc	-	-	-	-	-	-	-	-	-	-	-
Paper, printing etc	-	-	-	-	-	-	-	-	-	-	-
Other industries	-	-	-	-	-	-	-	-	-	-	-
Construction	-	-	-	-	-	-	-	-	-	-	-
Transport	-	53r	-	-	-	59	20,933	-	-	10,297	12
Air	-	-	-	-	-	59	-	-	-	10,297	-
Rail	-	-	-	-	-	-	-	-	-	-	12
Road	-	53r	-	-	-	-	20,933	-	-	-	-
National navigation	-	-	-	-	-	-	-	-	-	-	-
Pipelines	-	-	-	-	-	-	-	-	-	-	-
Other	-	750	119r	-	-	-	-	-	-	-	2,672
Domestic	-	284	69r	-	-	-	-	-	-	-	2,648
Public administration	-	-	-	-	-	-	-	-	-	-	12
Commercial	-	345	50r	-	-	-	-	-	-	-	-
Agriculture	-	122	1	-	-	-	-	-	-	-	12
Miscellaneous	-	-	-	-	-	-	-	-	-	-	-
Non energy use	1,529	584	342	263	1,594	-	-	54	96	-	-

(1) Stock fall (+), stock rise (-).
(2) Incorporates an extra adjustment for what are thought to be refinery losses. These data are the subject of ongoing investigations.
(3) Total supply minus total demand.

3.5 Commodity balances 2001 (continued)
Petroleum products

Thousand tonnes

Gas oil	Marine diesel oil	Fuel oils	Lubri-cants	Bitu-men	Petroleum wax	Petroleum coke	Orimul-sion	Misc. products	Total Products	
										Supply
26,796	-	11,912	656	1,707	416	1,346	-	724	82,093	Production
-	-	-	-	-	-	-	-	-	3,480	Other sources
4,098	-	1,011	251	238	17	633	-	-	16,978	Imports
-5,288	-	-5,440	-806	-269	-56	-460	-	-221	-19,088	Exports
-1,377	-56	-841	-	-	-	-	-	-	-2,274	Marine bunkers
49r	-	86r	-3r	-51r	-8r	-27r	-	-66r	-598r	Stock change (1)
-1,251r	+4r	-3,176r	+51r	+303r	-309r	-	-	+19r	-4,328r	Transfers (2)
23,027r	**-51r**	**3,552r**	**149r**	**1,928r**	**59r**	**1,492r**	**-**	**456r**	**76,264r**	**Total supply (2)**
-267r	-178r	-621r	-646r	+4r	+27r	+152r	-	-48r	+194r	**Statistical difference (3)**
23,294r	**126**	**4,173r**	**796**	**1,923**	**32**	**1,340**	**-**	**504**	**76,070r**	**Total demand**
63r	**-**	**1,475r**	**-**	**-**	**-**	**-**	**-**	**-**	**1,753r**	**Transformation**
32r	-	707r	-	-	-	-	-	-	955r	Electricity generation
10r	-	340r	-	-	-	-	-	-	349r	Major power producers
23r	-	367r	-	-	-	-	-	-	605r	Autogenerators
30	-	640	-	-	-	-	-	-	671	Heat generation
-	-	-	-	-	-	-	-	-	-	Petroleum refineries
-	-	-	-	-	-	-	-	-	-	Coke manufacture
-	-	128	-	-	-	-	-	-	128	Blast furnaces
-	-	-	-	-	-	-	-	-	-	Patent fuel manufacture
-	-	-	-	-	-	-	-	-	-	Other
178	**-**	**1,793r**	**-**	**-**	**-**	**581**	**-**	**32**	**4,981r**	**Energy industry use**
-	-	-	-	-	-	-	-	-	-	Electricity generation
-	-	-	-	-	-	-	-	-	-	Oil & gas extraction
50	-	1,793r	-	-	-	581	-	32	4,854r	Petroleum refineries
-	-	-	-	-	-	-	-	-	-	Coal extraction
-	-	-	-	-	-	-	-	-	-	Coke manufacture
127	-	-	-	-	-	-	-	-	127	Blast furnaces
-	-	-	-	-	-	-	-	-	-	Patent fuel manufacture
-	-	-	-	-	-	-	-	-	-	Pumped storage
-	-	-	-	-	-	-	-	-	-	Other
-	-	-	-	-	-	-	-	-	-	**Losses**
23,053	**126**	**905r**	**796**	**1,923**	**32**	**760**	**-**	**472**	**69,335r**	**Final Consumption**
3,384	**-**	**777**	**-**	**-**	**-**	**-**	**-**	**-**	**6,072r**	**Industry**
-	-	-	-	-	-	-	-	-	1,912r	Unclassified
81	-	16r	-	-	-	-	-	-	97r	Iron & steel
41	-	33	-	-	-	-	-	-	75r	Non-ferrous metals
238	-	30	-	-	-	-	-	-	268r	Mineral products
139r	-	177r	-	-	-	-	-	-	316r	Chemicals
169	-	58	-	-	-	-	-	-	227	Mechanical engineering etc
24	-	24	-	-	-	-	-	-	48	Electrical engineering etc
140	-	22	-	-	-	-	-	-	162	Vehicles
200r	-	57	-	-	-	-	-	-	256r	Food, beverages etc
90	-	114r	-	-	-	-	-	-	204r	Textiles, leather, etc
37	-	42r	-	-	-	-	-	-	79r	Paper, printing etc
1,756	-	201r	-	-	-	-	-	-	1,957r	Other industries
469	-	2	-	-	-	-	-	-	472	Construction
17,441r	**126**	**28r**	**-**	**-**	**-**	**-**	**-**	**-**	**48,949r**	**Transport**
-	-	-	-	-	-	-	-	-	10,356	Air
407r	-	-	-	-	-	-	-	-	414r	Rail
16,418	-	-	-	-	-	-	-	-	37,404r	Road
617	126	27	-	-	-	-	-	-	775r	National navigation
-	-	-	-	-	-	-	-	-	-	Pipelines
1,826	**-**	**101**	**-**	**-**	**-**	**-**	**-**	**-**	**5,468r**	**Other**
193	-	6	-	-	-	-	-	-	3,199r	Domestic
674	-	29r	-	-	-	-	-	-	714r	Public administration
406r	-	38r	-	-	-	-	-	-	838r	Commercial
448	-	11	-	-	-	-	-	-	594r	Agriculture
105r	-	16r	-	-	-	-	-	-	122r	Miscellaneous
403	**-**	**-**	**796**	**1,923**	**32**	**760**	**-**	**472**	**8,846**	**Non energy use**

3.6 Commodity balances 2000
Petroleum products

	Ethane	Propane	Butane	Other gases	Naphtha	Aviation spirit	Motor spirit	Industrial spirit	White spirit	Aviation turbine fuel	Burning oil
Supply											
Production	52	1,406	576	2,818	3,099	30	23,440	6	116	6,485	3,077
Other sources	1,411	977	995	-	-	-	-	-	-	-	-
Imports	-	78	253	-	348	16	2,443	34	3	4,675	86
Exports	-	-560	-150	-	-973	-	-4,708	-3	-6	-487	-199
Marine bunkers	-	-	-	-	-	-	-	-	-	-	-
Stock change (1)	-1	-18	-	+3	-58	+2	+260	-	-	-25	-70
Transfers	-60	-222	-438	-37	-568	-11	+625	-	-	+429	+587
Total supply	1,403	1,662	1,237	2,783	1,848	37	22,061	38	112	11,077	3,480
Statistical difference(2)	-188	+30	+797	-93	-515	-16	+458	-45	+25	+271	-358
Total demand	1,590	1,631	440	2,876	2,363	52	21,603	83	87	10,806r	3,838
Transformation	-	54	-	277r	-	-	-	-	-	-	-
Electricity generation	-	37	-	277r	-	-	-	-	-	-	-
Major power producers	-	-	-	-	-	-	-	-	-	-	-
Autogenerators	-	37	-	277r	-	-	-	-	-	-	-
Heat generation	-	17	-	-	-	-	-	-	-	-	-
Petroleum refineries	-	-	-	-	-	-	-	-	-	-	-
Coke manufacture	-	-	-	-	-	-	-	-	-	-	-
Blast furnaces	-	-	-	-	-	-	-	-	-	-	-
Patent fuel manufacture	-	-	-	-	-	-	-	-	-	-	-
Other	-	-	-	-	-	-	-	-	-	-	-
Energy industry use	50	16	26	2,432r	19	-	-	-	-	-	-
Electricity generation	-	-	-	-	-	-	-	-	-	-	-
Oil & gas extraction	-	-	-	-	-	-	-	-	-	-	-
Petroleum refineries	50	2	-	2,432r	19	-	-	-	-	-	-
Coal extraction	-	-	-	-	-	-	-	-	-	-	-
Coke manufacture	-	-	-	-	-	-	-	-	-	-	-
Blast furnaces	-	-	-	-	-	-	-	-	-	-	-
Patent fuel manufacture	-	-	-	-	-	-	-	-	-	-	-
Pumped storage	-	-	-	-	-	-	-	-	-	-	-
Other	-	14	26	-	-	-	-	-	-	-	-
Losses	-	-	-	-	-	-	-	-	-	-	-
Final consumption	1,540	1,562	414	166	2,344	52	21,603	83	87	10,806	3,838
Industry	80	746r	-	-	-	-	-	-	-	-	1,312
Unclassified	80	722r	-	-	-	-	-	-	-	-	1,312
Iron & steel	-	24r	-	-	-	-	-	-	-	-	-
Non-ferrous metals	-	-	-	-	-	-	-	-	-	-	-
Mineral products	-	-	-	-	-	-	-	-	-	-	-
Chemicals	-	-	-	-	-	-	-	-	-	-	-
Mechanical engineering etc	-	-	-	-	-	-	-	-	-	-	-
Electrical engineering etc	-	-	-	-	-	-	-	-	-	-	-
Vehicles	-	-	-	-	-	-	-	-	-	-	-
Food, beverages etc	-	-	-	-	-	-	-	-	-	-	-
Textiles, leather, etc	-	-	-	-	-	-	-	-	-	-	-
Paper, printing etc	-	-	-	-	-	-	-	-	-	-	-
Other industries	-	-	-	-	-	-	-	-	-	-	-
Construction	-	-	-	-	-	-	-	-	-	-	-
Transport	-	-	22	-	-	52	21,603	-	-	10,806	12
Air	-	-	-	-	-	52	-	-	-	10,806	-
Rail	-	-	-	-	-	-	-	-	-	-	12
Road	-	-	22	-	-	-	21,603	-	-	-	-
National navigation	-	-	-	-	-	-	-	-	-	-	-
Pipelines	-	-	-	-	-	-	-	-	-	-	-
Other	-	147	133	-	-	-	-	-	-	-	2,514
Domestic	-	147	133	-	-	-	-	-	-	-	2,490
Public administration	-	-	-	-	-	-	-	-	-	-	12
Commercial	-	-	-	-	-	-	-	-	-	-	-
Agriculture	-	-	-	-	-	-	-	-	-	-	12
Miscellaneous	-	-	-	-	-	-	-	-	-	-	-
Non energy use	1,460	670	259	166	2,344	-	-	83	87	-	-

(1) Stock fall (+), stock rise (-).
(2) Total supply minus total demand.

3.6 Commodity balances 2000 (continued)
Petroleum products

Thousand tonnes

Gas oil	Marine diesel oil	Fuel oils	Lubri-cants	Bitu-men	Petroleum wax	Petroleum coke	Orimul-sion	Misc. products	Total Products	
										Supply
28,292	6	11,621	703	1,438	436	1,796	-	943	86,341	Production
-	-	-	-	-	-	-	-	-	3,383	Other sources
3,815	-	596	211	255	23	657	-	718	14,212	Imports
-6,416	-	-5,360	-636	-283	-51	-502	-	-342	-20,677	Exports
-1,080	-61	-938	-	-	-	-	-	-	-2,079	Marine bunkers
-54	+1	+266	-26	+25	+35	+36	-	-707	-332	Stock change (1)
-794	+11	-2,773	+249	+319	-360	+1	-	-451	-3,493	Transfers
23,762	-43	3,411	501	1,754	83	1,989	-	161	77,357	**Total supply**
+270	-84	+61	-300	-221	+51	+236	-	-317	+63	Statistical difference (2)
23,493	41	3,350	801	1,975	32	1,753	-	478	77,294	**Total demand**
197r	-	1,503r	-	-	-	-	-	-	2,030r	**Transformation**
164r	-	649r	-	-	-	-	-	-	1,128r	Electricity generation
132r	-	224r	-	-	-	-	-	-	355r	Major power producers
32	-	425r	-	-	-	-	-	-	772r	Autogenerators
33	-	659	-	-	-	-	-	-	708r	Heat generation
-	-	-	-	-	-	-	-	-	-	Petroleum refineries
-	-	-	-	-	-	-	-	-	-	Coke manufacture
-	-	195	-	-	-	-	-	-	195	Blast furnaces
-	-	-	-	-	-	-	-	-	-	Patent fuel manufacture
-	-	-	-	-	-	-	-	-	-	Other
174	-	1,199r	-	-	-	977	-	15	4,907r	**Energy industry use**
-	-	-	-	-	-	-	-	-	-	Electricity generation
-	-	-	-	-	-	-	-	-	-	Oil & gas extraction
65	-	1,199r	-	-	-	977	-	15	4,759r	Petroleum refineries
-	-	-	-	-	-	-	-	-	-	Coal extraction
-	-	-	-	-	-	-	-	-	-	Coke manufacture
109	-	-	-	-	-	-	-	-	109	Blast furnaces
-	-	-	-	-	-	-	-	-	-	Patent fuel manufacture
-	-	-	-	-	-	-	-	-	-	Pumped storage
-	-	-	-	-	-	-	-	-	40	Other
-	-	-	-	-	-	-	-	-	-	Losses
23,122r	41	648r	801	1,975	32	776	-	463	70,356r	**Final Consumption**
2,881r	-	489r	-	-	-	-	-	-	5,507r	**Industry**
-	-	-	-	-	-	-	-	-	2,114r	Unclassified
69r	-	30r	-	-	-	-	-	-	123r	Iron & steel
29	-	9	-	-	-	-	-	-	38r	Non-ferrous metals
195	-	47	-	-	-	-	-	-	242	Mineral products
126	-	84r	-	-	-	-	-	-	211r	Chemicals
167	-	14r	-	-	-	-	-	-	180r	Mechanical engineering etc
22	-	12	-	-	-	-	-	-	34	Electrical engineering etc
116	-	9	-	-	-	-	-	-	125	Vehicles
139r	-	71r	-	-	-	-	-	-	210r	Food, beverages etc
53	-	89	-	-	-	-	-	-	142	Textiles, leather, etc
22	-	21r	-	-	-	-	-	-	43r	Paper, printing etc
1,516	-	101	-	-	-	-	-	-	1,617	Other industries
427	-	2	-	-	-	-	-	-	429	Construction
17,186r	41	40r	-	-	-	-	-	-	49,763r	**Transport**
-	-	-	-	-	-	-	-	-	10,858	Air
434r	-	-	-	-	-	-	-	-	444r	Rail
15,881	-	-	-	-	-	-	-	-	37,506	Road
871	41	40	-	-	-	-	-	-	954	National navigation
-	-	-	-	-	-	-	-	-	-	Pipelines
2,110r	-	119r	-	-	-	-	-	-	5,024r	**Other**
147	-	3	-	-	-	-	-	-	2,920	Domestic
872	-	78	-	-	-	-	-	-	961	Public administration
406r	-	28r	-	-	-	-	-	-	433r	Commercial
559	-	10	-	-	-	-	-	-	581	Agriculture
127r	-	1r	-	-	-	-	-	-	128r	Miscellaneous
945	-	-	801	1,975	32	776	-	463	10,062r	**Non energy use**

3.7 Supply and disposal of petroleum[(1)]

Thousand tonnes

	1998	1999	2000	2001	2002
Primary oils (Crude oil, NGLs and feedstocks)					
Indigenous production (2)	132,363	137,099	126,245	116,678r	115,944
Imports	47,958	44,869	54,387	53,551	56,690
Exports (3)	-84,610	-91,797	-92,918	-86,918r	-86,812
Transfers - Transfers to products (4)	-3,457	-3,323	-3,383	-3,480	-3,246
Product rebrands (5)	+1,255	+2,105	+3,493	+4,328	+2,333
Stock change (6) - Offshore	-127	-83	+550	-378	+68
Oil terminals	-466	-115	+548	-236r	+75
Use during production (7)	-353	-323	-295	..	..
Calculated refinery throughput (8)	92,563	88,432	88,627	83,545r	85,051
Overall statistical difference (9) (10)	-1,234	+146	+613	+202r	-337
Actual refinery throughput	**93,797**	**88,286**	**88,014**	**83,343r**	**85,389**
Petroleum products					
Losses in refining process	1,005	1,554	1,672	1,250	845
Refinery gross production (11)	92,792	86,733	86,341	82,093	84,543
Transfers - Transfers to products (4)	+3,457	+3,323	+3,383	+3,480	+3,246
Product rebrands (5)	-1,255	-2,105	-3,493	-4,328	-2,333
Imports	11,418	13,896	14,212	16,978	13,696
Exports (12)	-24,375	-21,730	-20,677	-19,088r	-22,827
Marine bunkers	-3,080	-2,329	-2,079	-2,274	-2,466
Stock changes (6) - Refineries	-65	+399	-425	+613	-1,223
Power generators	-28	+176	+94	-15r	-12
Calculated total supply	78,864	78,363	77,357	76,264r	75,095
Statistical difference (9)	+426	+388	+63	+194r	-160
Total demand (4)	**78,438**	**77,975**	**77,294**	**76,070r**	**75,255**
Of which:					
Energy use	67,752	67,242	67,232	67,223r	65,708
Of which, for electricity generation (13)	1,395	1,167	1,128	955r	678
total refinery fuels (13)	6,468	5,969	5,245	5,162	4,873
Non-energy use	10,686	10,733	10,062	8,846	9,547

(1) Aggregate monthly data on oil production, trade, refinery throughput and inland deliveries are available - see paragraph 3.91 and Annex C.

(2) Crude oil plus condensates and petroleum gases derived at onshore treatment plants.

(3) Includes NGLs, process oils and re-exports.

(4) Disposals of NGLs by direct sale (excluding exports) or for blending.

(5) Product rebrands (inter-product blends or transfers) represent petroleum products received at refineries/ plants as process for refinery or cracking unit operations.

(6) Impact of stock changes on supplies. A stock fall is shown as (+) as it increases supplies, and vice-versa for a stock rise (-).

(7) Own use in onshore terminals and gas separation plants. These figures ceased to be available from January 2001 with the advent of the new PPRS system.

(8) Equivalent to the total supplies reported against the upstream transformation sector in Tables 3.1 to 3.3.

(9) Supply greater than (+) or less than (-) recorded throughput or disposals.

(10) This total includes differences between the figures for indigenous production as recorded by individual fields and indigenous indigenous receipts, which is accounted for by own use in onshore terminals and gas separation plants, losses, platform and other field stock changes and the time lag between production on offshore loaders and tankers arrival at refineries. The size of this component of the overall statistical difference was previously given separately, and is given in the table below for information. See Chapter 3, paragraphs 3.35 to 3.39 for more information on the differences.

	1998	1999	2000	2001	2002
Indigenous receipts	133,125	137,220	126,116	116,678	115,944
Statistical difference - upstream production sector	-972	-527	+384	-	+1

(11) Includes refinery fuels.

(12) Excludes NGLs.

(13) Figures cover petroleum used to generate electricity by all major power producers and by all other generators, including petroleum used to generate electricity at refineries. These quantities are also included in the totals reported as used as refinery fuel, so there is thus some overlap in these figures.

3.8 Additional information on inland deliveries of selected products[(1)(2)(3)]

Thousand tonnes

	1998	1999	2000	2001	2002
Motor spirit					
Retail deliveries (4)					
Hypermarkets (5)					
Leaded premium / Lead Replacement Petrol (6)	1,001	641	339	213	142
Super premium unleaded	18	13	9	24	33
Premium unleaded	4,130	4,775	5,260r	5,498	5,776
Total hypermarkets	5,149	5,429	5,608	5,735	5,951
Refiners/other traders					
Leaded premium / Lead Replacement Petrol (6)	3,594	1,988r	1,123	624	252
Super premium unleaded	391	461r	395r	396	655
Premium unleaded	12,302	13,532	13,948r	13,597	12,359
Total Refiners/other traders	16,287	15,981	15,465r	14,617	13,266
Total retail deliveries					
Leaded premium / Lead Replacement Petrol (6)	4,595	2,629r	1,462	837	394
Super premium unleaded	409	474r	403	420	687
Premium unleaded	16,432	18,307	19,208r	19,095	18,135
Total retail deliveries	21,436	21,410	21,073r	20,352	19,217
Commercial consumers (7)					
Leaded premium / Lead Replacement Petrol (6)	91	61	44	34	19
Super premium unleaded	4	6	6	9	17
Premium unleaded	318	311	480	538	499
Total commercial consumers	413	378	530	581	535
Total motor spirit	**21,849**	**21,789**	**21,603**	**20,933**	**19,752**
Unleaded as % of Total motor spirit	78.6	87.6	93.0	95.8	97.9
Gas oil/diesel oil					
DERV fuel:					
Retail deliveries (4):					
Hypermarkets (5)	1,153	1,306	1,411	1,633	1,844
Refiners/other traders	5,449	5,831	6,052r	6,565	6,755
Total retail deliveries	6,602	7,137	7,463	8,198	8,599
Commercial consumers (7)	8,541	8,371	8,168	8,220	9,055
Total DERV fuel	15,143	15,508	15,632r	16,418	17,654
Gas oil	7,244	6,667	7,487r	6,882r	6,295
Marine diesel oil	1	15	41	126	39
Total gas oil/diesel oil	**22,388**	**22,190**	**23,160r**	**23,426r**	**23,988**
Fuel oils (8)					
Light	76	74	45r	43	85
Medium	259	419	390	521	791
Heavy	2,600	1,922	1,399	1,638	1,245
Total fuel oils	**2,935**	**2,415**	**1,833**	**2,202**	**2,121**

(1) Aggregate monthly data for inland deliveries of oil products are available - see paragraph 3.91 and Annex C.

(2) The end use section analyses are based partly on recorded figures and on estimates made by the Institute of Petroleum and the Department of Trade and Industry and are intended to be for general guidance only. See also the notes in the main text of this chapter.

(3) For a full breakdown of the end-uses of all oil products, see Commodity Balances in Tables 3.4 to 3.6.

(4) Retail deliveries - deliveries to garages, etc. mainly for resale to final consumers.

(5) Data for sales by super and hypermarket companies are collected via a separate reporting system, but are consistent with the main data collected from UKPIA member companies - see paragraph 3.71.

(6) Sales of Leaded Petrol ceased on 31 December 1999 - see paragraphs 3.46 and 3.48.

(7) Commercial consumers - direct deliveries for use in consumer's business.

(8) Inland deliveries excluding that used as a fuel in refineries, but including that used for electricity generation by major electricity producers and other industries.

3.9 Inland deliveries by country[1]

	England and Wales (2)			Scotland			Northern Ireland		
	2000	2001	2002	2000	2001	2002	2000	2001	2002
Energy use									
Gases for gasworks and other uses									
Butane and propane	995	1,076	957	79	86	91	30	30	29
Other gases	-	-	-	80	81	72	-	-	-
Aviation spirit	45	53	51	4	3	2	4	3	-
Motor spirit:									
Dealers	19,641r	18,992	17,962	1,145	1,061	946	287	298	309
Commercial consumers	484	540	473	30	22	38	16	19	23
Total motor spirit	20,125	19,532	18,435	1,175	1,083	985	303	317	332
Kerosenes									
Aviation turbine fuel	10,216	9,751	9,601	411	473	476	71	73	72
Burning oil	2,889	3,316	2,824	230	232	309	629	696	718
Gas oil/diesel oil									
DERV fuel	14,382r	15,207	16,406	1,089	1,039	1,045	160	171	203
Other (3)	5,213	5,168	4,941	1,004	980	719	366	450	468
Fuel oils	1,464	1,843	1,789	215	207	197	154	153	135
Total products used as energy	**55,329r**	**55,946**	**55,003**	**4,287**	**4,184**	**3,895**	**1,717**	**1,893**	**1,957**
Non-energy use									
Feedstock for petroleum chemical plants	3,580	2,547	2,504	2,302	2,211	2,640	-	-	2
Industrial spirit	83	53	41	-	-	-	-	-	-
White spirit	87	96	124	-	-	-	-	-	-
Lubricating oils	765	773	819	31	20	27	6	3	3
Bitumen	1,710	1,618	1,662	193	197	210	72	109	111
Petroleum wax	31	32	48	1	-	-	-	-	-
Total products used as non-energy (4)	**7,489**	**6,349**	**6,552**	**2,531**	**2,430**	**2,879**	**78**	**112**	**116**
Total all products	**62,818r**	**62,295**	**61,556**	**6,818**	**6,614**	**6,774**	**1,795**	**2,005**	**2,073**

(1) Excludes products used as a fuel within refineries that are included in Tables 3.4 to 3.6.

(2) Includes the Channel Islands and the Isle of Man.

(3) Includes deliveries of marine diesel oil.

(4) Includes deliveries of miscellaneous products and petroleum coke.

3.10 Stocks of crude oil and petroleum products at end of year[(1)]

				Thousand tonnes	
	1998	1999	2000	2001	2002
Crude and process oils					
Refineries (2)	5,074	4,560	3,917	4,183	4,503
Terminals (3)	1,832	2,461	2,556	2,526	2,126
Offshore (4)	917	1,000	450	828	760
Total crude and process oils (5)	7,883	8,080	6,992	7,637	7,499
Petroleum products					
Ethane	6	6	6	6r	6
Propane	120	144	162	188r	108
Butane	92	89	88	105r	117
Other petroleum gases	3	3	-	-	2
Naphtha	461	349	428	424r	404
Aviation spirit	12	5	4	4r	2
Motor spirit	1,984	1,425	1,078	1,375r	1,280
Industrial spirit	17	7	14	12	11
White spirit	14	15	21	23	22
Aviation turbine fuel	637	461	487	779r	510
Burning oil	257	339	414	292r	300
Gas oil (6) (7)	3,703	2,984	1,908	2,232r	2,363
Marine diesel oil	-	1	-	-	-
Fuel oils (7)	1,466	1,401	1,122	1,180r	1,196
Lubricating oils	292	169	199	202	214
Bitumen	194	189	165	215r	192
Petroleum wax	3	36	1	9	15
Petroleum coke	287	327	291	318	302
Miscellaneous products	217	320	1,031	1,097r	670
Total all products	9,765	8,269	7,419	8,461r	7,712
Of which : net bilateral stocks (8)	2,228	1,307	77	514	1,008

(1) Aggregate monthly data on the level of stocks of crude oil and oil products are available - see paragraph 3.91 and Annex C.

(2) Stocks of crude oil, NGLs and process oils at UK refineries.

(3) Stocks of crude oil and NGLs at UKCS pipeline terminals.

(4) Stocks of crude oil in tanks and partially loaded tankers at offshore fields.

(5) Includes process oils held abroad for UK use approved by bilateral agreements.

(6) Includes middle distillate feedstock.

(7) The increase in gas oil stocks and the decrease in fuel oil stocks can be attributed to the change in patterns of stocks held abroad, under bilateral agreements, by UK companies as part of their national stocking obligation.

(8) The difference between stocks held abroad for UK use under approved bilateral agreements and the equivalent stocks held in the UK for foreign use.

Chapter 4
Natural gas

Introduction

4.1   This chapter presents figures on the production, transmission and consumption of natural gas and colliery methane. Three tables are presented and a map showing the gas transmission system in Great Britain is included (page 110). The commodity balances for natural gas and colliery methane form the first table (Table 4.1). This is followed by a 5 year table showing the supply, transmission and consumption of these gases as a time series (Table 4.2). A more detailed examination of the various stages of natural gas from gross production through to consumption is given in Table 4.3. Long term trends commentary and table on production and consumption of gas back to 1970 is to be found on the DTI Energy Statistics web site www.dti.gov.uk/energy/inform/dukes/dukes2003/04longterm.pdf.

4.2   Petroleum gases are covered in Chapter 3. Gases manufactured in the coke making and iron and steel making processes (coke oven gas and blast furnace gas) appear in Chapter 2. Biogases (landfill gas and sewage gas) are part of Chapter 7. Details of net selling values of gas for the domestic sector are to be found in Chapter 1.

The gas supply industry Great Britain

4.3   When British Gas was privatised in 1986, it was given a statutory monopoly over supplies of natural gas (methane) to premises taking less than 732,000 kWh (25,000 therms) a year. Under the Oil and Gas (Enterprise) Act 1982, contract customers taking more than this were able to buy their gas from other suppliers but no other suppliers entered the market until 1990.

4.4   In 1991, the Office of Fair Trading (OFT) followed up an examination of the contract market by the Monopolies and Mergers Commission (MMC) that had taken place in 1988. It reviewed progress towards a competitive market and found that the steps taken in 1988 had been ineffective in encouraging self-sustaining competition. British Gas undertook in March 1992 to allow competitors to take by 1995 at least 60 per cent of the contract market above 732,000 kWh (25,000 therms) a year (subsequently redefined as 45 per cent of the market above 73,200 kWh (2,500 therms)); to release to competitors the gas necessary to achieve this; and to establish a separate transport and storage unit with regulated charges. At the same time, the Government took powers in the 1992 Competition and Service (Utilities) Act to reduce or remove the tariff monopoly, and in July 1992 it lowered the tariff threshold from 732,000 kWh (25,000 therms) to 73,200 kWh (2,500 therms).

4.5   Difficulties in implementing the March 1992 undertakings led to further references to the MMC. As a result of the new recommendations made by the MMC in 1993, the President of the Board of Trade decided in December 1993 to require full internal separation of British Gas's supply and transportation activities, but not divestment, and to accelerate removal of the tariff monopoly to April 1996, with a phased opening of the domestic market by the regulator over the following two years.

4.6   In November 1995 the Gas Bill received Royal Assent, clearing the way for the extension of competition into the domestic gas supply market on a phased basis between 1996 and 1998. This was carried out in stages between April 1996 and May 1998. By December 2002 almost 7½ million gas consumers (37 per cent) were no longer supplied by British Gas. Table 4A gives market penetration in more detail, by local distribution zone (LDZ). For all types of domestic customer it is in the markets in Northern England that new suppliers have had most success. At the end of Q4, 2002

British Gas had lost around 34 per cent of the credit and 43 per cent of the direct debit market compared to 23 per cent of the pre-payment market, although it should be noted that British Gas's pre-payment prices are below the average of new suppliers. At the end of 2002, 27 suppliers were licensed to supply gas to domestic customers.

Table 4A: Domestic gas market penetration (in terms of percentage of customers supplied) by local distribution zone and payment type, fourth quarter of 2002

Region	British Gas Trading			Non-British Gas		
	Credit	Direct Debit	Prepayment	Credit	Direct Debit	Prepayment
Northern	60	44	62	40	56	38
Wales	60	57	64	40	43	36
North East	63	52	71	37	48	29
East Midlands	65	53	73	35	47	27
North West	65	60	82	35	40	18
South East	65	55	80	35	45	20
North Thames	66	66	81	34	34	19
Scotland	66	57	86	34	43	14
Eastern	68	59	80	32	41	20
Southern	68	51	73	32	49	27
South West	72	59	75	28	41	25
West Midlands	73	64	77	27	36	23
Great Britain	66	57	77	34	43	23

4.7   Following the 1995 Act, the business of British Gas was fully separated into two corporate entities. The supply and shipping businesses were devolved to a subsidiary, British Gas Trading Limited, while the transportation business (Transco) remained within British Gas plc. In February 1997, Centrica plc was demerged from British Gas plc (which was itself renamed as BG plc) completing the division of the business into two independent entities. Centrica became the holding company for British Gas Trading, British Gas Services, the Retail Energy Centres and the company producing gas from the North and South Morecambe fields. BG plc comprised the gas transportation and storage business of Transco, along with British Gas's other exploration and production, international downstream, research and technology and property activities. In October 2000 BG plc demerged into two separately listed companies, of which Lattice Group plc was the holding company for Transco, while BG Group plc included the international and gas storage businesses. On 21 October 2002 Transco and the National Grid Company merged to form National Grid Transco.

4.8   From 1 October 2001, under the Utilities Act, gas pipeline companies have been able to apply for their own national Gas Transporter Licences so that they can compete with Transco. In some areas low pressure spur networks had already been developed by new transporters competing with Transco to bring gas supplies to new customers (mainly domestic). In addition, some very large loads (above 60 GWh) are serviced by pipelines operated independently, some by North Sea producers.

4.9   By the end of 1994, competitors had exceeded the target 45 per cent of the market above 73,200 kWh (2,500 therms), but virtually all of this was in the firm gas market. From 1995 British Gas's competitors made inroads into the interruptible market and in 2002 Centrica's share of the industrial and commercial market had fallen to around 11 per cent. At the end of 2002, 58 suppliers (together owned by about 13 company groups) were active in the contract market. The structure of the gas industry in Great Britain as it stood at the end of 2002 is shown in Chart 4.1.

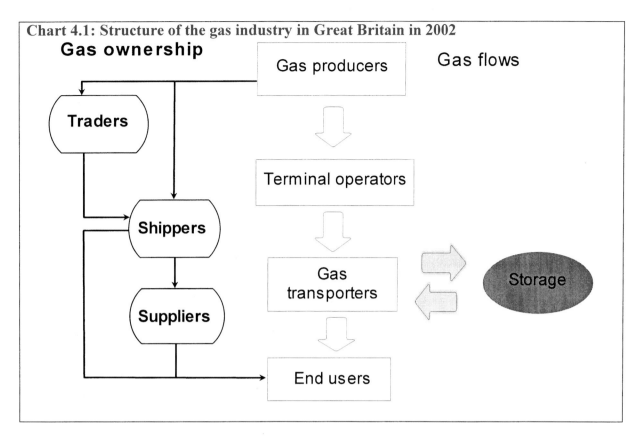

Chart 4.1: Structure of the gas industry in Great Britain in 2002

Gas ownership — Gas flows

Gas producers → Terminal operators → Gas transporters ↔ Storage → End users

Traders → Shippers → Suppliers → End users

Regional analysis

4.10   Table 4B gives the number of consumers with a gas demand below 73,200 kWh per year in 2002.   It covers both domestic and small business customers receiving gas from the national transmission system. It is this section of the market that was progressively opened up to competition between April 1996 and May 1998. The regions shown are Transco's 13 local distribution zones (LDZs). Table 4B also gives the corresponding information for all consumers of gas.

Table 4B: Consumption by gas customers by gas zone in 2002

Local distribution zones	Consumption by customers below 73,200 kWh (2,500 therms) annual demand		Consumption by all customers	
	Number of consumers (thousands)	Gas sales 2002 (GWh)	Number of consumers (thousands)	Gas sales 2002 (GWh)
North Western	2,594	51,764	2,644	89,957
South Eastern	2,358	46,413	2,405	76,210
North Thames	2,200	44,060	2,255	74,637
East Midlands	2,108	41,945	2,145	80,698
West Midlands	1,885	37,056	1,921	64,409
Scotland	1,643	33,805	1,677	64,414
Eastern	1,640	33,754	1,672	53,008
Southern	1,476	30,041	1,505	47,562
South West	1,299	23,228	1,321	38,105
North Eastern	1,277	25,380	1,304	48,945
Northern	1,122	23,824	1,140	44,840
Wales South	771	15,281	782	35,037
Wales North	214	4,391	218	9,287
Great Britain	20,587	410,944	20,990	727,111

Source: Transco

Northern Ireland

4.11   Before 1997, Northern Ireland did not have a public natural gas supply. The construction of a natural gas pipeline from Portpatrick in Scotland to Northern Ireland was completed in 1996 and provided the means of establishing such a system. The primary market is Ballylumford power station, which was purchased by British Gas in 1992 and converted from oil to gas firing (with a heavy fuel oil back up). The onshore line has been extended to serve wider industrial, commercial and domestic markets and this extension is continuing. In 2002, 80 per cent of all gas supplies in Northern Ireland were used to generate electricity.

Competition

4.12   Paragraphs 4.3 to 4.11 above referred to the developments in recent years in opening up the non-domestic market to competition. About three-quarters of this market (by volume) in the United Kingdom was opened to competition at the end of 1982, and the remainder in August 1992 (with the reduction in the tariff threshold). As mentioned above, however, no other suppliers entered the market until 1990. After 1990 there was a rapid increase in the number of independent companies supplying gas, although by 1999 there were signs of some consolidation. Chart 4.2 shows that in recent years sales of gas have become more concentrated in the hands of the largest companies in the domestic, industrial and commercial sectors. This has come about through larger companies absorbing smaller suppliers and through mergers between already significant suppliers. The three largest suppliers now jointly account for 84 per cent of sales to domestic customers whereas in 2000 the proportion was 79 per cent. For the industrial sector the share of the largest three suppliers has fallen a little from 47 per cent in 2000 to 42 per cent in 2002 but through mergers the largest 8 firms have increased their joint share to 95 per cent from only 76 per cent in 2000. For the purpose of this chart industrial sales include sales of gas to autogenerators in the industrial sector. For commercial sector sales, in 2002 the three largest suppliers accounted for 64 per cent of sales, up from 38 per cent in 2000. Whereas in 2000 the 10 largest suppliers accounted for 82 per cent of sales by 2002 this proportion had moved up to 94 per cent.

Commodity balances for gas (Table 4.1)

4.13   For all three years shown on this table, production of natural gas has been greater than supply because exports have been larger than imports. However, net exports of natural gas, although growing rapidly, were not large in absolute terms, amounting to only 7½ per cent of total production in 2002. Imports and exports of natural gas are described in greater detail below in paragraph 4.18.

4.14   Demand for natural gas is traditionally less than supply because of the various measurement differences described in paragraphs 4.42 to 4.45.

4.15   In 2002, 29½ per cent of natural gas demand was for electricity generation (transformation sector), slightly higher than the proportion in 2001 largely due to gas prices falling back from the very high levels of that year. A further 8 per cent was consumed for heating purposes within the energy industries. One per cent was accounted for by distribution losses within the gas network. (For an explanation of the items included under losses, see paragraphs 4.42 to 4.45.) Of the remaining 61½ per cent, 2 per cent was transformed into heat for sale to a third party, 16 per cent was accounted for by the industrial sector with the chemicals industry (excluding natural gas for petrochemical feedstocks), iron and steel and the food industry being the largest consumers. The chemicals sector accounted for over a quarter of the industrial consumption of natural gas.

4.16   Sales of gas to households (domestic sector) produced 34 per cent of gas demand, while public administration (including schools and hospitals) consumed 4 per cent of total demand, almost as much gas as the chemicals sector. The commercial, agriculture and miscellaneous sectors together took up 5 per cent. Non energy use of gas accounted for the remaining ½ per cent. This is much lower

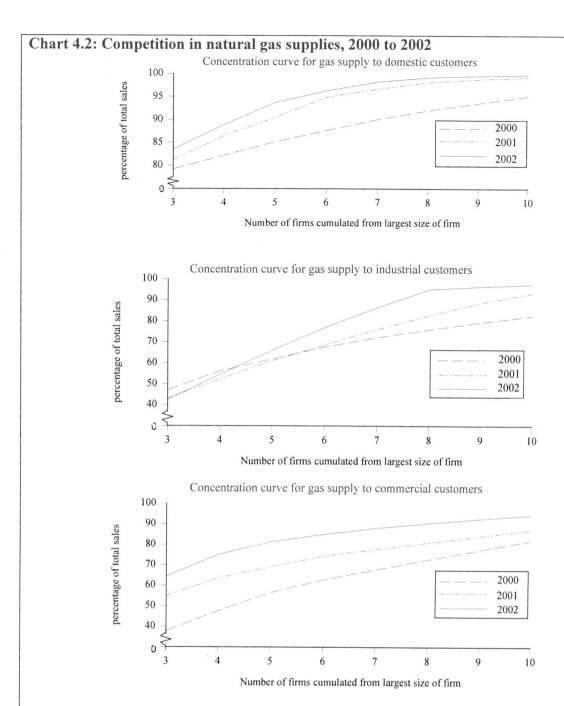

Chart 4.2: Competition in natural gas supplies, 2000 to 2002

Concentration curve for gas supply to domestic customers

Concentration curve for gas supply to industrial customers

Concentration curve for gas supply to commercial customers

Illustrating increasing competition using concentration curves:

Concentration curves are one way of showing the increase or decrease in competition within an industry. The sets of curves for the three sectors shown in Chart 4.2 are all constructed in the same way. In any particular year, in a particular sector, the proportion (expressed as a percentage) of total sales of gas (by volume) accounted for by the three firms with the largest sales is calculated. This calculation is repeated for the largest four firms, the largest five firms and so on up to the largest 10 firms. These percentages of total sales are plotted. If each of the 10 firms had an equal share of gas sales the plot would form a straight diagonal line from the origin to 100 per cent at the 10 firm point. For a monopoly the curve lies on the vertical axis. When an industry is concentrated in the hands of a few firms, the curve is well above and to the left of the diagonal line and moves towards the diagonal as the competition increases. In 2000 the three largest firms in terms of sales to the domestic sector accounted for 79 per cent of sales, the six largest 88 per cent, and the ten largest 95 per cent. By 2002 the curve had moved upwards to the left indicating less competition since the largest three firms accounted for only 84 per cent of total sales to the domestic sector and the largest six firms 96 per cent, and the largest ten for over 99 per cent. This apparent reduction in competitiveness (evident in all three sectors) has been brought about by mergers between some of the larger gas suppliers.

than in previous years because one of the plants using natural gas as a feedstock closed in 2001. As Table 4C, below, shows, non-energy use of gas is small relative to total use (see the technical notes section, paragraph 4.35, for more details on non-energy use of gas).

Table 4C: Non-energy use: share of natural gas demand	
	Continental shelf and onshore natural gas
1998	1.2%
1999	1.2%
2000	1.2%
2001	1.0%
2002	0.4%

4.17   Care should be exercised in interpreting the figures for individual industries in these commodity balance tables. As companies switch contracts between gas suppliers, it has not been possible to ensure consistent classification between and within industry sectors and across years. The breakdown of final consumption includes a substantial amount of estimated data. For about 18½ per cent of consumption the allocation to consuming sector is estimated.

4.18   Imports of natural gas from the Norwegian sector of the North Sea began to decline in the late 1980s as output from the Frigg field tailed off. The interconnector linking the UK's transmission network with Belgium via a Bacton to Zeebrugge pipeline began to operate in October 1998. Since 1998 there was an increase in imports brought about by inflows through the Bacton to Zeebrugge interconnector (although the UK has been a net exporter through this interconnector in all three years that it has operated). Imports added only about 2½ per cent to UK production. Exports to mainland Europe from the United Kingdom's share of the Markham field began in 1992 with Windermere's output being added in 1997. Exports to the Republic of Ireland began in 1995. In 2002, exports accounted for 12½ per cent of UK production. Exports of natural gas exceeded imports for the first time in 1997 and grew rapidly to 2000, fell by 5½ per cent in 2001 partly due to higher gas prices in the UK, but rose by 9 per cent to a new peak in 2002.

4.19   Chart 4.3 shows the increase in indigenous production and consumption of natural gas over the past five years and relative size of net exports.

Supply and consumption of natural gas and colliery methane (Table 4.2)
4.20   This table summarises the production and consumption of gas from these sources in the United Kingdom over the last 5 years.

4.21   As Chart 4.4 shows, the growth in consumption for electricity generation has dominated the growth in natural gas consumption over the last 10 years. Most of this gas was used in Combined Cycle Gas Turbine (CCGT) stations, although the use of gas in dual fired conventional steam stations was a growth area in 1997 and 1998. However, gas use for electricity generation grew by only 3 per cent in 2000 and in 2001 fell by 4½ per cent as higher gas prices made it more difficult for gas fired stations to compete with large coal fired stations but this was reversed by a 5½ per cent growth in 2002 when gas prices eased. In 2002 the transformation sector as a whole accounted for 31½ per cent of gas demand compared with 26 per cent in 1997.

4.22   Between 1998 and 2000, industrial use of gas grew by 8 per cent, but in 2001 it fell slightly by ½ per cent and declined sharply by 3½ per cent in 2002. This decline cuts across all industrial sectors partly due to the downturn in economic activity, relatively high gas prices and mild weather. Use by the public administration sector and the commercial sector was 5 per cent and 3½ per cent lower respectively in 2002 than in 2001. Use in the energy industries other than electricity (and heat) generation fell by ½ per cent partly due to the closure of one large iron and steel making plant.

Chart 4.3: Natural gas production, net imports, and consumption, 1997 to 2002

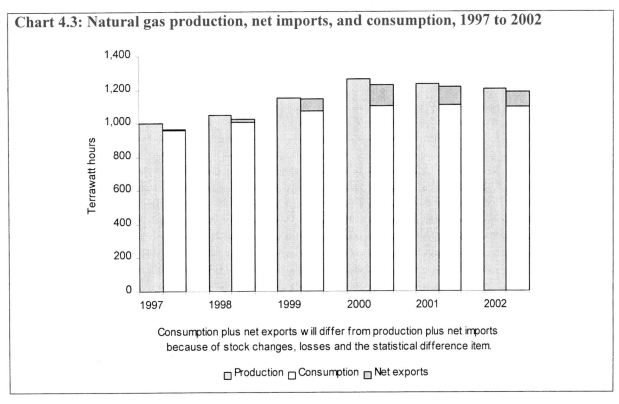

Consumption plus net exports will differ from production plus net imports because of stock changes, losses and the statistical difference item.

□ Production □ Consumption ■ Net exports

Chart 4.4: Consumption of town gas and natural gas, 1970 to 2002

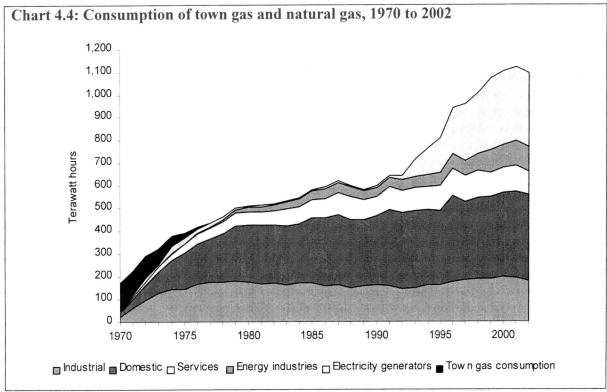

▨ Industrial ▨ Domestic ▢ Services ▨ Energy industries ▢ Electricity generators ■ Town gas consumption

4.23   Gas use in the domestic sector is particularly dependent on winter temperatures and in 2002 the average temperatures in 4 out of the 6 winter months were lower than in 2001, contributing to a slight decline in demand of ½ a per cent in 2002. Although demand from the domestic sector increased by 5½ per cent between 1998 and 2002, its share of total demand fell from 35½ per cent to 34 per cent.

4.24   Maximum daily demand for natural gas through the National Transmission System in winter 2002/03 was 4,965 GWh on 8th January 2003. On that day natural gas demand in Northern Ireland was 13 GWh. This total maximum daily demand was 4½ per cent higher than January 2002's previous record level and about 19 per cent higher than the peak daily level recorded during the particularly colder winter of 1996 (February).

4.25   It is estimated that sales of gas supplied on an interruptible basis accounted for around 22 per cent of total gas sales in 2002, a small decrease on the proportion in 2001.

UK continental shelf and onshore natural gas (Table 4.3)
4.26   Table 4.3 shows the flows for natural gas from production through transmission to consumption. The footnotes to the table give more information about each table row. This table departs from the standard balance methodology and definitions in order to maintain the link with past data and with monthly data given at DTI's energy statistics web site (see paragraph [4.41]). The relationship between total UK gas consumption shown in this table and total demand for gas given in the balance tables (4.1 and 4.2) is illustrated for 2002 as follows:

		GWh
Total UK consumption (Table 4.3)		1,009,068
plus Producers' own use		79,298
plus Operators' own use		7,017
equals		
"Consumption of natural gas" (see paragraph 4.31)		1,095,383
plus Other losses and metering differences (upstream)		-
plus Downstream losses - leakage assessment	5,284)	7,845
- own use gas	427)	
- theft	2,134)	
plus Metering differences (transmission)		1,821
equals		
Total demand (Tables 4.1 and 4.2)		1,105,049

4.27   Gross production rose by 20 per cent between 1998 and 2000 but eased back by 2½ per cent in 2001 and fell again by 2 per cent in 2002, though the production level in 2002 was still 15 per cent higher than in 1998. Gas available at UK terminals has increased by a lesser amount (8 per cent) over this period mainly because of the increase in exports and decrease in imports described in paragraph 4.18. Producers' and operators' own use of gas have tended to grow in proportion to the volumes of gas produced and transmitted. Output from the transmission system increased by 7½ per cent between 1998 and 2002, while total UK consumption of natural gas increased by 8 per cent. Consumption increased by more than the output from the transmission system because distribution losses and metering differences have been reduced as a proportion of consumption over these four years.

4.28   For a discussion of the various losses and statistical differences terms in this table, see paragraphs 4.42 to 4.45 in the technical notes and definitions section below. The statistical difference between output from the National Transmission System and total UK consumption has been disaggregated using information obtained from Transco on leakage from local distribution zone pipes, theft and use regarded as own use by pipeline operators. The convention used is set out in paragraph 4.45.

4.29   Losses and metering differences attributable to the information provided on the upstream gas industry are zero in 2001 and 2002 because these data are no longer reported in the revised Petroleum Production Reporting System. This simplified system for reporting the production of crude oil, NGLs and natural gas in the UK was implemented from 1st January 2001; it reduced the burden on the respondents and improved the quality of data reported on gas production.

Technical notes and definitions

4.30   These notes and definitions are in addition to the technical notes and definitions covering all fuels and energy as a whole in Chapter 1, paragraphs 1.24 to 1.58. For notes on the commodity balances and definitions of the terms used in the row headings see Annex A, paragraphs A.7 to A.42.

Definitions used for production and consumption

4.31   **Natural gas** production in Tables 4.1 and 4.2 relates to the output of indigenous methane at land terminals and gas separation plants (includes producers' and processors' own use). For further explanation, see the Annex F, paragraph F.19 on DTI's Energy Statistics web site under 'Production of oil and gas'. Output of the Norwegian share of the Frigg and Murchison fields is included under imports. A small quantity of onshore produced methane (other than colliery methane) is also included.

4.32   Table 4.3 shows production, transmission and consumption figures for UK continental shelf and onshore natural gas. Production includes waste and own use for drilling, production and pumping operations, but excludes gas flared. Gas available in the United Kingdom excludes waste, own use for drilling etc, stock change, and includes imports net of exports. Gas transmitted (input into inland transmission systems) is after stock change, own use, and losses at inland terminals. The amount consumed in the United Kingdom differs from the total gas transmitted by the gas supply industry, because of losses in transmission, differences in temperature and pressure between the points at which the gas is measured, delays in reading meters and consumption in the works, offices, shops, etc of the undertakings. The figures include an adjustment to the quantities billed to consumers to allow for the estimated consumption remaining unread at the end of the year.

4.33   **Colliery methane** production is colliery methane piped to the surface and consumed at collieries or transmitted by pipeline to consumers. As the output of deep-mined coal declines so does the production of colliery methane, unless a use can be found for gas that was previously vented. The supply of methane from coal measures that are no longer being worked or from drilling into coal measures is licensed under the same legislation as used for offshore gas production. Production data, when it becomes available, will be reported as natural gas in the balances. If possible, separate production details will be included in future versions of Annex F.

4.34   **Transfers** of natural gas include natural gas use within the iron and steel industry for mixing with blast furnace gas to form a synthetic coke oven gas. For further details see paragraph 2.48 in Chapter 2.

4.35   **Non-energy gas**: Non-energy use is gas used as feedstock for petrochemical plants in the chemical industry as raw material for the production of ammonia (an essential intermediate chemical in the production of nitrogen fertilisers) and methanol. The contribution of liquefied petroleum gases (propane and butane) and other petroleum gases is shown in Tables 3.4 to 3.6 of Chapter 3. Firm data for natural gas are not available, but estimates for 1998 to 2002 are shown in Table 4.2. and estimates for 2000 to 2002 in Table 4.1   Estimates for the years up to 2001 have been obtained from the National Atmospheric Emissions Inventory (NAEI); 2002 data are DTI extrapolations.

Sectors used for sales/consumption

4.36   For definitions of the various sectors used for sales and consumption analyses see the Chapter 1 paragraphs 1.54 to 1.58 and Annex A, paragraphs A.31 to A.42. However, **miscellaneous** has a wider coverage than in the commodity balances of other fuels. This is because some gas supply companies are unable to provide a full breakdown of the services sector and the gas they supply to consumers is allocated to miscellaneous when there is no reliable basis for allocating it elsewhere.

Data collection

4.37   Production figures are generally obtained from returns made under the Department of Trade and Industry's Petroleum Production Reporting System (PPRS) and from other sources. DTI obtain data on the transmission of natural gas from National Grid Transco (who operate the National Transmission System) and from other pipeline operators. Data on consumption are based on returns from gas suppliers and UKCS producers who supply gas directly to customers.

4.38   The production data are for the United Kingdom (including natural gas from the UKCS - offshore and onshore). The restoration of a public gas supply to parts of Northern Ireland in 1997 (see paragraph 4.11) means that all tables in this chapter (except Tables 4A and 4B) cover the UK.

4.39   DTI carry out an annual survey of gas suppliers to obtain details of gas sales to the various categories of consumer. Estimates are included for the suppliers with the smallest market share since the DTI inquiry covers only the largest suppliers (i.e. those with more than about a ½ per cent share of the UK market up to 1997 and those known to supply more than 1,750 GWh per year for 1998 onwards).

Period covered

4.40   Figures generally relate to years ended 31 December. However, data for natural gas for electricity generation relate to periods of 52 weeks as set out in Chapter 5, paragraphs 5.54 and 5.55.

Monthly and quarterly data

4.41   Monthly data on natural gas production and supply are available from the DTI's Energy Statistics web site www.dti.gov.uk/energy/inform/energy_stats/ in monthly Table 4.2. A quarterly commodity balance for natural gas (which includes consumption data) is published in DTI's quarterly statistical bulletin *Energy Trends* and is also available from quarterly Table 4.1 at DTI's Energy Statistics web site. See Annex C for more information about *Energy Trends* and the DTI Energy Statistics web site.

Statistical and metering differences

4.42   In Table 4.3 there are several headings that refer to statistical or metering differences. These arise because measurement of gas flows, in volume and energy terms, takes place at several points along the supply chain. The main sub-headings in the table represent the instances in the supply chain where accurate reports are made of the gas flows at that particular key point in the supply process. It is possible to derive alternative estimates of the flow of gas at any particular point by taking the estimate for the previous point in the supply chain and then applying the known losses and gains in the subsequent part of the supply chain. The differences seen when the actual reported flow of gas at any point and the derived estimate are compared are separately identified in the table wherever possible, under the headings statistical or metering differences.

4.43   The differences arise from several factors:-

- Limitations in the accuracy of meters used at various points of the supply chain. While standards are in place on the accuracy of meters, there is a degree of error allowed which, when large flows of gas are being recorded, can become significant.

- Differences in the methods used to calculate the flow of gas in energy terms. For example, at the production end, rougher estimates of the calorific value of the gas produced are used which may be revised only periodically, rather than the more accurate and more frequent analyses carried out further down the supply chain. At the supply end, although the calorific value of gas shows day-to-day variations, for the purposes of recording the gas supplied to customers a single calorific value is used. Until 1997 this was the lowest of the range of calorific values for the actual gas being supplied within each LDZ, resulting in a "loss" of gas in energy terms. In 1997 there was a change to a "capped flow-weighted average" algorithm for calculating calorific values resulting in a reduction in the losses shown in the penultimate row of Table 4.3. This change in algorithm, along with improved meter validation and auditing procedures, also reduced the level of the "metering differences" row within the downstream part of Table 4.3.

- Differences in temperature and pressure between the various points at which gas is measured. Until February 1997 British Gas used "uncorrected therms" on their billing system for tariff customers when converting from a volume measure of the gas used to an energy measure. This made their supply figure too small by a factor of 2.2 per cent, equivalent to about 1 per cent of the wholesale market.

- Differences in the timing of reading meters. While National Transmission System meters are read daily, customers' meters are read less frequently (perhaps only annually for some domestic customers) and profiling is used to estimate consumption. Profiling will tend to underestimate consumption in a strongly rising market.

- Other losses from the system, for example, theft through meter tampering by consumers.

4.44   The headings in Table 4.3 show where, in the various stages of the supply process, it has been possible to identify these metering differences as having an effect. Usually they are aggregated with other net losses as the two factors cannot be separated. Whilst the factors listed above can give rise to either losses or gains, losses are more common.

4.45   The box below shows how in 2002 the wastage, losses and metering differences figures in Table 4.3 are related to the losses row in the balance Tables 4.1 and 4.2. It should be noted that losses in 2001 and 2002 are lower than in previous years because figures for losses and metering differences in the upstream gas industry are no longer available (see above):

Table 4.3	GWh
Upstream gas industry:	
Other losses and metering differences	-
Downstream gas industry:	
Transmission system metering differences	1,821
Leakage assessment	5,284
Own use gas	427
Theft	2,134
Tables 4.1 and 4.2	
Losses	9,666

Similarly the statistical difference row in Tables 4.1 and 4.2 is made up of the following components in 2002:

Table 4.3	GWh
Statistical difference between gas available from upstream and gas input to downstream	-61
plus Downstream gas industry:	
Distribution losses and metering differences	2,031
Tables 4.1 and 4.2	
Statistical difference	+1,970

Contact: *Mike Janes (Statistician)*   *John Castle*
              Energy Markets Information and Analysis   *Energy Information Systems*
              mike.janes@dti.gsi.gov.uk   *john.castle@dti.gsi.gov.uk*
              020-7215 5186   *020-7215 2718*

              James Achur
              Energy Markets Information and Analysis
              james.achur@dti.gsi.gov.uk
              020-7215 2717

The National gas transmission system, 2002

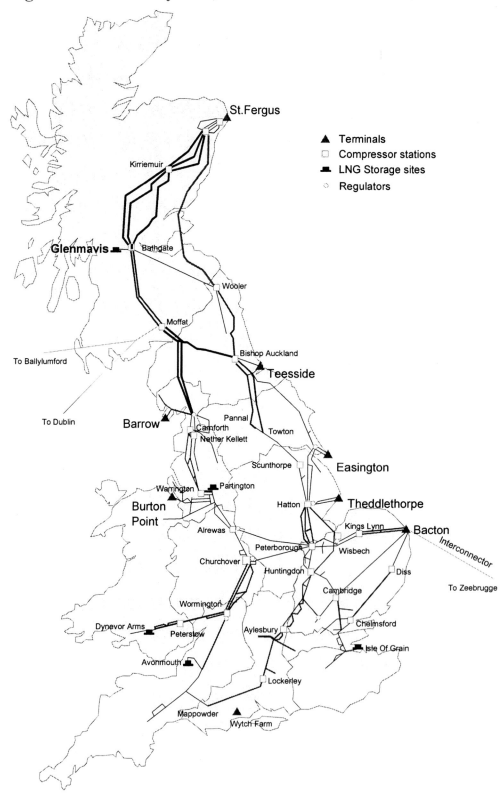

Legend:
- ▲ Terminals
- ☐ Compressor stations
- ◤ LNG Storage sites
- ◌ Regulators

Source: National Grid Transco

4.1 Commodity balances

Natural gas

GWh

	2000			2001			2002		
	Natural gas	Colliery methane	Total Natural gas	Natural gas	Colliery methane	Total Natural gas	Natural gas	Colliery methane	Total Natural gas
Supply									
Production	1,260,168r	488	1,260,656r	1,230,533r	389r	1,230,922r	1,204,714	396	1,205,110
Other sources	-	-	-	-	-	-	-	-	-
Imports	26,032	-	26,032	30,463	-	30,463	60,491	-	60,491
Exports	-146,342	-	-146,342	-138,331r	-	-138,331r	-150,731	-	-150,731
Marine bunkers	-	-	-	-	-	-	-	-	-
Stock change (1)	-11,068r	-	-11,068r	-661	-	-661	-7,356	-	-7,356
Transfers (3)	-442r	-	-442r	-65r	-	-65r	-99	-	-99
Total supply	1,128,348r	488	1,128,836r	1,121,939	389r	1,122,328r	1,107,019	396	1,107,415
Statistical difference (2)	+3,384	-	+3,384	+2,657	-	+2,657	+1,970	-	+1,970
Total demand	1,124,963r	488	1,125,451r	1,119,282r	389r	1,119,671r	1,105,049	396	1,105,445
Transformation	349,304r	150	349,454r	332,650r	77r	332,727r	345,874	110	345,984
Electricity generation	324,413r	150	324,563r	309,732r	77r	309,809r	326,220	110	326,330
Major power producers	283,784	-	283,784	276,764	-	276,764	291,264	-	291,264
Autogenerators	40,629r	150	40,779r	32,968r	77r	33,045r	34,956	110	35,066
Heat generation (6)	24,891r		24,891r	22,918r		22,918r	19,654		19,654
Petroleum refineries	-	-	-	-	-	-	-	-	-
Coke manufacture	-	-	-	-	-	-	-	-	-
Blast furnaces	-	-	-	-	-	-	-	-	-
Patent fuel manufacture	-	-	-	-	-	-	-	-	-
Other	-	-	-	-	-	-	-	-	-
Energy industry use	77,723r	218	77,941r	91,248r	207	91,455r	90,888	196	91,084
Electricity generation	-	-	-	-	-	-	-	-	-
Oil and gas extraction	65,555r	-	65,555r	78,458r	-	78,458r	79,298	-	79,298
Petroleum refineries	3,641	-	3,641	4,192	-	4,192	3,240	-	3,240
Coal extraction	6	218	224	4	207	211	-	196	196
Coke manufacture	17	-	17	9	-	9	-	-	-
Blast furnaces	712	-	712	375	-	375	222	-	222
Patent fuel manufacture	-	-	-	-	-	-	-	-	-
Pumped storage	-	-	-	-	-	-	-	-	-
Other	7,792r	-	7,792r	8,210	-	8,210	8,128	-	8,128
Losses (4)	20,480	-	20,480	9,755r	-	9,755r	9,666	-	9,666
Final consumption	677,456r	120	677,576r	685,629r	105	685,734r	658,621	90	658,711
Industry	183,320r	120	183,440r	182,787r	105	182,892r	176,528	90	176,618
Unclassified	-	120	120	-	105	105	-	90	90
Iron and steel	22,551r	-	22,551r	20,969r	-	20,969r	19,533	-	19,533
Non-ferrous metals	5,468r	-	5,468r	5,217r	-	5,217r	4,946	-	4,946
Mineral products	13,894r	-	13,894r	13,788r	-	13,788r	12,647	-	12,647
Chemicals	46,557r	-	46,557r	48,508r	-	48,508r	47,731	-	47,731
Mechanical Engineering, etc	9,774r	-	9,774r	8,585r	-	8,585r	8,363	-	8,363
Electrical engineering, etc	4,695r	-	4,695r	4,417r	-	4,417r	4,154	-	4,154
Vehicles	10,824r	-	10,824r	11,158r	-	11,158r	10,743	-	10,743
Food, beverages, etc	27,585r	-	27,585r	27,441r	-	27,441r	27,205	-	27,205
Textiles, leather, etc	7,755r	-	7,755r	7,464r	-	7,464r	7,363	-	7,363
Paper, printing, etc	16,085r	-	16,085r	15,711r	-	15,711r	14,555	-	14,555
Other industries	15,153r	-	15,153r	16,585r	-	16,585r	16,433	-	16,433
Construction	2,979r	-	2,979r	2,944r	-	2,944r	2,855	-	2,855
Transport	-	-	-	-	-	-	-	-	-
Air	-	-	-	-	-	-	-	-	-
Rail	-	-	-	-	-	-	-	-	-
Road (5)	-	-	-	-	-	-	-	-	-
National navigation	-	-	-	-	-	-	-	-	-
Pipelines	-	-	-	-	-	-	-	-	-
Other	480,365r	-	480,365r	491,953r	-	491,953r	477,631	-	477,631
Domestic	369,909	-	369,909	379,163	-	379,163	376,327	-	376,327
Public administration	44,552r	-	44,552r	46,121r	-	46,121r	43,715	-	43,715
Commercial	36,216r	-	36,216r	37,025r	-	37,025r	35,741	-	35,741
Agriculture	1,522r	-	1,522r	1,623r	-	1,623r	1,509	-	1,509
Miscellaneous	28,166r	-	28,166r	28,021r	-	28,021r	20,339	-	20,339
Non energy use	13,771r	-	13,771r	10,889r	-	10,889r	4,462	-	4,462

(1) Stock fall (+), stock rise (-).
(2) Total supply minus total demand.

(3) Natural gas used in the manufacture of synthetic coke oven gas.

(4) See paragraph 4.45.
(5) See footnote 5 to Table 4.2.
(6) See footnote 6 to Table 4.2.

4.2 Supply and consumption of natural gas and colliery methane[1]

GWh

	1998	1999	2000	2001	2002
Supply					
Production	1,048,859	1,152,635	1,260,656r	1,230,922r	1,205,110
Imports	10,582	12,862	26,032	30,463	60,491
Exports	-31,604	-84,433	-146,342	-138,331r	-150,731
Stock change (2)	-374	+7,787	-11,068r	-661	-7,356
Transfers	-608	-506	-442r	-65r	-99
Total supply	1,026,855	1,088,345	1,128,836r	1,122,328r	1,107,415
Statistical difference (3)	+5,295	+704	+3,384r	+2,657r	+1,970
Total demand	1,021,560	1,087,641	1,125,451r	1,119,671r	1,105,445
Transformation	267,733	341,678	349,454r	332,727r	345,984
Electricity generation	267,733	315,493	324,563r	309,809r	326,330
Major power producers	236,300	281,988	283,784	276,764r	291,264
Autogenerators	31,433	33,505	40,779r	33,045r	35,066
Heat generation (6)	-	26,185	24,891r	22,918r	19,654
Other	-	-	-	-	-
Energy industry use	75,993	76,973	77,941r	91,455r	91,084
Electricity generation	-	-	-	-	-
Oil and gas extraction	65,500	64,634	65,555r	78,458r	79,298
Petroleum refineries	3,753	4,155	3,641	4,192	3,240
Coal extraction	331	252	224	211	196
Coke manufacture	7	13	17	9	-
Blast furnaces	527	643	712	375	222
Other	5,875	7,276	7,792r	8,210	8,128
Losses (4)	16,254	14,678	20,480r	9,755r	9,666
Final consumption	661,580	654,312	677,576r	685,734r	658,711
Industry	176,084	176,815	183,440r	182,892r	176,618
Unclassified	180	150	120	105	90
Iron and steel	20,105	21,622	22,551r	20,969r	19,533
Non-ferrous metals	5,532	5,549	5,468r	5,217r	4,946
Mineral products	14,689	14,533	13,894r	13,788r	12,647
Chemicals	46,386	46,792	46,557r	48,508r	47,731
Mechanical engineering, etc	10,022	10,173	9,774r	8,585r	8,363
Electrical engineering, etc	3,507	3,941	4,695r	4,417r	4,154
Vehicles	10,274	10,616	10,824r	11,158r	10,743
Food, beverages, etc	27,269	27,901	27,585r	27,441r	27,205
Textiles, leather, etc	7,268	6,966	7,755r	7,464r	7,363
Paper, printing, etc	14,241	12,532	16,085r	15,711r	14,555
Other industries	14,415	13,905	15,153r	16,585r	16,433
Construction	2,196	2,135	2,979r	2,944r	2,855
Transport	-	-	-	-	-
Road (5)	-	-	-	-	-
Other	473,519	464,553	480,365r	491,953r	477,631
Domestic	355,895	358,066	369,909	379,163	376,327
Public administration	51,976	43,253	44,552r	46,121r	43,715
Commercial	40,722	36,622	36,216r	37,025r	35,741
Agriculture	953	1,155	1,522r	1,623r	1,509
Miscellaneous	23,973	25,457	28,166r	28,021r	20,339
Non energy use	11,977	12,944	13,771r	10,889r	4,462

(1) Colliery methane figures included within these totals are as follows:

	1998	1999	2000	2001	2002
Total production	474	481	488	389r	396
Electricity generation	30	93	150	77r	110
Coal extraction	264	238	218	207	196
Other industries	180	150	120	105	90
Total consumption	474	481	488	389r	396

(2) Stock fall (+), stock rise (-).

(3) Total supply minus total demand.

(4) For an explanation of what is included under losses see paragraphs 4.45.

(5) A small amount of natural gas is consumed by road transport, but gas use in this sector is predominantly of petroleum gas, hence road use of gas is reported in the petroleum products balances in Chapter 3.

(6) Heat generation data are not available before 1999. For earlier years gas used to generate heat for sale is allocated to final consumption by the industry sector making the sale.

4.3 UK continental shelf and onshore natural gas production and supply[(1)]

GWh

	1998	1999	2000	2001	2002
Upstream gas industry:					
Gross production (2)	1,048,385	1,152,154	1,260,168r	1,230,533r	1,204,714
Minus Producers' own use (3) (18)	65,500	64,634	65,556r	78,458r	79,298
Exports	31,604	84,433	146,342	138,331r	150,731
Stock change (pipelines) (4) (18)	-1,721	-842	+161	-	-
Waste (5) (18)	89	-	-	-	-
Other losses and metering differences (6)(7)(18)	7,419	5,634	10,281r	-	-
Plus Imports of gas	10,582	12,862	26,032	30,463	60,491
Gas available at terminals (8)	956,076	1,011,157	1,063,858r	1,044,207r	1,035,176
Minus Statistical difference (7)	+734	-127	+251r	-694r	-61
Downstream gas industry:					
Gas input into the national transmission system (9)	955,342	1,011,284	1,063,607r	1,044,901r	1,035,237
Minus Operators' own use (10)	4,337	5,626	6,701	6,549	7,017
Stock change (storage sites) (11)	+2,095	-6,945	+10,907r	+661	+7,356
Metering differences (7)	509	633	2,088r	1,798r	1,821
Gas output from the national transmission system (12)	948,401	1,011,970	1,043,911	1,035,893r	1,019,043
Minus Leakage assessment (13)	5,688	5,722	5,464r	5,360r	5,284
Own use gas (14)	364	448	442r	433r	427
Theft (15)	2,185	2,241	2,206r	2,164r	2,134
Transfers (16)	608	506	441r	65r	99
Statistical difference and metering differences (7)	4,561	831	3,128r	3,354r	2,031
Total UK consumption (17)	**934,995**	**1,002,222**	**1,032,230r**	**1,024,517r**	**1,009,068**

(1) For details of where to find monthly updates of natural gas production and supply see paragraph 4.41.

(2) Includes waste and producers' own use, but excludes gas flared.

(3) Gas used for drilling, production and pumping operations.

(4) Gas held within the UKCS pipeline system. As sections are opened and closed between fields, gas moves in and out of the system, hence it is regarded as a change in stocks.

(5) Gas vented from oil and gas platforms as part of the production process. With effect from 1999 gas vented is deducted from the Gross Production figure.

(6) Losses due to pipeline leakage.

(7) Measurement of gas flows, in volume and energy terms, occurs at several points along the supply chain. As such, differences are seen between the actual recorded flow through any one point and estimates calculated for the flow of gas at that point. More detail on the reasons for these differences is given in the technical notes and definitions section of this chapter, paragraphs 4.42 to 4.45.

(8) The volume of gas available at terminals for consumption in the UK as recorded by the terminal operators. The percentage of gas available for consumption in the UK from indigenous sources in 2002 was 94.2 per cent, compared with 97.1 per cent in 2001.

(9) Gas received as reported by the pipeline operators. The pipeline operators include Transco, who run the national pipeline network, and other pipelines that take North Sea gas supplies direct to consumers.

(10) Gas consumed by pipeline operators in pumping operations and on their own sites, office, etc.

(11) Stocks of gas held in specific storage sites, either as liquefied natural gas, pumped into salt cavities or stored by pumping the gas back into an offshore field. Stock rise (+), stock fall (-).

(12) Including public gas supply, direct supplies by North Sea producers, third party supplies and stock changes.

(13) This is a Tranco assessment of leakage through the local distribution system based on the National Leakage Reduction Monitoring Model. The 2002 figure is a DTI estimate.

(14) Equivalent to about 0.06 per cent of LDZ throughput this is an assessment of the energy used to counter the effects of gas cooling on pressure reduction.

(15) Calculated by Transco as 0.3 per cent of LDZ throughput, this is theft before the gas reaches customer meters.

(16) Transfers are the use within the iron and steel industry for use in the manufacture of synthetic coke oven gas.

(17) See paragraph 4.27 for an explanation of the relationship between these "Total UK consumption" figures and "Total demand" shown within the balance tables.

(18) A simplified PPRS reporting system was introduced in January 2001 requiring less data from respondents - see paragraph 4.27.

Chapter 5
Electricity

Introduction

5.1   This Chapter presents statistics on electricity from generation through to sales. In addition, statistics on generating capacity, on fuel used for generation and on load factors and efficiencies are included along with a map showing the transmission system in Great Britain and the location of the main power stations (page 125).

5.2   Commodity balances for electricity, for each of the last three years, form the introductory table (Table 5.1). The supply and consumption elements of the electricity balance are presented as 5-year time series in Table 5.2. Table 5.3 separates out the public distribution system for electricity from electricity generated and consumed by autogenerators and uses a commodity balance format. Fuels used to generate electricity in the United Kingdom in each of the last five years are covered in Table 5.4. Table 5.5 shows the relationship between the commodity balance definitions and traditional Digest definitions for electricity, so that the most recent data can be linked to the long term trends data, which can be found on the DTI energy statistics web site. Table 5.6 shows the relationship between fuels used, generation and supply in each of the latest five years. As in previous years, tables on plant capacity (Tables 5.7 and 5.8) and on plant loads and efficiency (Table 5.9) have been included and the table that lists individual power stations in operation is Table 5.10. The long term trends commentary and tables on fuel use, generation, supply and consumption back to 1970 are on DTI's energy statistics web site www.dti.gov.uk/energy/inform/dukes/dukes2003/05longterm.pdf.

Structure of the industry

5.3   On 27 March 2001, the means of trading electricity changed with the introduction in England and Wales of the New Electricity Trading Arrangements (NETA). These arrangements are based on bi-lateral trading between generators, suppliers, traders and customers and are designed to be more efficient and provide greater choice for market participants, whilst maintaining the operation of a secure and reliable electricity system. The system includes forwards and futures markets, a balancing mechanism to enable the National Grid Company, as systems operator, to balance the system, and a settlement process. The system is shown in simplified form in Chart 5.1.

5.4   Since the period immediately after privatisation of the industry in 1989, when there were 7 generating companies in England and Wales and 12 Regional Electricity companies distributing and supplying electricity to customers in their designated area, there have been many structural and business changes. At the end of 2002 there were 32 major power producers operating in England and Wales. Competition developed as follows:

(a)   From 1 April 1990, customers with peak loads of more than 1 MW (about 45 per cent of the non-domestic market) were able to choose their supplier.

(b)   From 1 April 1994, customers with peak loads of more than 100 kW were able to choose their supplier.

(c)   Between September 1998 and May 1999, the remaining part of the electricity market (ie below 100 kW peak load) was opened up to competition. Paragraph 5.8 and Table 5A give more details of the opening up of the domestic gas and electricity markets to competition.

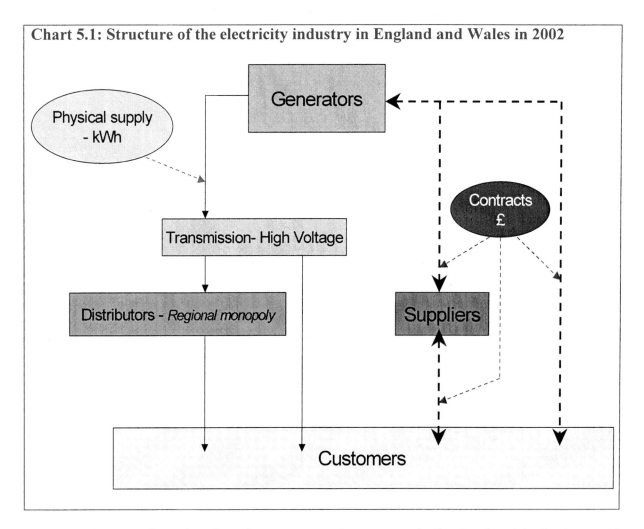

Chart 5.1: Structure of the electricity industry in England and Wales in 2002

Physical supply - kWh

Generators

Transmission- High Voltage

Contracts £

Distributors - *Regional monopoly*

Suppliers

Customers

5.5   At the same time, there have been moves to integrate vertically the electricity business with former generating companies acquiring electricity supply companies and supply companies purchasing generating stations or acquiring interests in companies building new power stations. Distribution businesses have been sold or acquired and merged. The National Grid Company, now part of National Grid Transco, operates the high voltage transmission system linking generators to distributors and some large customers. The Grid system of England and Wales is linked to that of Scotland via two interconnectors and to the grid of continental Europe via in interconnector to France under the English Channel. (See Table 5.10).

5.6   In Scotland, the two main companies, Scottish Power and Scottish and Southern Energy, cover the full range of electricity provision. They operate generation, transmission, distribution and supply businesses. The entire output of the two nuclear power stations in Scotland, which are owned by British Energy plc, is sold to these two suppliers under long-term contracts. In addition, there are about 25 small independent hydro stations and some independent generators operating fossil-fuelled stations, which sell their output to Scottish Power and Scottish and Southern Energy.

5.7   The electricity supply industry in Northern Ireland is also in private hands. Northern Ireland Electricity plc (NIE) (part of the Viridian Group) is responsible for power procurement, transmission, distribution and supply in the Province. Generation is in the hands of three private sector companies who own the four major power stations. There is a link (re-established in 1996) between the Northern Ireland grid and that of the Irish Republic, along which electricity is both imported and exported. In December 2001, the link between Northern Ireland's grid and that of Scotland was inaugurated.

5.8   By December 2002, just over 9.2 million electricity consumers (37 per cent) were no longer with their home supplier. Table 5A gives market penetration in the fourth quarter of 2002. For quarterly credit customers it is in the markets in Yorkshire, the North West, North Wales and Merseyside, and the East and West Midlands that new suppliers had the most success. By the end of 2002, the former regional electricity companies had lost around 35 per cent of the credit and 41 per cent of the direct debit market, but the biggest change during the year was in the number of prepayment customers who had switched supplier.

Table 5A: Domestic electricity market penetration (in terms of percentage of customers supplied) by Public Electricity Supply area and payment type, fourth quarter of 2002

Region	Home Supplier			Non-Home Supplier		
	Credit	Direct Debit	Prepayment	Credit	Direct Debit	Prepayment
Yorkshire	57	58	65	43	42	35
North West	57	52	59	43	48	41
Merseyside and North Wales	58	56	56	42	44	44
West Midlands	61	58	62	39	42	38
East Midlands	61	60	58	39	40	42
North East	63	53	59	37	47	41
South Scotland	67	52	67	33	48	33
South Wales	68	74	75	32	26	25
South East	68	63	54	32	37	46
Eastern	68	57	59	32	43	41
London	70	59	64	30	41	36
South	71	66	67	29	34	33
South West	75	56	67	25	44	33
North Scotland	86	80	89	14	20	11
Great Britain	65	59	64	35	41	36

Commodity balances for electricity (Table 5.1)

5.9   The first page of this balance table shows that 98 per cent of UK electricity supply in 2002 was home produced and 2 per cent was from imports net of exports. Under a ¼ per cent of home produced electricity was exported. Of the 384 TWh produced (excluding pumped storage production), 91½ per cent was from major power producers and 8½ per cent from autoproducers, 24½ per cent was from primary sources and 75½ per cent from secondary sources.

5.10   Electricity generated by each type of fuel is shown on the second page of the commodity balance table. The link between electricity generated and electricity supplied is made in Table 5.6 and electricity supplied by each type of fuel is illustrated in Chart 5.3. Paragraph 5.26 examines further the ways of presenting each fuel's contribution to electricity production.

5.11   Demand for electricity is predominantly from final consumers, who accounted for 84½ per cent in 2002. The remaining 15½ per cent is split 8 per cent to energy industries' use and 7½ per cent to losses.   The electricity industry itself uses 54½ per cent of the energy industries' total use of electricity, with a further 11 per cent used for pumping at pumped storage stations. Petroleum refineries are the next most significant consumer. The losses item has three components. First, transmission losses from the high voltage transmission system represented about 19 per cent of the figure in 2002. Second, distribution losses, which occur between the gateways to the public supply system's network and the customers' meters, accounted for about 75 per cent of losses. Third, a small amount was lost through theft or meter fraud (6 per cent) (see also paragraphs 5.62).

5.12   Industrial consumption was 33½ per cent of final consumption in 2002, slightly less than the consumption by households (34½ per cent), with transport and the services sector accounting for the remaining 32 per cent.   Within the industrial sector the three largest consuming industries are chemicals, food, and paper, which together account for 41½ per cent of industrial consumption.   The iron and steel sector is also a large user of electricity and would rank fourth largest, but part of its consumption is included against blast furnaces and coke ovens under energy industry uses.   This is because electricity is used by coke ovens and blast furnaces in the transformation of solid fuels into coke, coke oven gas and blast furnace gas.   Taken together, the engineering industries accounted for a further 18 per cent of final consumption of electricity.   A note on the estimates included within these figures is to be found at paragraph 5.63.   Chart 5.2 shows diagrammatically the demand for electricity in 2002.

5.13   The transport sector covers electricity consumed by companies involved in transport, storage and communications.   Within the overall total of 8,500 GWh, it is known that national railways consume about 2,700 GWh each year for traction purposes, and this figure has been shown separately in the balances.

Chart 5.2: Electricity demand by sector, 2002

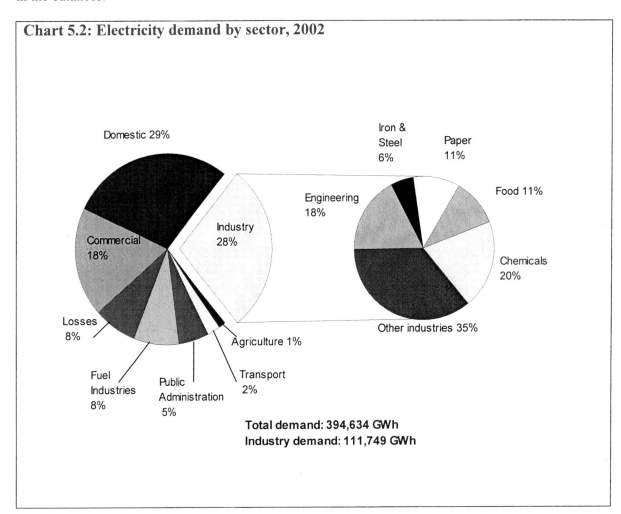

Total demand: 394,634 GWh
Industry demand: 111,749 GWh

Supply and consumption of electricity (Table 5.2)

5.14   There was a marginal increase in the supply of electricity in 2002 (less than ½ per cent). Production (including pumped storage production) increased by ½ per cent.   There was a 14 per cent fall in imports of electricity, because low UK prices made it less attractive to French exporters, while higher prices in continental Europe fostered a growth in exports, which were three times their level in 2001.

5.15   Energy industry use of electricity as a proportion of electricity demand (8 per cent) was slightly higher in 2002 than 2001, while losses as a proportion of total demand, at 7½ per cent, were the same as in the two previous years. Industrial consumption of electricity was virtually unchanged on 2001's level, while consumption in the services sector rose by 1 per cent. Consumption by transport, storage and communications fell by 4 per cent and domestic sector consumption fell by ½ per cent. Temperatures influence the actual level of consumption in any one year in the winter months, as customers adjust heating levels in their homes. On average, temperatures in the winter months were lower in 1999, 2000 and 2001 than in the milder years of 1998 and 2002. Temperatures in the first and fourth quarters of 2002 were particularly mild.

Regional electricity data

5.16   The restructuring of the electricity industry in 1990 and the privatisation of the electricity companies meant that it was no longer possible for this Digest to present regional data on the supply of electricity, as it would disclose information about individual businesses that were in competition with each other. Now that competition has been fully introduced, the Department of Trade and Industry has started to examine ways in which electricity data can be collected at a regional (and sub-regional) level, in order to meet the requirements of users. Further information is available on the DTI Energy statistics web site www.dti.gov.uk/energy/inform/energy_stats/. Distribution, the physical delivery of electricity, is a monopoly activity for each public electricity supplier inside its own geographic area. Data on electricity distributed is given in Table 5B. The areas covered by each company vary in terms of square kilometres covered, number of customers and electricity distributed within the area. As the map on page 125 shows some companies are now responsible for distribution in more than one area.

5.17   The difference between total electricity distributed, shown in Table 5B, and total consumption is accounted for by electricity sold directly to large users by generators via the high voltage grid without passing through the distribution network of the regional companies, electricity consumed by the company generating the electricity (autogeneration plus electricity industry own use), and transmission losses.

Table 5B: Electricity distributed by public electricity suppliers, 2002[1] [2]

	Area (sq km)	Number of customers (thousand)	Customer density (No. per sq. km)	Electricity distributed (GWh)
Eastern	20,300	3,394	167	35,012
South	16,900	2,827	167	32,584
East Midlands	16,000	2,459	154	28,201
Midlands	13,300	2,383	179	26,711
London	665	2,305	3,467	25,946
North West	12,500	2,300	184	24,852
Yorkshire	10,700	2,169	203	23,945
South Scotland	22,950	2,075	90	22,968
South East	8,200	2,136	261	20,634
North East	14,400	1,548	108	16,760
South West	14,400	1,454	101	15,329
Merseyside & North Wales	12,200	1,443	118	16,651
South Wales	11,800	1,053	89	12,222
North Scotland	54,390	830	15	8,527
Northern Ireland	13,506	692	51	7,328
Total	242,211	29,068	120	317,670

(1) The figures for the area and number of customers were provided by OFGEM and Northern Ireland Electricity and relate to 2000. Number of customers figures are number of meter points. Electricity distributed is taken from returns made to DTI for 2002.
(2) The figures for electricity distributed exclude electricity sold directly to customers over high voltage lines.

Commodity balances for the public distribution system and for other generators (Table 5.3)

5.18   Table 5.3 expands on the commodity balance format to show consumption divided between electricity distributed over the public distribution system and electricity provided by other generators (autogeneration). Autogeneration is the generation of electricity wholly or partly for a company's own use as an activity which supplements the primary activity. However, most generators of electricity from renewable sources (apart from large scale hydro and some biofuels) are included as other generators because of their comparatively small size, even though their main activity is electricity generation. For a full list of companies included as major power producers see paragraph 5.46.

5.19   Table 5.3 also expands the domestic sector to show consumption by payment type and the commercial sector is expanded to show detailed data beyond that presented in Tables 5.1 and 5.2.

5.20   The proportion of electricity supplied by generators other than major power producers rose slightly in 2002 to 8½ per cent, but it is still below the 9½ per cent it reached in 2000 following steady yearly growth. The proportion of this electricity transferred to the public distribution system increased from 20 per cent in 1999 to 23½ per cent in 2000 and 27½ per cent in 2001, but fell back to 22½ per cent in 2002. High gas prices and low electricity prices made it more difficult for electricity produced by other generators to compete in the electricity market in 2002.

5.21   In 2002, 5½ per cent of final consumption of electricity was by other generators and did not pass over the public distribution system. This was slightly higher than 2001's 5 per cent lower than the 6 per cent achieved in 2000. A substantial proportion of electricity is self-generated in the energy industries with the proportion close to or above 20 per cent in all three years shown in the table. At petroleum refineries the proportion is even higher and in 2002 three quarters of electricity was self-generated.

5.22   In 2002, about 13 per cent of the industrial demand for electricity was met by autogeneration. There was also a lesser proportion (about 2½ per cent) from autogeneration within the commercial and transport sectors. Table 1.9 in Chapter 1 shows the fuels used by autogenerators to generate this electricity within each major sector and also the quantities of electricity generated and consumed.

5.23   Within the domestic sector, about a third of the electricity consumed was purchased under some form of off-peak pricing structure (the same as in the previous two years). About 16 per cent of consumption was through prepayment systems, a proportion that has varied little over the three years shown.

Fuel used in generation (Table 5.4)

5.24   In this table fuel used by electricity generators is measured in both original units and for comparative purposes, in the common unit of million tonnes of oil equivalent. In Table 5.6 figures are quoted in a third unit, namely GWh, in order to show the link between fuel use and electricity generated.

5.25   The energy supplied basis defines the primary input (in million tonnes of oil equivalent) needed to produce 1 TWh of hydro, wind, or imported electricity as:

$$\text{Electricity generated (TWh)} \times 0.085985$$

The primary input needed to produce 1 TWh of nuclear electricity is similarly

$$\frac{\text{Electricity generated (TWh)} \times 0.085985}{\text{Thermal efficiency of nuclear stations}}$$

In the United Kingdom the thermal efficiency of nuclear stations has risen in stages from 32 per cent in 1982 to 37½ per cent in 2002 (see Table 5.9 and paragraph 5.53 for the definition)[1]. The factor of 0.085985 is the energy content of one TWh divided by the energy content of one million tonnes of oil equivalent (see page 202 and inside back cover flap).

5.26   Figures on fuel use for electricity generation can be compared in two ways. Table 5.4 illustrates one way by using the volumes of **fuel input** to power stations (after conversion of inputs to an oil equivalent basis), but this takes no account of how efficiently that fuel is converted into electricity. The fuel input basis is the most appropriate to use for analysis of the quantities of particular fuels used in electricity generation (eg to determine the amount of coal at risk from displacement by gas or other fuels). A second way uses the amount of electricity generated and supplied by each fuel. This **output** basis is appropriate for comparing how much, and what percentage, of electricity generation comes from a particular fuel. It is the most appropriate method to use to examine the dominance of any fuel, and for diversity issues. Percentage shares based on fuel outputs reduce the contribution of coal and nuclear, and increase the contribution of gas (by about 5 percentage points in 2001) compared with the fuel input basis, because of the higher conversion efficiency of the latter. This output basis is used in Chart 5.3, taking electricity supplied (gross) figures from Table 5.6. Trends in fuel used on this electricity supplied basis are described in the section on Table 5.6, in paragraphs 5.29 to 5.32, below.

5.27   An historical series of fuel used in generation on a consistent, energy supplied, fuel input basis is available at Table 5.1.1 on DTI's energy statistics web site.

Relating measurements of supply, consumption and availability (Table 5.5)
5.28   The balance methodology uses terms that cannot be readily employed for earlier years' data because statistics were not available in sufficient detail. Table 5.5 shows the relationship between these terms for the latest five years. For the full definitions of the terms used in the commodity balances see the Annex A, paragraphs A.7 to A.42.

Electricity generated, and supplied (Table 5.6)
5.29   The main data on generation and supply in Table 5.6 are presented by type of fuel. However, before 1996 data were presented by type of station and in order to maintain a link with this earlier data the final part of the table shows generation from conventional steam stations and from combined cycle gas turbine stations over the most recent five years.

5.30   Total electricity generated in the United Kingdom in 2002 exceeded generation in 2001 by ½ per cent. This rate of growth was well below the average rate of growth over the previous four years of 2¼ per cent per year. Major power producers (as defined in paragraph 5.45) accounted for 91½ per cent of electricity generation in 2002. Generation by other generators was 3 per cent up on a year earlier.

5.31   Generation from coal-fired stations was 5½ per cent lower in 2002 than in 2001 but higher than in the four preceding years. Generation from gas rose by 7 per cent in 2002 to a new record level, 3 per cent above 2000's previous record. One new CCGT station came on stream during the year and two others made their first full year contributions. Generation from nuclear sources fell by 2 per cent. Slightly lower gas prices, except during the winter peak demand period, enabled gas fired generation to recapture some of the generation market that it had lost to coal in the face of high gas prices and cheap (imported) coal during 2001. A high level of outages for repairs and maintenance at nuclear stations caused the decline in generation from nuclear sources.

---

[1] *Note that the International Energy Agency uses 0.33 in its calculations, which is the European average thermal efficiency of nuclear stations in 1989, measured in net terms rather than the UK's gross terms.*

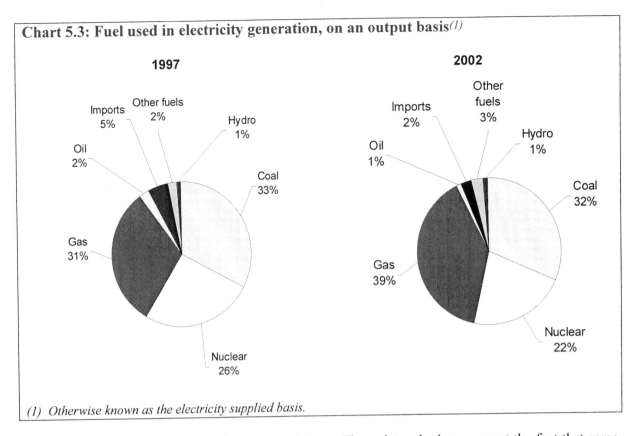

Chart 5.3: Fuel used in electricity generation, on an output basis *(1)*

1997

Imports 5%
Other fuels 2%
Hydro 1%
Oil 2%
Coal 33%
Gas 31%
Nuclear 26%

2002

Imports 2%
Other fuels 3%
Hydro 1%
Oil 1%
Coal 32%
Gas 39%
Nuclear 22%

(1) Otherwise known as the electricity supplied basis.

5.32   Table 5.6 also shows electricity supplied data. These data take into account the fact that some stations use relatively more electricity than others in the generation process itself. In total, electricity supplied (gross) was 4½ per cent less than the volume generated in 2002, but for nuclear stations it was 8 per cent less, while for gas fired stations it was only 2 per cent less. Chart 5.3 shows how shares of the generation market in terms of electricity output have changed over the last five years. Gas' share of electricity supplied (net) plus imports has moved up from 31 per cent in 1997 to 39 per cent in 2002, more than recovering it 2 percentage point loss of share in 2001. Coal's share at 32 per cent was 1 percentage point lower than in 1997 and 1 percentage point lower than in 2001. Nuclear's 22 per cent share was not as low as its share in 2000 (21 per cent) but considerably lower than the peak 26 per cent share of 1997. Oil's share has halved to 1 per cent over the five years shown and imports' share has fallen from 5 per cent in 1997 to 2 per cent in 2002.

Plant capacity (Tables 5.7 and 5.8)

5.33   Table 5.7 shows capacity, ie the maximum power available at any one time, for major power producers and other generators by type of plant.

5.34   In 2002, there was a decrease of just under 2,800 MW (4 per cent) in the capacity of major power producers. This is due to the mothballing of all or part of some coal, oil and CCGT plant. New capacity coming on stream in 2002 amounted to only 32 MW. In December 2002, major power producers accounted for 92 per cent of the total generating capacity, the same proportion as at the end of 2001. The capacity of other generators decreased by 2 per cent. Renewables capacity of other generators increased by 122 MW but capacity of good quality CHP fell by 11 MWe (see Chapter 6) and of other non-CHP capacity amounting to 231 MW was closed.

5.35   A breakdown of the capacity of the major power producers' plants at the end of March each year from 1993 to 1996 and at the end of December for 1996 to 2002 is shown in Chart 5.4.

5.36 In Table 5.8, data for the generating capacity of industrial, commercial and transport undertakings are shown, according to the industrial classification of the generator. A fifth of the capacity is in the chemicals sector. Petroleum refineries have 16 per cent of capacity, engineering and other metal trades, and paper, printing and publishing each have a 10 per cent share.

Plant loads, demand and efficiency (Table 5.9)

5.37 Table 5.9 shows the maximum load met each year, load factors (by type of plant and for the system in total) and indicators of thermal efficiency. Maximum demand figures cover the winter period ending the following March.

5.38 Maximum demand during the winter of 2002/2003 occurred in December 2002. This was 5.3 per cent higher than the previous maximum in January 2002. Maximum demand in 2002/2003 was 87.6 per cent of the capacity of major power producers (Table 5.7) as measured at the end of December 2002, compared with 80 per cent in 2001/02, and 81 per cent in 2000. The sharp increase in this percentage is because major power producers have closed or mothballed about 2,800 MW of capacity, see 5.34 above.

5.39 Plant load factors measure how intensively each type of plant has been used. The recent trend had been for conventional thermal plant to be used less intensively and CCGT stations more intensively. However, in 2000 increased maintenance and repair at nuclear stations and at CCGT stations, coupled with high gas prices at the end of the year, led to a departure from this trend. Continuing high gas prices in 2001 and 2002 have brought about the lower load factors for 2001 and 2002. Further problems at nuclear stations in 2002 saw nuclear's load factor fall back from the recovery in 2001. The use of coal-fired stations to make up for the nuclear shortfall and in competition with gas (see paragraph 5.31) is reflected in the increased load factor for conventional thermal stations in 2001 and 2002.

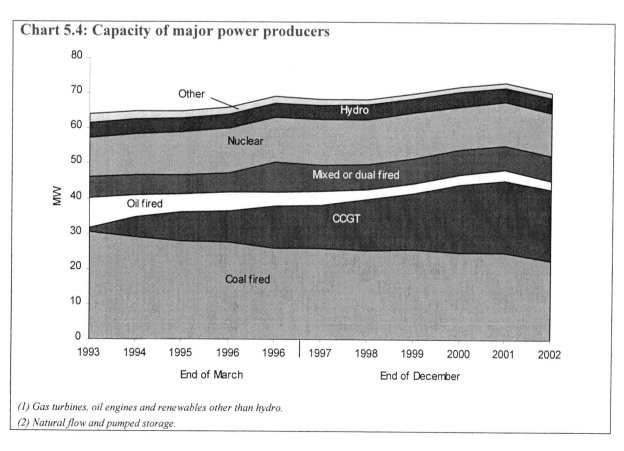

Chart 5.4: Capacity of major power producers

(1) Gas turbines, oil engines and renewables other than hydro.
(2) Natural flow and pumped storage.

5.40 2001 was a particularly dry year in the areas where hydro electricity is produced. As a result the load factors for natural flow hydro (and to a lesser extent for pumped storage) were lower in 2001 than in 2000. Both showed a recovery in the wetter year of 2002, but a dry end to the year again restricted use of these stations.

5.41 Thermal efficiency measures the efficiency with which the heat energy in fuel is converted into electrical energy. The efficiency of coal-fired stations had been on a downward trend as coal became the marginal fuel for generation, but coal's increased role in 2000 saw an increase in the thermal efficiency of coal-fired generation. In 2001 efficiency fell back to 1999 levels, but in 2002 it recovered with the mothballing of some less efficient stations. CCGT efficiency in each of the last five years has been very consistent with a slight upward trend reflecting the influence of more modern stations coming on stream. The efficiency of nuclear stations rose slightly in 2002. The efficiencies presented in this table are calculated using **gross** calorific values to obtain the energy content of the fuel inputs. If **net** calorific values are used, efficiencies are higher, for example CCGT efficiencies rise by about 5 percentage points.

The Electricity Supply System in Great Britain in 2002

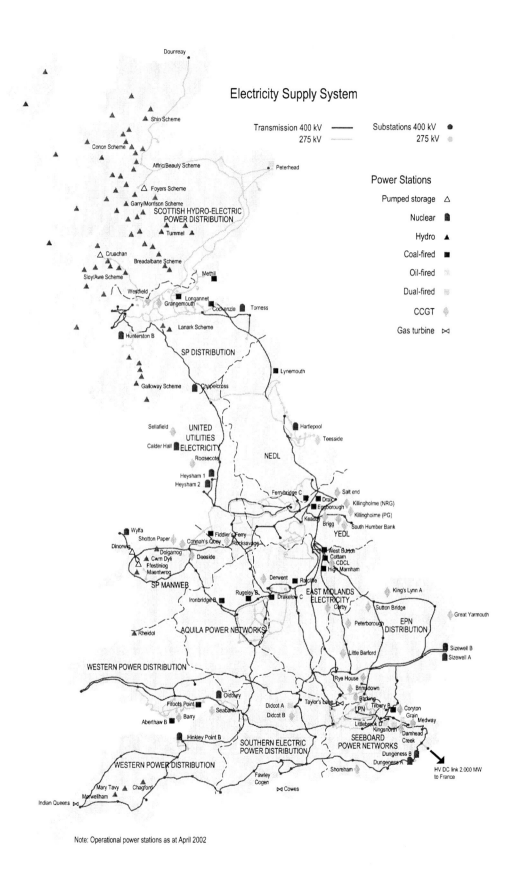

Note: Operational power stations as at April 2002

Source: Electricity Association

Technical notes and definitions

5.42   These notes and definitions are in addition to the technical notes and definitions covering all fuels and energy as a whole in Chapter 1, paragraphs 1.24 to 1.58. For notes on the commodity balances and definitions of the terms used in the row headings see the Annex A, paragraphs A.7 to A.42.

Electricity generation from renewable sources

5.43   Figures on electricity generation from renewable energy sources are included in the tables in this section. Further detailed information on renewable energy sources is included in Chapter 7.

Combined heat and power

5.44   Electricity generated from combined heat and power (CHP) schemes, CHP generating capacities and fuel used for electricity generation are included in the tables in this chapter. However, more detailed analyses of CHP schemes are set out in Chapter 6.

Generating companies

5.45   Following the restructuring of the electricity supply industry in 1990, the term "Major generating companies" was introduced into the electricity tables to describe the activities of the former nationalised industries and distinguish them from those of autogenerators and new independent companies set up to generate electricity. The activities of the autogenerators and the independent companies were classified under the heading "Other generating companies". In the 1994 Digest, a new terminology was adopted to encompass the new independent producers, who were then beginning to make a significant contribution to electricity supply. Under this terminology, all companies whose prime purpose is the generation of electricity are included under the heading "Major power producers" (or MPPs). The term "Other generators" ("Autogenerators" in the balance tables) is restricted to companies who produce electricity as part of their manufacturing or other commercial activities, but whose main business is not electricity generation. "Other generators" also covers generation by energy services companies at power stations on an industrial or commercial site where the main purpose is the supply of electricity to that site, even if the energy service company is a subsidiary of a major power producer. Most generators of electricity from renewable sources (apart from large scale hydro and some biofuels) are also included as "Other generators" because of their comparatively small size, even though their main activity is electricity generation.

5.46   **Major power producers at the end of 2002 were:**
AES Electric Ltd., American Electric Power, Anglian Power Generators Ltd, Baglan Generation Ltd., Barking Power Ltd., BNFL Magnox., British Energy plc., Coolkeeragh Power Ltd., Corby Power Ltd., Coryton Energy Company Ltd., Deeside Power, Derwent Cogeneration Ltd., Edison Mission Energy Ltd., Enfield Energy Centre Ltd., Entergy Power Group Ltd., Fellside Heat and Power Ltd., Fibrogen Ltd., Fibropower Ltd., Fibrothetford Ltd., Fife Power Ltd., Great Yarmouth Power Ltd, Humber Power Ltd., Innogy plc., International Power plc., Killingholme Power Ltd., Lakeland Power Ltd., London Power Company, Medway Power Ltd., NIGEN, Peterborough Power Ltd., PowerGen plc, Premier Power Ltd., Regional Power Generators Ltd., Rocksavage Power Company Ltd., Saltend Co-generation Company Ltd., Sita Tyre Recycling Ltd., Scottish Power plc., Scottish and Southern Energy plc., Seabank Power Ltd., SELCHP Ltd., South Coast Power Ltd., South Western Electricity, Sutton Bridge Power Ltd., Teesside Power Ltd.

Types of station

5.47   The various types of station identified in the tables of this chapter are as follows:

Conventional steam stations are stations that generate electricity by burning fossil fuels to convert water into steam, which then powers steam turbines.

Nuclear stations are also steam stations but the heat needed to produce the steam comes from nuclear fission.

Gas turbines use pressurised combustion gases from fuel burned in one or more combustion chambers to turn a series of bladed fan wheels and rotate the shaft on which they are mounted. This then drives the generator. The fuel burnt is usually natural gas or gas oil.

Combined cycle gas turbine (CCGT) stations combine in the same plant gas turbines and steam turbines connected to one or more electrical generators. This enables electricity to be produced at higher efficiencies than is otherwise possible when either gas or steam turbines are used in isolation. The gas turbine (usually fuelled by natural gas or oil) produces mechanical power (to drive the generator) and waste heat. The hot exhaust gases (waste heat) are fed to a boiler, where steam is raised at pressure to drive a conventional steam turbine that is also connected to an electrical generator.

Natural flow hydro-electric stations use natural water flows to turn turbines.

Pumped storage hydro-electric stations use electricity to pump water into a high level reservoir. This water is then released to generate electricity at peak times. Where the reservoir is open, the stations also generate some natural flow electricity; this is included with natural flow generation. As electricity is used in the pumping process, pumped storage stations are net consumers of electricity.

Other stations include wind turbines and stations burning fuels such as landfill gas, sewage sludge and waste.

Public distribution system
5.48   This comprises the grids in England and Wales, Scotland and Northern Ireland.

Sectors used for sales/consumption
5.49   The various sectors used for sales and consumption analyses are standardised across all chapters of the 2003 Digest. For definitions of the sectors see the Chapter 1 paragraphs 1.54 to 1.58 and Annex A paragraphs A.31 to A.42.

Declared net capability and declared net capacity
5.50   Declared net capability is the maximum power available for export from a power station on a continuous basis minus any power imported by the station from the network to run its own plant. It represents the nominal maximum capability of a generating set to supply electricity to consumers. The registered capacity of a generating set differs from declared net capability in that, for registered capacity, not all power consumed by the plant is subtracted from the normal full load capacity, only the MW consumed by the generating set through its transformer when generating at its normal full load capacity.

5.51   Declared net capacity is used to measure the maximum power available from generating stations that use renewable resources. For wind and tidal power a factor is applied to declared net capability to take account of the intermittent nature of the energy source (eg 0.43 for wind).

Load factors
5.52   The following definitions are used in Table 5.9:

Maximum load - Twice the largest number of units supplied in any consecutive thirty minutes commencing or terminating at the hour.

Simultaneous maximum load met - The maximum load on the grid at any one time. It is measured by the sum of the maximum load met in England and Wales and the loads met at the same time by companies in other parts of the United Kingdom. In 2002/03 the maximum load in England and Wales occurred on 10 December 2002 at 17.30. However in Scotland and Northern Ireland the maximum load occurred on 7 January 2003 at 17.30, but the combined UK load was less than on 10 December.

Plant load factor - The average hourly quantity of electricity supplied during the year, expressed as a percentage of the average output capability at the beginning and the end of year.

System load factor - The average hourly quantity of electricity available during the year expressed as a percentage of the maximum demand nearest the end of the year or early the following year.

Thermal efficiency

5.53 Thermal efficiency is the efficiency with which heat energy contained in fuel is converted into electrical energy. It is calculated for fossil fuel burning stations by expressing electricity generated as a percentage of the total energy content of the fuel consumed (based on average gross calorific values). For nuclear stations it is calculated using the quantity of heat released as a result of fission of the nuclear fuel inside the reactor. The efficiency of CHP systems is discussed separately in Chapter 6, paragraph 6.24 and Table 6D. Efficiencies based on gross calorific value of the fuel (sometimes referred to as higher heating values or HHV) are lower than the efficiencies based on net calorific value (or lower heating value LHV). The difference between HHV and LHV is due to the energy associated with the latent heat of the evaporation of water products from the steam cycle which cannot be recovered and put to economic use.

Period covered

5.54 Figures for the major power producers relate to periods of 52 weeks as follows (although some data provided by electricity supply companies relate to calendar months):

Year	53 weeks ended
1998	3 January 1999
	52 weeks ended
1999	2 January 2000
2000	31 December 2000
2001	30 December 2001
2002	29 December 2002

5.55 Figures for industrial, commercial and transport undertakings relate to years ended 31 December, except for the iron and steel industry where figures relate to the following 52 week periods:

Year	53 weeks ended
1998	2 January 1999
	52 weeks ended
1999	1 January 2000
2000	30 December 2000
2001	29 December 2001
2002	28 December 2002

5.56 Statistical years that contain 53 weeks are adjusted to 52-week equivalents by taking 5/6ths of the 6-week December period values.

Monthly and quarterly data

5.57 Monthly and quarterly data on fuel use, electricity generation and supply and electricity availability and consumption are available on DTI's Energy Statistics web site www.dti.gov.uk/energy/inform/energy_stats/. Monthly data on fuel used in electricity generation by major power producers are given in Monthly Table 5.3 and monthly data on supplies by type of plant and type of fuel are given in Monthly Table 5.4, while monthly data on availability and consumption of electricity by the main sectors of the economy are given in Monthly Table 5.5. A quarterly commodity balance for electricity is published in DTI's quarterly statistical bulletin *Energy Trends* (Quarterly Table 5.2) along with a quarterly table of fuel use for generation by all generators and electricity supplied by major power producers (Quarterly Table 5.1). Both these quarterly tables are also available from DTI's Energy Statistics web site. See Annex C for more information about *Energy Trends*.

Data collection

5.58 For Major Power Producers, as defined in paragraph 5.45, the data for the tables in this Digest are obtained from the results of an annual DTI inquiry, sent to each company, covering generating capacity, fuel use, generation, sales and distribution of electricity.

5.59 Another annual inquiry is sent to licensed suppliers of electricity to establish electricity sales by these companies. Similarly, an annual inquiry is sent to electricity distributors to establish electricity distributed by these companies.

5.60 Companies that generate electricity mainly for their own use (known as autogenerators or autoproducers - see paragraph 5.45, above) are covered by an annual inquiry commissioned by DTI but carried out by the Office for National Statistics (ONS) from their Newport offices. Where autogenerators operate a combined heat and power (CHP) plant, this survey is now supplemented by information from the CHP Quality Assessment scheme (for autogenerators who have registered under the scheme - see Chapter 6 on CHP). The ONS inquiry only covers generators with capacities greater than 200 kWe and DTI estimates fuel use and electricity generation for smaller companies or includes estimates made by FES for CHP electricity, described in Chapter 6. There are two areas of autogeneration that are covered by direct data collection by DTI, mainly because the return contains additional energy information needed by the Department. These are the Iron and Steel industry, and generation on behalf of London Underground.

Losses and statistical differences

5.61 Statistical differences are included in Tables 5.1, 5.2 and 5.3. These arise because data collected on production and supply do not match exactly with data collected on sales or consumption. One of the reasons for this is that some of the data are based on different calendars as described in paragraphs 5.54 and 5.55, above. Sales data based on calendar years will always include more electricity consumption than the slightly shorter statistical year of exactly 52 weeks.

5.62 Of the losses shown in the commodity balance for electricity of 30,000 GWh in 2002, it is estimated that about 5,600 GWh (1½ per cent of electricity available) were lost from the high voltage transmission system of the National Grid and 22,500 GWh (6 per cent) between the grid supply points (the gateways to the public supply system's distribution network) and customers' meters. The balance (about ½ per cent of electricity available) is accounted for by theft and meter fraud, accounting differences and calendar differences (as described in paragraph 5.61, above).

5.63 Care should be exercised in interpreting the figures for individual industries in the commodity balance tables. As new suppliers have entered the market and companies have moved between suppliers, it has not been possible to ensure consistent classification between and within industry sectors and across years. The breakdown of final consumption includes some estimated data. For about 6 per cent of consumption of electricity supplied by the public distribution system, the sector figures are partially estimated.

Contact: *Mike Janes (Statistician)*   *Joe Ewins*
           Energy Markets Information and Analysis   *Energy Information Systems*
           mike.janes@dti.gsi.gov.uk   *joe_ewins@dti.gsi.gov.uk*
           020-7215 5186   *020-7215 5190*

5.1 Commodity balances

Electricity

GWh

	2000	2001	2002
Total electricity			
Supply			
Production	374,375r	382,327r	384,490
Other sources *(1)*	2,694	2,356	2,652
Imports	14,308	10,663	9,182
Exports	-134	-264	-768
Marine bunkers	-	-	-
Stock change *(2)*	-	-	-
Transfers	-	-	-
Total supply	**391,243r**	**395,082r**	**395,556**
Statistical difference *(3)*	+1,494r	+1,078r	+922
Total demand	**389,749r**	**394,004r**	**394,634**
Transformation	-	-	-
Electricity generation	-	-	-
Major power producers	-	-	-
Autogenerators	-	-	-
Heat generation	-	-	-
Petroleum refineries	-	-	-
Coke manufacture	-	-	-
Blast furnaces	-	-	-
Patent fuel manufacture	-	-	-
Other	-	-	-
Energy industry use	**30,681r**	**30,107r**	**31,874**
Electricity generation	16,304r	17,114r	17,360
Oil and gas extraction	527	675	540
Petroleum refineries	6,362r	5,231r	6,554
Coal extraction	-	-	
Coke manufacture	1,283	1,223	1,218
Blast furnaces	877	885	815
Patent fuel manufacture	-	-	-
Pumped storage	3,499	3,210	3,463
Other	1,829r	1,769r	1,924
Losses	**29,649**	**30,902**	**29,980**
Final consumption	**329,419r**	**332,995r**	**332,780**
Industry	**114,112r**	**111,709r**	**111,749**
Unclassified	-	-	-
Iron and steel	9,229r	8,428r	6,352
Non-ferrous metals	6,002r	7,172r	6,308
Mineral products	7,864r	7,186r	6,997
Chemicals	23,242r	20,830r	22,284
Mechanical engineering, etc	9,097r	8,226r	8,592
Electrical engineering, etc	5,985r	5,463r	5,779
Vehicles	6,093r	5,576r	5,370
Food, beverages, etc	11,329r	11,120r	12,186
Textiles, leather, etc	3,470r	3,206r	3,414
Paper, printing, etc	11,141r	11,216r	11,745
Other industries	19,074r	21,727r	21,109
Construction	1,586	1,559	1,613
Transport	**8,623r**	**8,834**	**8,480**
Air	-	-	-
Rail *(4)*	2,700	2,700	2,700
Road	-	-	-
National navigation	-	-	-
Pipelines	-	-	-
Other	**206,684r**	**212,452r**	**212,551**
Domestic	111,842	115,336	114,535
Public administration	20,913r	20,645r	20,893
Commercial	69,571r	72,014	72,964
Agriculture	4,358r	4,457r	4,159
Miscellaneous	-	-	-
Non energy use			

5.1 Commodity balances (continued)

Electricity

	GWh		
	2000	2001	2002
Electricity production			
Total production (5)	**374,375r**	**382,327r**	**384,490**
Primary electricity			
Major power producers	**89,394**	**93,085r**	**91,968**
Nuclear	85,063	89,870r	88,043
Large scale hydro (5)	4,331	3,215r	3,925
Small scale hydro	-	-	-
Wind	-	-	-
Autogenerators	**1,701**	**1,805r**	**2,117r**
Nuclear	-	-	-
Large scale hydro	540	630	657r
Small scale hydro	214	210	204r
Wind	947	965r	1,256
Secondary electricity			
Major power producers	**249,696r**	**257,329r**	**259,588**
Coal	117,025	127,121	121,074
Oil	2,415r	2,472	2,011
Gas	129,558	126,999	135,741
Renewables	698	737r	762
Other	-	-	-
Autogenerators	**33,584r**	**30,108r**	**30,817**
Coal	2,925r	4,345r	3,327
Oil	4,109r	2,781r	2,810
Gas	18,519r	14,991r	16,408
Renewables	3,630r	4,318r	4,544
Other	4,401r	3,673r	3,728
Primary and secondary production (6)			
Nuclear	85,063	89,870r	88,043
Hydro	5,085	4,055r	4,786
Wind	947	965r	1,256
Coal	119,950r	131,466r	124,401
Oil	6,524r	5,253r	4,821
Gas	148,077r	141,990r	152,149
Other renewables	4,328r	5,055r	5,306
Other	4,401r	3,673r	3,728
Total production	374,375r	382,327r	384,490

(1) Pumped storage production.
(2) Stock fall (+), stock rise (-).
(3) Total supply minus total demand.
(4) See paragraph 5.13.
(5) Excludes pumped storage production.
(6) These figures are the same as the electricity generated figures in Table 5.6 except that they exclude pumped storage production. Table 5.6 shows that electricity used on works is deducted to obtain electricity supplied. It is electricity supplied that is used to produce Chart 5.3 showing each fuel's share of electricity output (see paragraph 5.26).

5.2 Electricity supply and consumption

GWh

	1998	1999	2000	2001	2002
Supply					
Production	361,078	365,250	374,375r	382,327r	384,490
Other sources (1)	1,624	2,902	2,694	2,356	2,652
Imports	12,599	14,507	14,308	10,663	9,182
Exports	-131	-263	-134	-264	-768
Total supply	**375,170**	**382,396**	**391,243r**	**395,082r**	**395,556**
Statistical difference (2)	+1,861	+1,564	+1,494r	+1,078r	+922
Total demand	**373,309**	**380,832**	**389,749r**	**394,004r**	**394,634**
Transformation	-	-	-	-	-
Energy industry use	**29,674**	**29,790**	**30,681r**	**30,107r**	**31,874**
Electricity generation	17,408	16,707	16,304r	17,114r	17,360
Oil and gas extraction	537	408	527	675	540
Petroleum refineries	5,136	4,981	6,362r	5,231r	6,554
Coal and coke	1,334	1,358	1,283	1,223	1,218
Blast furnaces	948	948	877	885	815
Pumped storage	2,594	3,774	3,499	3,210	3,463
Other	1,717	1,614	1,829r	1,769r	1,924
Losses	**27,957**	**28,298**	**29,649**	**30,902**	**29,980**
Final consumption	**315,678**	**322,744**	**329,419r**	**332,995r**	**332,780**
Industry	**107,177**	**110,978**	**114,112r**	**111,709r**	**111,749**
Unclassified	-	-	-	-	-
Iron and steel	9,571	9,779	9,229r	8,428r	6,352
Non-ferrous metals	5,698	5,895	6,002r	7,172r	6,308
Mineral products	7,142	7,265	7,864r	7,186r	6,997
Chemicals	20,916	21,677	23,242r	20,830r	22,284
Mechanical engineering. etc	8,520	8,824	9,097r	8,226r	8,592
Electrical engineering, etc	5,996	6,006	5,985r	5,463r	5,779
Vehicles	5,586	5,615	6,093r	5,576r	5,370
Food, beverages, etc	11,852	12,524	11,329r	11,120r	12,186
Textiles, leather, etc	3,666	3,751	3,470r	3,206r	3,414
Paper, printing, etc	10,684	10,989	11,141r	11,216r	11,745
Other industries	16,012	17,125	19,074r	21,727r	21,109
Construction	1,534	1,528	1,586	1,559	1,613
Transport	**8,511**	**8,579**	**8,623r**	**8,834r**	**8,480**
Other	**199,990**	**203,187**	**206,684r**	**212,452r**	**212,551**
Domestic	109,410	110,308	111,842	115,336	114,535
Public administration	21,577	21,951	20,913r	20,645r	20,893
Commercial	64,952	66,748	69,571r	72,014	72,964
Agriculture	4,051	4,180	4,358r	4,457r	4,159
Miscellaneous	-	-	-	-	-
Non energy use	-	-	-	-	-

(1) Pumped storage production.
(2) Total supply minus total demand.

5.3 Commodity balances

Public distribution system and other generators

GWh

	2000			2001			2002		
	Public distribution system	Other generators	Total	Public distribution system	Other generators	Total	Public distribution system	Other generators	Total
Supply									
Major power producers	339,090r	-	339,090r	350,414r	-	350,414r	351,556	-	351,556
Other generators	-	35,285r	35,285r	-	31,913r	31,913r	-	32,934	32,934
Other sources (1)	2,694	-	2,694	2,356	-	2,356	2,652	-	2,652
Imports	14,308	-	14,308	10,663	-	10,663	9,182	-	9,182
Exports	-134	-	-134	-264	-	-264	-768	-	-768
Transfers	+8,220r	-8,220r	-	+8,808r	-8,808r	-	+7,438	-7,438	-
Total supply	364,178r	27,065r	391,243r	371,977r	23,105r	395,082r	370,060	25,496	395,556
Statistical difference (2)	+1,493r	+1r	+1,494r	+1,079r	-1r	+1,078r	+921	+1	+922
Total demand	362,685r	27,064r	389,749r	370,898r	23,106r	394,004r	369,139	25,495	394,634
Transformation	-	-	-	-	-	-	-	-	-
Energy industry use	23,160	7,521r	30,681r	24,194r	5,913r	30,107r	24,173	7,701	31,874
Electricity generation	14,952	1,352r	16,304r	15,779r	1,335r	17,114r	15,960	1,400	17,360
Oil and gas extraction	527	-	527	675	-	675	540	-	540
Petroleum refineries	1,665	4,697r	6,362r	1,912	3,319r	5,231r	1,598	4,956	6,554
Coke manufacture	1,097	186	1,283	1,047	176	1,223	1,064	154	1,218
Blast furnaces	-	877	877	-	885	885	-	815	815
Pumped storage	3,499	-	3,499	3,210	-	3,210	3,463	-	3,463
Other fuel industries	1,420	409r	1,829r	1,571	198r	1,769r	1,548	376	1,924
Losses	29,568	81	29,649r	30,843	59	30,902	29,914	66	29,980
Final consumption	309,957r	19,462r	329,419r	315,861r	17,134r	332,995r	315,052	17,728	332,780
Industry	97,316r	16,796r	114,112r	97,021r	14,688r	111,709r	96,843	14,906	111,749
Iron and steel	7,868r	1,361r	9,229r	7,768r	660r	8,428r	5,690	662	6,352
Non-ferrous metals	4,112	1,890	6,002r	4,157r	3,015r	7,172r	4,180	2,128	6,308
Mineral products	7,626r	238	7,864r	6,987r	199r	7,186r	6,997	-	6,997
Chemicals	15,249r	7,993r	23,242r	14,410r	6,420r	20,830r	14,984	7,300	22,284
Mechanical engineering, etc	8,556r	541r	9,097r	8,122r	104r	8,226r	8,370	222	8,592
Electrical engineering, etc	5,976r	9	5,985r	5,450r	13r	5,463r	5,777	2	5,779
Vehicles	6,008r	85	6,093r	5,452r	124r	5,576r	5,360	10	5,370
Food, beverages, etc	10,324r	1,005r	11,329r	10,216r	904r	11,120r	10,541	1,645	12,186
Textiles, leather, etc	3,367r	103r	3,470r	3,097r	109r	3,206r	3,305	109	3,414
Paper, printing, etc	8,139r	3,002r	11,141r	8,572r	2,644r	11,216r	9,392	2,353	11,745
Other industries	18,520	554r	19,074r	21,246r	481r	21,727r	20,649	460	21,109
Construction	1,571	15	1,586	1,544	15	1,559	1,598	15	1,613
Transport	7,142	1,481r	8,623r	7,452	1,382r	8,834r	7,051	1,429	8,480
Of which National Rail (3)	2,700	-	2,700	2,700	-	2,700	2,700	-	2,700
Other	205,499	1,185r	206,684r	211,388	1,064r	212,452r	211,158	1,393	212,551
Domestic	111,842	-	111,842	115,336	-	115,336	114,535	-	114,535
Standard	60,993r	-	60,993r	63,377r	-	63,377r	63,225	-	63,225
Economy 7 and other off-peak	32,880	-	32,880	32,949r	-	32,949r	32,207	-	32,207
Prepayment (standard)	12,059r	-	12,059r	12,474r	-	12,474	12,608	-	12,608
Prepayment (off-peak)	5,507r	-	5,507r	6,163r	-	6,163r	6,055	-	6,055
Sales under any other arrangement	403r	-	403r	373r	-	373r	440	-	440
Public administration	20,307r	606r	20,913r	19,938r	707r	20,645r	19,514	1,379	20,893
Public lighting (4)	1,986	-	1,986	2,044	-	2,044	1,923	-	1,923
Other public sector	18,321r	606r	18,927r	17,894r	707r	18,601r	17,591	1,379	18,970
Commercial	69,571r	-	69,571r	72,014r	-	72,014r	72,964	-	72,964
Shops	31,906	-	31,906	32,652	-	32,652	33,769	-	33,769
Offices	20,361r	-	20,361r	21,765r	-	21,765r	21,928	-	21,928
Hotels	8,000	-	8,000	8,206	-	8,206	8,253	-	8,253
Combined domestic/ commercial premises	1,711	-	1,711	1,746	-	1,746	1,767	-	1,767
Post and telecommunications	5,393	-	5,393	5,545	-	5,545	5,597	-	5,597
Unclassified	2,200	-	2,200	2,100	-	2,100	1,650	-	1,650
Agriculture	3,779	579	4,358r	4,100	357r	4,457r	4,145	14	4,159

(1) Pumped storage production.
(2) Total supply minus total demand.
(3) See paragraph 5.15.
(4) Sales for public lighting purposes are increasingly covered by wider contracts that cannot distinguish the public lighting element.

5.4 Fuel used in generation[1]

	Unit	1998	1999	2000	2001	2002
					Original units of measurement	
Major power producers *(2)*						
Coal	M tonnes	46.63	39.58	44.76	49.29r	46.14
Oil *(3)*	"	0.82	0.79	0.75	0.79	0.67
Gas	GWh	236,300	281,988	283,784	276,764r	291,264
Other generators *(2)*						
Transport undertakings:						
Gas	GWh	2,555	2,496	2,194	2,238	1,793
Undertakings in industrial and commercial sectors:						
Coal *(4)*	M tonnes	1.96	1.59	1.47r	1.64	1.57
Oil *(5)*	"	0.79	0.76	0.71	0.54	0.55
Gas *(6)*	GWh	28,878	31,009	38,585r	30,807r	33,273
Major power producers *(2)*				**Millions of tonnes of oil equivalent**		
Coal		28.722	24.506	27.765	30.575r	28.623
Oil *(3)*		0.845	0.817	0.772	0.818r	0.689
Gas		20.318	24.247	24.401	23.797r	25.044
Nuclear		23.443	22.216	19.635	20.717r	20.323
Hydro (natural flow) *(7)*		0.364	0.381	0.372	0.276	0.337
Other renewables *(7)*		0.177	0.223	0.237r	0.253r	0.274
Net imports		1.072	1.225	1.219	0.894	0.724
Total major power producers *(2)*		**74.941**	**73.615**	**74.401r**	**77.330r**	**76.014**
Of which: conventional thermal and other stations *(9)*		32.751	28.626	32.793r	34.061r	32.248
combined cycle gas turbine stations		17.311	21.167	20.382r	21.382r	22.382
Other generators *(2)*						
Transport undertakings:						
Gas		0.220	0.215	0.189	0.192	0.154
Undertakings in industrial and commercial sectors:						
Coal *(4)*		1.174	1.006	0.905r	1.026r	0.981
Oil *(5)*		0.685	0.724	0.777r	0.604r	0.603
Gas *(6)*		2.483	2.666	3.318r	2.649r	2.861
Hydro (natural flow) *(7)*		0.076	0.078	0.065	0.072	0.074
Other renewables *(7)*		1.040	1.248	1.416r	1.670r	1.799
Other fuels *(8)*		1.380	1.392	1.354r	1.004r	1.087
Total other generators *(2)*		**7.058**	**7.329**	**8.024r**	**7.217r**	**7.559**
All generating companies						
Coal *(4)*		29.896	25.512	28.670r	31.601r	29.604
Oil *(3)(5)*		1.530	1.541	1.549r	1.422r	1.292
Gas *(6)*		23.021	27.128	27.908r	26.638r	28.059
Nuclear		23.443	22.216	19.635	20.717r	20.323
Hydro (natural flow) *(7)*		0.440	0.459	0.437	0.348r	0.411
Other renewables *(7)*		1.217	1.471	1.653r	1.923r	2.073
Other fuels *(8)*		1.380	1.392	1.354r	1.004r	1.087
Net imports		1.072	1.225	1.219	0.894	0.724
Total all generating companies		**81.999**	**80.944**	**82.425r**	**84.547r**	**83.573**

(1) For details of where to find monthly updates of fuel used in electricity generation by major power producers and quarterly updates of fuel used in electricity generation by all generating companies see paragraph 5.58.

(2) See paragraphs 5.45 and 5.46 for information on companies covered.

(3) Includes Orimulsion, oil used in gas turbine and diesel plants, and oil used for lighting up coal fired boilers.

(4) Includes coke oven coke

(5) Includes refinery gas.

(6) Includes colliery methane.

(7) Renewable sources, which are included under hydro and other renewables in this table, are shown separately in Table 7.6 of Chapter 7.

(8) Main fuels included are coke oven gas, blast furnace gas, and waste products from chemical processes.

(9) Includes gas turbines, oil engines and plants producing electricity from renewable sources other than hydro.

5.5 Electricity supply, electricity supplied (net), electricity available, electricity consumption and electricity sales

GWh

	1998	1999	2000	2001	2002
Total supply					
(as given in Tables 5.1 and 5.2)	375,170	382,396	391,243r	395,082r	395,556
less imports of electricity	-12,599	-14,507	-14,308	-10,663	-9,182
plus exports of electricity	+131	+263	+134	+264	+768
less electricity used in pumped storage	-2,594	-3,774	-3,499	-3,210	-3,463
less electricity used on works	-17,408	-16,707	-16,304r	-17,114r	-17,360
equals					
Electricity supplied (net)	342,700	347,671	357,267r	364,359r	366,318
(as given in Tables, 5.6, 5.1.2 and 5.1.3)					
Total supply					
(as given in Tables 5.1 and 5.2)	375,170	382,396	391,243r	395,082r	395,556
less electricity used in pumped storage	-2,594	-3,774	-3,499	-3,210	-3,463
less electricity used on works	-17,408	-16,707	-16,304r	-17,114r	-17,360
equals					
Electricity available	355,168	361,915	371,440r	374,758r	374,733
(as given in Tables 5.1.2)					
Final consumption					
(as given in Tables 5.2 and 5.3)	315,678	322,744	329,419r	332,995r	332,780
plus Iron and steel consumption counted as energy industry use	+1,266	+1,272	+1,174	+1,158	+1,074
equals					
Final users	316,944	324,016	330,593r	334,153r	333,854
(as given in Tables 5.1.2)					
Final consumption					
Public distribution system					
(as given in Table 5.3)	298,961	304,255	309,957r	315,861r	315,052
plus Oil and gas extraction use	+537	+408	+527	+675	+540
plus Petroleum refineries use	+1,646	+1,214	+1,665	+1,912	+1,598
plus Coke manufacture use	+1,150	+1,174	+1,097	+1,047	+1,064
plus Other fuel industries use	+1,190	+1,307	+1,420	+1,571	+1,548
equals					
UK Electricity sales (1)	303,484	308,358	314,666r	321,066r	319,802

(1) The renewables obligation percentage is calculated using total renewables generation on an obligation basis from Table 7.4 (x 100) as the numerator, and this figure as the denominator. Separate electricity sales data for public electricitiy suppliers are given for England and Wales, Scotland and Northern Ireland in Table 5.5 of Energy Trends on the DTI web site at http://www.dti.gov.uk/energy/energy_trends/index.shtml

5.6 Electricity fuel use, generation and supply

GWh

| | Thermal sources | | | | | | | Non-thermal sources | | | |
	Coal	Oil	Gas	Nuclear	Renew-ables (1)	Other (3)	Total	Hydro-natural flow	Hydro-pumped storage	Other (4)	Total All sources
1998											
Major power producers (2)											
Fuel used	334,037	9,827	236,298	272,642	2,338	-	855,142	4,237	1,624	-	861,003
Generation	118,595	3,442	105,804	99,486	576	-	327,903	4,237	1,624	-	333,764
Used on works	5,701	231	1,116	8,896	129	-	16,072	12	55	-	16,140
Supplied (gross)	112,894	3,211	104,688	90,590	447	-	311,830	4,225	1,569	-	317,624
Used in pumping											2,594
Supplied (net)											315,030
Other generators (2)											
Fuel used	13,659	7,966	31,433	-	11,221	16,046	80,325	881	-	877	82,083
Generation	4,376	3,913	11,994	-	2,661	4,236	27,180	881	-	877	28,938
Used on works	235	290	392	-	145	194	1,256	12	-	-	1,268
Supplied	4,141	3,623	11,602	-	2,516	4,042	25,924	869	-	877	27,670
All generating companies											
Fuel used	347,696	17,793	267,731	272,642	13,559	16,046	935,467	5,118	1,624	877	943,086
Generation	122,971	7,355	117,798	99,486	3,237	4,236	355,083	5,118	1,624	877	362,702
Used on works	5,936	521	1,508	8,896	274	194	17,329	24	55	-	17,408
Supplied (gross)	117,035	6,834	116,290	90,590	2,963	4,042	337,754	5,094	1,569	877	345,294
Used in pumping											2,594
Supplied (net)											342,700
1999											
Major power producers (2)											
Fuel used	285,005	9,502	281,986	258,372	2,547	-	837,412	4,431	2,902	-	844,744
Generation	102,074	2,943	128,365	95,133	760	-	329,275	4,431	2,902	-	336,608
Used on works	4,726	210	2,759	7,461	186	-	15,342	22	98	-	15,462
Supplied (gross)	97,348	2,733	125,606	87,672	574	-	313,933	4,409	2,804	-	321,146
Used in pumping											3,774
Supplied (net)											317,372
Other generators (2)											
Fuel used	11,702	8,420	33,562	-	13,659	16,187	83,530	905	-	851	85,287
Generation	4,106	3,606	14,537	-	3,227	4,312	29,788	905	-	851	31,544
Used on works	197	267	471	-	100	199	1,234	11	-	-	1,245
Supplied	3,909	3,339	14,066	-	3,127	4,113	28,554	894	-	851	30,299
All generating companies											
Fuel used	296,707	17,922	315,548	258,372	16,206	16,187	920,942	5,336	2,902	851	930,031
Generation	106,180	6,549	142,902	95,133	3,987	4,312	359,063	5,336	2,902	851	368,152
Used on works	4,923	477	3,230	7,461	286	199	16,576	33	98	-	16,707
Supplied (gross)	101,257	6,072	139,672	87,672	3,701	4,113	342,487	5,303	2,804	851	351,445
Used in pumping											3,774
Supplied (net)											347,671
2000											
Major power producers (2)											
Fuel used	322,907	8,978	283,781	228,355	2,919r	-	846,940r	4,331	2,694	-	853,966r
Generation	117,025	2,415r	129,558	85,063	698	-	334,759r	4,331	2,694	-	341,784r
Used on works	5,175	291	2,593	6,729	58	-	14,846	15	91	-	14,952
Supplied (gross)	111,850	2,124r	126,965	78,334	640	-	319,913r	4,316	2,603	-	326,832r
Used in pumping											3,499
Supplied (net)											323,333r
Other generators (2)											
Fuel used	10,522r	9,042r	40,779r	-	15,517r	15,743r	91,603r	755	-	947	93,304r
Generation	2,925r	4,109r	18,519r	-	3,630r	4,401r	33,584r	755	-	947	35,285r
Used on works	39	304	592r	-	203r	202r	1,340r	12	-	-	1,352r
Supplied	2,887r	3,805r	17,927r	-	3,427r	4,198r	32,244r	743	-	947	33,933r
All generating companies											
Fuel used	333,429r	18,020r	324,560r	228,355	18,436r	15,743r	938,543r	5,086	2,694	947	947,270r
Generation	119,950r	6,524r	148,077r	85,063	4,328r	4,401r	368,343r	5,086	2,694	947	377,070r
Used on works	5,214	595	3,185r	6,729	261r	202r	16,186r	27	91	-	16,304r
Supplied (gross)	114,737r	5,929r	144,892r	78,334	4,067r	4,198r	352,157r	5,059	2,603	947	360,766r
Used in pumping											3,499
Supplied (net)											357,267r

5.6 Electricity fuel use, generation and supply (cont'd)

GWh

	Thermal sources							Non-thermal sources			Total All sources
	Coal	Oil	Gas	Nuclear	Renew-ables (1)	Other (3)	Total	Hydro-natural flow	Hydro-pumped storage	Other (4)	
2001											
Major power producers (2)											
Fuel used	355,587r	9,513r	276,761r	240,939r	3,105r	-	885,905r	3,215r	2,356r	-	891,477r
Generation	127,121	2,472	126,999	89,870r	737r	-	347,199r	3,215r	2,356	-	352,770r
Used on works	5,823	280	2,710	6,885r	54r	-	15,752r	11r	16r	-	15,779r
Supplied (gross)	121,298	2,192	124,289	82,985	683	-	331,447	3,204	2,340	-	336,991
Used in pumping											3,210
Supplied (net)											333,781
Other generators (2)											
Fuel used	11,927r	7,025r	33,045r	-	18,456r	11,674r	82,127r	840	-	965r	83,931r
Generation	4,345r	2,781r	14,991r	-	4,318r	3,673r	30,108r	840	-	965r	31,913r
Used on works	231r	195r	483r	-	246r	169r	1,324r	11	-	-	1,335r
Supplied	4,114r	2,586r	14,508r	-	4,072r	3,504r	28,784r	829	-	965r	30,578r
All generating companies											
Fuel used	367,514r	16,538r	309,806r	240,939r	21,561r	11,674r	968,032r	4,055r	2,356	965r	975,408r
Generation	131,466r	5,253r	141,990r	89,870r	5,055r	3,673r	377,307r	4,055r	2,356	965r	384,683r
Used on works	6,054r	475r	3,193r	6,885r	300r	169r	17,076r	22r	16	-	17,114r
Supplied (gross)	125,412r	4,778r	138,797r	82,985	4,755r	3,504r	360,231r	4,033	2,340	965r	367,569r
Used in pumping											3,210
Supplied (net)											364,359r
2002											
Major power producers (2)											
Fuel used	332,885	8,013	291,261	236,356	3,187	-	871,703	3,925	2,652	-	878,280
Generation	121,074	2,011	135,741	88,043	762	-	347,631	3,925	2,652	-	354,208
Used on works	5,580	378	2,877	6,953	71	-	15,859	11	90	-	15,960
Supplied (gross)	115,494	1,633	132,864	81,090	691	-	331,772	3,914	2,562	-	338,248
Used in pumping											3,463
Supplied (net)											334,785
Other generators (2)											
Fuel used	11,413	7,019	35,066	-	19,664	12,640	85,802	860	-	1,256	87,918
Generation	3,327	2,810	16,408	-	4,544	3,728	30,817	860	-	1,256	32,934
Used on works	230	207	527	-	252	171	1,389	11	-	-	1,400
Supplied	3,097	2,603	15,881	-	4,292	3,556	29,429	849	-	1,256	31,534
All generating companies											
Fuel used	344,298	15,032	326,328	236,356	22,851	12,640	957,505	4,785	2,652	1,256	966,198
Generation	124,401	4,821	152,149	88,043	5,306	3,728	378,448	4,785	2,652	1,256	387,142
Used on works	5,810	586	3,405	6,953	323	171	17,248	23	90	-	17,360
Supplied (gross)	118,591	4,235	148,744	81,090	4,983	3,556	361,200	4,763	2,562	1,256	369,781
Used in pumping											3,463
Supplied (net)											366,318

	1998		1999		2000		2001		2002	
	Conv-entional thermal (5)	CCGT	Conv-entional thermal (5)	CCGT	Conv-entional thermal (5)	CCGT	Conv-entional thermal (5)	CCGT	Conv-entional thermal (5)	CCGT
Major power producers (2)										
Generated	134,585	93,832	119,522	114,620	131,761r	117,935	139,363r	117,966r	135,695	123,893
Supplied (gross)	128,235	93,005	113,493	112,768	125,469r	116,110	132,568r	115,894r	128,796	121,886
Other generators										
Generated	21,752	5,428	22,661	7,127	22,725r	10,859r	21,129r	8,979r	20,296	10,521
Supplied (gross)	20,766	5,157	21,782	6,771	21,926r	10,318r	20,253r	8,531r	19,433	9,996
All generating companies										
Generated	156,337	99,260	142,183	121,747	154,486r	128,794r	160,492r	126,945r	155,991	134,414
Supplied (gross)	149,001	98,162	135,275	119,539	147,395r	126,428r	152,821r	124,425r	148,229	131,882

(1) Thermal renewable sources are those included under biofuels in Chapter 7.
(2) See paragraphs 5.45 and 5.46 on companies covered.
(3) Other thermal sources include coke oven gas, blast furnace gas and waste products from chemical processes.
(4) Other non-thermal sources include wind, wave and solar photovoltaics.
(5) Includes gas turbines, oil engines and plants producing electricity from renewable sources other than hydro.

5.7 Plant capacity

MW

	1998	1999	2000	2001	2002
				end December	
Major power producers *(1)*					
Total declared net capability	**68,390**	**70,058**	**72,030**	**73,219**	**70,439**
Of which:					
Conventional steam stations:	35,081	35,427	34,640	34,640	32,032
Coal fired	25,324	25,581	24,835	24,835	22,452
Oil fired	2,829	2,829	2,933	2,933	2,708
Mixed or dual fired *(2)*	6,928	7,017	6,872	6,872	6,872
Combined cycle gas turbine stations	14,638	16,110	19,349	20,517	20,249
Nuclear stations	12,956	12,956	12,486	12,486	12,486
Gas turbines and oil engines	1,492	1,333	1,323	1,323	1,463
Hydro-electric stations:					
Natural flow	1,327	1,327	1,327	1,348r	1,304
Pumped storage	2,788	2,788	2,788	2,788	2,788
Renewables other than hydro	108	117	117	117	117
Other generators *(1)*					
Total capacity of own generating plant	**4,990**	**5,388**	**6,258r**	**6,269r**	**6,149**
Of which:					
Conventional steam stations *(3)*	3,248r	3,315r	3,544r	3,437r	3,132
Combined cycle gas turbine stations	1,005r	1,243r	1,709r	1,777r	1,840
Hydro-electric stations (natural flow)	148	150	158	160	162
Renewables other than hydro	589	680	847	895	1,015
All generating companies					
Total capacity	**73,380**	**75,446**	**78,288r**	**79,488r**	**76,588**
Of which:					
Conventional steam stations *(3)*	38,329r	38,742r	38,184r	38,077r	35,164
Combined cycle gas turbine stations	15,643r	17,353r	21,058r	22,294r	22,089
Nuclear stations	12,956	12,956	12,486	12,486	12,486
Gas turbines and oil engines	1,492	1,333	1,323	1,323	1,463
Hydro-electric stations:					
Natural flow	1,475	1,477	1,485	1,508	1,466
Pumped storage	2,788	2,788	2,788	2,788	2,788
Renewables other than hydro	697	797	964	1,012	1,132

(1) See paragraphs 5.45 and 5.46 for information on companies covered.
(2) Includes gas fired stations that are not Combined Cycle Gas Turbines.
(3) For other generators, conventional steam stations include combined heat and power plants (electrical capacity only), but exclude combined cycle gas turbine plants, hydro-electric stations and plants using renewable sources.

5.8 Capacity of other generators

					MW
			end-December		
	1998	1999	2000	2001	2002

Capacity of own generating plant [1]

Undertakings in industrial and commercial sector:

	1998	1999	2000	2001	2002
Petroleum refineries	757	887	1,003	1,001r	954
Iron and steel	355	355	373	379r	309
Chemicals	1,237	1,253	1,266r	1,263r	1,251
Engineering and other metal trades	506	518	615r	612r	608
Food, drink and tobacco	334	406	409r	396r	392
Paper, printing and publishing	483	483	573r	544r	597
Other [2]	1,035	1,204	1,736r	1,791r	1,934r
Total industrial and commercial sector	4,707	5,105	5,975r	5,986r	6,046r
Undertakings in transport sector	283	283	283	283	103
Total other generators	**4,990**	**5,388**	**6,258r**	**6,269r**	**6,149r**

(1) For combined heat and power plants the electrical capacity only is included. Further CHP capacity is included under major
power producers in Table 5.7. A detailed analysis of CHP capacity is given in the tables of Chapter 6.

(2) Includes companies in the commercial sector.

5.9 Plant loads, demand and efficiency

Major power producers [1]

	Unit	1998	1999	2000	2001	2002
Simultaneous maximum load met (2)	MW	56,312	57,849	58,452	58,589	61,717
Maximum demand as a percentage of UK capacity	Per cent	82.3	82.6	81.1	80.0	87.6
Plant load factor						
Combined cycle gas turbine stations	Per cent	79.2	84.0	75.0	66.6r	68.4
Nuclear stations	"	80.1	77.5r	70.5	76.1	74.3
Hydro-electric stations:						
Natural flow	"	36.7	38.0	37.2	27.4	33.8
Pumped storage	"	6.4	11.5	10.7	9.6	10.5
Conventional thermal and other stations (3)	"	38.8	35.3	39.4	42.1r	42.3
All plant	"	**53.2**	**53.1**	**52.7**	**53.1**	**53.9**
System load factor	"	**67.5r**	**66.7r**	**67.4r**	**68.7r**	**64.6**
Thermal efficiency						
(gross calorific value basis)						
Combined cycle gas turbine stations	"	46.6	46.6	46.6	46.7r	47.1
Coal fired stations	"	35.5	35.8	36.2	35.7	36.1
Nuclear stations	"	36.5	36.8	37.3	37.3	37.3

(1) See paragraphs 5.45 and 5.46 for information on companies covered.

(2) Data cover the 12 months ending March of the following year eg 2002 data are for the year ending March 2003.

(3) Conventional steam plants, gas turbines, oil engines and plants producing electricity from renewable sources other
than hydro.

5.10 Power Stations in the United Kingdom

(operational at the end of May 2003)[1]

Company Name	Station Name	Fuel	Installed Capacity (MW)	Year of Commission or year generation began
AES	Drax	coal	3,870	1974
	Drax GT	gas oil	75	1971
	Fifoots Point (2)	coal	393	2000
	Kilroot	coal/oil	520	1981
	Barry	CCGT	250	1998
	Indian Queens	oil	140	1996
American Electric Power	Ferrybridge C	coal	1,955	1966
	Fiddler's Ferry	coal	1,961	1971
	Ferrybridge GT	gas oil	34	1966
	Fiddler's Ferry GT	gas oil	34	1969
Alcan	Lynemouth	coal	248	1995
	Fort William	hydro	62	1929
	Kinlochleven	hydro	30	1907
Baglan Generation Ltd	Baglan Bay	CCGT	575	2002
Barking Power	Barking	CCGT	1,000	1994
British Energy	Dungeness B	nuclear	1,110	1985
	Hartlepool	nuclear	1,210	1989
	Heysham1	nuclear	1,150	1989
	Heysham 2	nuclear	1,250	1989
	Hinkley Point B	nuclear	1,220	1976
	Sizewell B	nuclear	1,188	1995
	Hunterston B	nuclear	1,190	1976
	Torness	nuclear	1,250	1988
	Eggborough	coal	1,960	1967
	Bridgewater District Energy	gas	10	2000
	Solutia District Energy	gas	10	2000
	Sevington District Energy	gas	10	2000
BNFL Magnox	Chapelcross	nuclear	196	1959
	Dungeness A	nuclear	450	1965
	Oldbury	nuclear	434	1967
	Sizewell A	nuclear	420	1966
	Wylfa	nuclear	980	1971
	Maentwrog	hydro	20	1928
Calpine Corporation	Saltend	CCGT	1,200	2000
Centrica	Kings Lynn	CCGT	340	1996
	Peterborough	CCGT	380	1993
	Roosecote	CCGT	229	1991
Citigen (London) Ltd	Charterhouse St, London	gas/gas oil	31	1995
Coolkeeragh Power	Coolkeeragh	oil	293	1959
Corby Power	Corby	CCGT	401	1993
Coryton Energy Company Ltd	Coryton	CCGT	750	2001
Derwent Cogeneration	Derwent	CHP	236	1994
Edison Mission Energy	Dinorwig	pumped storage	1,728	1983
	Ffestiniog	pumped storage	360	1961
Enfield Energy Centre Ltd	Brimsdown	CCGT	406	1999
Entergy	Damhead Creek	CCGT	792	2000
Fellside Heat and Power	Fellside	CHP	168	1993
Fibrogen	Glanford	meat & bone meal	13	1993
Fibropower Ltd	Eye, Suffolk	poultry litter	13	1992
Fibrothetford	Thetford	poultry litter	39	1998
Fife Power	Westfield Development Centre (2)	CCGT	120	1998

5.10 Power Stations in the United Kingdom
(operational at the end of May 2003)[1] (continued)

Company Name	Station Name	Fuel	Installed Capacity (MW)	Year of Commission or year generation began
Humber Power	South Humber Bank 1	CCGT	785	1996
	South Humber Bank 2	CCGT	527	1998
Innogy Plc	Aberthaw B	coal	1,455	1971
	Tilbury B (4)	coal/oil	1,020	1968
	Didcot A	coal/gas	1,925	1972
	Aberthaw GT	gas oil	51	1971
	Cowes	gas oil	70	1982
	Didcot GT	gas oil	100	1972
	Fawley GT	gas oil	34	1969
	Littlebrook GT	gas oil	105	1982
	Tilbury GT	gas oil	34	1968
	Fawley (4)	oil	484	1969
	Littlebrook D (4)	oil	685	1982
	Didcot B	CCGT	1,370	1998
	Little Barford	CCGT	655	1995
	Cwm Dyli	hydro	10	1989 (3)
	Dolgarrog	hydro	37	1924
International Power	Deeside (4)	CCGT	250	1994
	Rugeley	coal	1,006	1972
	Rugeley GT	gas oil	50	1972
London Power Company	Sutton Bridge	CCGT	803	1999
	Cottam	coal	2,008	1969
	West Burton	coal	1,932	1967
Medway Power	Medway	CCGT	688	1995
National Grid	Kielder	hydro	5.5	1984
NRG Energy	Killingholme	CCGT	650	1994
PowerGen	Kingsnorth	coal/oil	1,940	1970
	Ironbridge	coal	970	1970
	Ratcliffe	coal	2,000	1968
	Grain GT	gas oil	55	1978
	Kingsnorth GT	gas oil	34	1967
	Ratcliffe GT	gas oil	34	1966
	Taylor's Lane GT	gas oil	132	1979
	Connahs Quay	CCGT	1,380	1996
	Cottam Development Centre	CCGT	400	1999
	Rheidol	hydro	50	1961
Premier Power Ltd	Ballylumford	oil/gas	823	1968
Regional Power Generators Ltd	Glanford Brigg	CCGT	240	1993
Rocksavage Power Co. Ltd	Rocksavage	CCGT	750	1997
Scottish & Southern Energy plc **Schemes:**				
Affric/Beauly	Mullardoch Tunnel	hydro	2.4	1955
	Fasnakyle	hydro	69	1951
	Deanie	hydro	38	1963
	Culligran	hydro	24	1962
	Aigas	hydro	20	1962
	Kilmorack	hydro	20	1962
Breadalbane	Lubreoch	hydro	4	1958
	Cashlie	hydro	11	1959
	Lochay	hydro	47	1958
	Finlarig	hydro	16.5	1955
	Lednock	hydro	3	1961
	St. Fillans	hydro	16.8	1957
	Dalchonzie	hydro	4	1958
Conon	Achanalt	hydro	3	1956
	Grudie Bridge	hydro	18.7	1950
	Mossford	hydro	18.7	1957
	Luichart	hydro	34	1954
	Orrin	hydro	18	1959
	Torr Achilty	hydro	15	1954

5.10 Power Stations in the United Kingdom

(operational at the end of May 2003)[1] (continued)

Company Name	Station Name	Fuel	Installed Capacity (MW)	Year of Commission or year generation began
Scottish & Southern Energy plc (continued)				
Foyers	Foyers	hydro/pumped storage	300	1974
Great Glen	Foyers Falls	hydro	5.2	1968
	Mucomir	hydro	2	1962
	Ceannacroc	hydro	20	1956
	Livishie	hydro	15	1962
	Glenmoriston	hydro	37	1957
	Quoich	hydro	18.1	1955
	Ivergarry	hydro	20	1956
Shin	Cassley	hydro	10	1959
	Lairg	hydro	3.5	1959
	Shin	hydro	18.6	1958
Sloy/Awe	Sloy	hydro	152.5	1950
	Sron Mor	hydro	5	1957
	Clachan	hydro	40	1955
	Alt-na-Lairgie	hydro	6	1956
	Nant	hydro	15	1963
	Inverawe	hydro	25	1963
	Kilmelfort	hydro	2	1956
	Loch Gair	hydro	6	1961
	Lussa	hydro	2.4	1952
	Striven	hydro	8	1951
Tummel	Gaur	hydro	6.4	1953
	Cuaich	hydro	2.5	1959
	Loch Ericht	hydro	2.2	1962
	Rannoch	hydro	44.1	1930
	Tummel	hydro	34	1933
	Errochty	hydro	75	1955
	Clunie	hydro	61.2	1950
	Pitlochry	hydro	15	1950
Small Hydros:	Chliostair	hydro	1.1	1960
	Kerry Falls	hydro	1.3	1951
	Loch Dubh	hydro	1.2	1954
	Nostie Bridge	hydro	1.3	1950
	Storr Lochs	hydro	2.4	1952
	Cuileag	hydro	3	2002
Thermal:	Peterhead	oil/gas	1,550	1980
	Lerwick	diesel/gas	67.2	1953
	Keadby	CCGT	720	1994
	Chickerell	gas	45	1998
	Burghfield	gas	45	1998
	Thatcham	diesel	9.6	1994
	Five Oaks	diesel	11.5	1995
	Chippenham	gas	10	2002
	Wheldale	gas	10	2002
Island Generation	Stornoway	diesel	23.5	1950
	Arnish	diesel	3	2001
	Kirkwall	diesel	16.2	1953
	Loch Carnan, South Uist	diesel	11.8	1971
	Bowmore	diesel	6	1946
	Tiree	diesel	2.5	1945
	Barra	diesel	2.1	1990
Scottish Power **Schemes:**				
Galloway	Carsfad	hydro	12	1936
	Drumjohn	hydro	2	1985
	Earlstoun	hydro	14	1936
	Glenlee	hydro	24	1935
	Kendoon	hydro	24	1936
	Tongland	hydro	33	1935
Lanark	Bonnington	hydro	11	1927
	Stonebyres	hydro	5	1927
Cruachan	Cruachan	pumped storage	399	1966

5.10 Power Stations in the United Kingdom
(operational at the end of May 2003)[1] (continued)

Company Name	Station Name	Fuel	Installed Capacity (MW)	Year of Commission or year generation began
Scottish Power (continued)				
Thermal:	Cockenzie	coal	1,152	1967
	Longannet	coal	2,304	1970
	Knapton	gas oil	40	1994
	Rye House	CCGT	715	1993
Seabank Power Limited	Seabank 1	CCGT	812	1998
	Seabank 2	CCGT	410	2000
Sita Tyre Recycling Ltd	Wolverhampton	waste	20	1994
South Coast Power	Shoreham	CCGT	400	2000
South East London Combined Heat & Power Ltd	Landmann Way, London	waste	32	1994
Teesside Power Ltd	Teesside Power Station	CCGT	1,875	1992
Western Power Generation	St Marys	gas oil	6	1958
	Princetown	kerosene	3	1959
	Lynton	gas oil	2	1961
	Roseland	kerosene	5	1963
Total			**70,430**	

(1) This list covers stations of more than 1 MW capacity, but excludes some renewables stations of over 1 MW which are included in the section below.
(2) AES Fifoots and Fife Power are both in receivership/administration and not operating.
(3) Recommissioning date.
(4) Excludes mothballed capacity.

Other power stations[5]

Station type	Fuel	Capacity (MW)
Renewable sources	wind	534
and combustible wastes	landfill gas	473
	sewage gas	96
	hydro	81
	waste	247
	other	68
CHP schemes other than major power producers and renewables	mainly gas	3,815
Other autogenerators	various fuels	878

(5) As at end December 2002.

Interconnectors

	Capacity (MW)
England - Scotland (6)	2,200
England - France	2,000
Scotland - Northern Ireland	500
Northern Ireland - Irish Republic	600

(6) The capacity of the interconnector has been increased from 1,200 MW but the increase will only be useable on completion of the second Yorkshire line.

Chapter 6
Combined heat and power

Introduction

6.1   This chapter sets out the contribution made by Combined Heat and Power (CHP) to the United Kingdom's energy requirements. The data presented in this Chapter have been derived from information submitted to the CHP Quality Assurance programme (CHPQA). This programme was introduced by Government to provide the methods and procedures to assess and certify the quality of the full range of CHP schemes. It is a rigorous system for the Government to ensure that the incentives on offer are targeted fairly and benefit schemes in relation to their environmental performance. The data presented in this chapter have been derived from information submitted to CHPQA or by following the same procedures where no information has been provided directly.

6.2   CHP is the simultaneous generation of usable heat and power (usually electricity) in a single process. The term CHP is synonymous with cogeneration and total energy, which are terms often used in other Member States of the European Community and the United States. CHP uses a variety of fuels and technologies across a wide range of sites and scheme sizes. The basic elements of a CHP plant comprise one or more prime movers (a reciprocating engine, gas turbine, or steam turbine) driving electrical generators, where the steam or hot water generated in the process is utilised via suitable heat recovery equipment for use either in industrial processes, or in community heating and space heating.

6.3   A CHP plant provides primary energy savings compared to separate generation of heat and power. In addition, CHP is typically sized to make use of the available heat, and connected to the lower voltage distribution system (ie embedded). This provides efficiency gains compared to electricity-only plant, which is larger, and connected at very high voltage to the grid transmission system, by avoiding significant transmission and distribution losses. CHP can also provide important network services such as black start, improvements to power quality, and the ability to operate in island mode if the grid goes down.

6.4   There are four principal types of CHP systems: steam turbine, gas turbine, combined cycle systems and reciprocating engines. Each of these is defined in paragraph 6.34 below.

Government policy towards CHP

6.5   To reduce carbon emissions and help deliver the UK's Climate Change Programme, the Government has a target of achieving at least 10,000 MWe of Good Quality CHP capacity by 2010. At the end of the year 2001, installed Good Quality CHP capacity was 4,753 MWe. During 2002, there was a decrease in the total number of CHP schemes from 1,561 at the beginning of the year to 1,539 at the end, but a decrease of only 11 MWe in capacity (to 4,742 MWe).

6.6   In May 2002, the Government published a consultation on its strategy to reach the 2010 target (www.defra.gov.uk/environment/consult/chpstrat/index.htm). The final version of the strategy is due to be published during the course of 2003.

6.7   The Chancellor announced in the Budget of 2002 that the Government is committed to providing relief from the Climate Change Levy (CCL) for electricity generated by CHP. The Budget contained measures that provide a framework for relief from CCL by extending the exemption from levy to electricity from Good Quality CHP schemes if the electricity is sold to end-users via third party electricity utilities (www.hmce.gov.uk/business/othertaxes/ccl/tec18.pdf).

6.8 The Government published a White Paper on Energy (Our energy future – creating a low carbon economy) in February 2003. The White Paper reaffirms the Government's commitment to a target of 10 GWe of Good Quality CHP capacity installed by 2010. In addition to the measures already put in place, the White Paper introduced a number of other measures. These include:

- A review of the existing guidance on information required to accompany power station consent applications. Applicants will need to demonstrate clearly that they have considered all economically viable options for CHP and community heating;
- Emphasis on the benefits of CHP and community heating whenever Planning Policy Guidance, Regional Planning Guidance or Sustainable Development Guidance is introduced or reviewed;
- Working with OFGEM to keep developments in the New Electricity Trading Arrangements (NETA) under review to ensure a level playing field for smaller generators;
- Proceed with considering setting targets for Government Departments to use CHP generated electricity;
- Exploring the opportunities for providing incentives to CHP in an expansion of the energy efficiency commitment;
- Supporting field trials designed to evaluate the benefits of micro-CHP;
- Inviting the Energy Saving Trust and the Carbon Trust to review their current and future programmes to ensure that they reinforce the delivery of the Governments CHP target;
- Work on the framework for pilot projects within the Emissions Trading Scheme (ETS) for which CHP projects may be eligible. Under the UK ETS, carbon savings can already be traded and the European Union ETS will further encourage low carbon technologies such as CHP.

UK Energy markets, and their effect on CHP

6.9   Two major factors affecting the economics of CHP are the relative cost of fuel (principally natural gas) and the value that can be realised for electricity. At the end of the 1990s, gas prices increased and the price of electricity decreased. In the last two years, gas prices have started to decline again but electricity prices are also low.

6.10   Concerns have been raised that the New Electricity Trading Arrangements (NETA) have had an adverse impact on the development of CHP. The Government has identified a range of measures to improve the position of CHP within NETA and will keep the position under review. A number of modifications have been made to the market rules since the introduction of NETA that have improved the position of smaller generators.

Use of CHPQA in producing CHP statistics

6.11   The CHPQA programme is now the major source for CHP statistics. The following factors need to be kept in mind when using the statistics produced:

- Scheme operators have previously determined the boundary of a CHP scheme (what is regarded as part of the CHP installation and what is not). Now, through CHPQA, scheme operators have been given guidance on how to determine scheme boundaries. A scheme can include multiple CHP prime movers, along with supplementary boilers and generating plant, subject to appropriate metering installed to support the CHP scheme boundaries proposed, and subject to appropriate metering and threshold criteria (see CHPQA Guidance Note 11 available at www.chpqa.com).

- The output of a scheme is based on gross power output, ignoring parasitic loads (ie ignoring power used in pumps, fans, etc within the scheme itself). Parasitic loads vary from around 5.8 per cent for pass out condensing steam turbines, down to 1.6 per cent for combined cycle gas turbines (CCGT). The capacity weighted average is 2.2 per cent of both capacity and output (see Table

6D). In practice, most parasitic loads exist because of the existence of the heat network rather than because of the generation of electricity.

- The main purpose of a number of CHP schemes is the generation of electricity including export to others. Such schemes may not be sized to use all of the available heat. The total capacity and output of these schemes have been scaled back using the methodologies outlined in CHPQA. Only the portion of the capacity and output that qualifies as Good Quality is counted in this chapter and the remaining capacity and output are regarded as power only. The fuel use for these partial schemes is also scaled back by assigning fuel use to the power-only portion of the output based on the overall electrical efficiency of the scheme. The remaining fuel is accounted for in this Chapter. For some schemes, this convention can result in high apparent heat efficiencies particularly when the fuel is allocated separately to power and heat (see paragraphs 6.35 to 6.37). All electricity capacity and generation, not just that which qualifies as Good Quality CHP (CHP Total Power Capacity CHP_{TPC} and CHP Total Power Output CHP_{TPO}) is included in the Electricity Chapter (Chapter 5) of this Digest. For further details of CHP_{QPC} and CHP_{QPO} see the Technical Notes and definitions section at paragraph 6.38 and CHPQA Guidance Notes 26 and 27 available at www.chpqa.com .

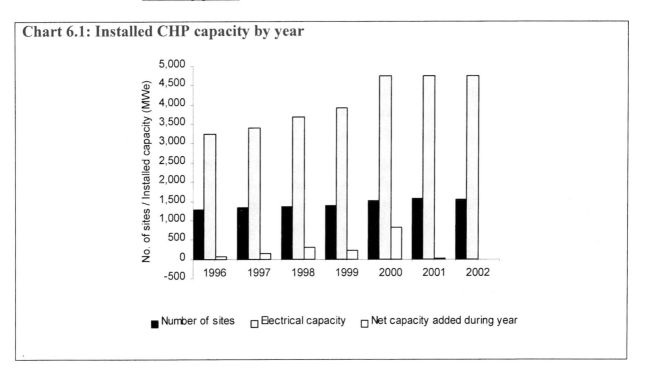

Chart 6.1: Installed CHP capacity by year

Progress towards the Government's targets
6.12 Chart 6.1 shows the change in installed CHP capacity over the last seven years. Installed capacity at the end of 2002 stood at 4,742 MWe. In the decade to 2000, capacity more than doubled, representing an average growth rate over the period of 8 per cent per annum. However, difficult market conditions slowed this growth rate in 2001, and in 2002 there was a small decrease of 11 MWe, as shown in Table 6A.

Capacity in 2002
6.13 In 2002, 13 new schemes came into operation and 35 ceased to operate. The net loss in the number of schemes reflects the slowing of the market in 2001 and 2002 due to unfavourable energy prices.

6.14 In the current market conditions, a number of operators have chosen to mothball their CHP Schemes rather than continue to operate. As these schemes are still able to operate they have been included in the total capacity. At the end of 2002, there were 19 mothballed schemes with a total capacity of 21 MWe.

6.15   Over 65 per cent of capacity is now gas turbine based, with about 80 per cent of this in combined cycle mode. Capacity in all technologies, except combined cycle gas turbines, decreased (see Tables 6A and 6.5). In the years up to 2000, heat output remained broadly stable, whilst electricity generation increased. However between 2000 and 2001, electricity generation decreased by 15 per cent partly as a result of a decrease in electricity exported from CHP sites. This reflected the difficulties encountered by smaller generators faced with rising gas prices, and falling electricity prices under NETA. As a result CHP plants were used less and the average load factor fell from 64 per cent in 2000 to 54 per cent in 2001. Between 2001 and 2002, electricity generation increased by 7½ per cent and the load factor recovered by 4 percentage points to 58 per cent in 2002.

Table 6A: A summary of the recent development of CHP

	Unit	1998	1999	2000	2001	2002
Number of schemes		1,357	1,383	1,522	1,561	1,539
Net number of schemes added during year		*14*	*27*	*139*	*39*	*-22*
Electrical capacity (CHP$_{QPC}$)	MWe	3,680	3,912	4,730	4,753	4,742
Net capacity added during year		*292*	*232*	*818*	*23*	*-11*
Capacity added in percentage terms	Per cent	*9*	*6*	*21*	*1*	*-*
Heat capacity	MWth	15,262	14,800	11,888	12,004	11,483
Heat to power ratio *(1)*		4.15	3.78	2.51	2.53	2.31
Fuel input	GWh	113,198	113,019	117,450	114,432	117,887
Electricity generation (CHP$_{QPO}$)	GWh	18,684	20,256	26,539	22,568	24,236
Heat generation (CHP$_{QHO}$)	GWh	62,227	60,439	62,121	61,025	60,738
Overall efficiency *(2)*	Per cent	71.5	71.4	75.5	73.1	72.1
Load factor	Per cent	58.0	59.1	64.1	54.2	58.3

(1)   Heat to power ratios are calculated from the qualifying heat output (QHO) and the qualifying power output (QPO).
(2)   These are calculated using gross calorific values; overall net efficiencies are some 5 percentage points higher.

Installed capacity and output in 2002

6.16   Table 6A gives a summary of the overall CHP market. The electricity generated by CHP schemes was 24,236 GWh. This represents just over 6 per cent of the total electricity generated in the UK in 2002. Across the commercial and industrial sectors (including the fuel industries other than electricity generation) electrical output from CHP accounted for around 10 per cent of electricity consumption. CHP schemes in total supplied 60,738 GWh of heat.

6.17   In terms of electrical capacity, schemes larger than 10 MWe represent 80 per cent of the total electrical capacity of CHP schemes as shown in Table 6B. However, in terms of number of schemes, the largest share (43 per cent) is in schemes less than 100 kWe. Schemes of 1 MWe or larger make up just over 16 per cent of the total number of schemes. Table 6.5 provides data on electrical capacity for each type of CHP installation.

Table 6B: CHP schemes by capacity size ranges in 2002

Electrical capacity size range	Number of schemes	Share of total (per cent)	Total electricity capacity (MWe)	Share of total (per cent)
Less than 100 kWe	664	43.1	40.5	0.9
100 kWe - 999 kWe	625	40.6	151.2	3.2
1 MWe - 9.9 MWe	182	11.8	759.9	16.0
Greater than 10 MWe	68	4.4	3,790.8	79.9
Total	**1,539**	**100.0**	**4,742.4**	**100.0**

6.18   In terms of heat capacity, combined cycle gas turbines now make up the largest proportion, 42½ per cent, with steam turbines providing the next largest proportion, 34½ per cent. Table 6.7 provides data on heat capacity for each type of CHP installation.

Fuel used by types of CHP installation

6.19   Table 6.1 shows the fuel used to generate electricity and heat in CHP schemes, (see paragraphs 6.35 to 6.37, below for an explanation of the convention for dividing fuel between electricity and heat production). Table 6.3 gives the overall fuel used by types of CHP installation (which are explained in paragraph 6.34). Total fuel use is summarised in Chart 6.2. In 2002, 64 per cent of the total fuel use was natural gas, an increase over the 2001 figure (61 per cent). CHP schemes accounted for 7½ per cent of UK gas consumption in 2002 (see Table 4.3).

6.20   Non-conventional fuels (liquids, solids or gases which are by-products or waste products from industrial processes, or are renewable fuels) account for a quarter of fuel used in CHP. These are fuels that are not commonly used by the mainstream electricity generating industry, and some would otherwise be flared or disposed of by some means. These fuels (with the exception of some waste gases) will always be burnt in external combustion engines, such as boilers feeding steam turbines. In almost all cases, the technical nature of the combustion process (lower calorific value of the fuel, high moisture content of the fuel, the need to maintain certain combustion conditions to ensure complete disposal etc) will always imply a lower efficiency. However, given that the use of such fuels avoids the use of fossil fuels, and since they need to be disposed of in some way, the use of these fuels in CHP provides environmental benefits.

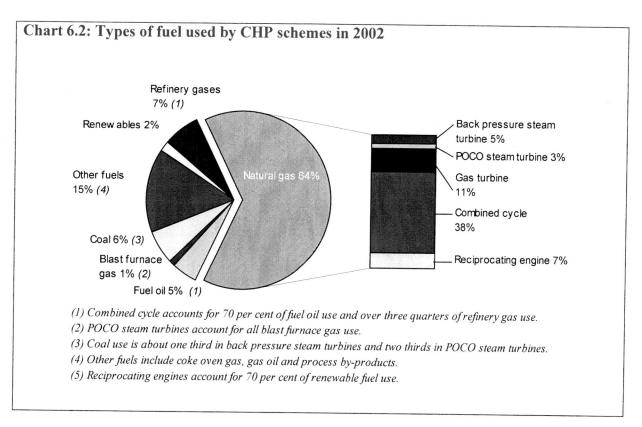

Chart 6.2: Types of fuel used by CHP schemes in 2002

Refinery gases 7% *(1)*
Renew ables 2%
Other fuels 15% *(4)*
Coal 6% *(3)*
Blast furnace gas 1% *(2)*
Fuel oil 5% *(1)*
Natural gas 64%

Back pressure steam turbine 5%
POCO steam turbine 3%
Gas turbine 11%
Combined cycle 38%
Reciprocating engine 7%

(1) Combined cycle accounts for 70 per cent of fuel oil use and over three quarters of refinery gas use.
(2) POCO steam turbines account for all blast furnace gas use.
(3) Coal use is about one third in back pressure steam turbines and two thirds in POCO steam turbines.
(4) Other fuels include coke oven gas, gas oil and process by-products.
(5) Reciprocating engines account for 70 per cent of renewable fuel use.

CHP capacity, output and fuel use by sector

6.21   Table 6.8 gives data on all operational schemes by economic sector. A definition of the sectors used in this table can be found in Chapter 1, paragraph 1.57 and Table 1F:

- 303 schemes 90½ per cent of electrical capacity) are in the industrial sector and 1,236 schemes (9½ per cent of capacity) are in the agricultural, commercial, public administration, residential and transport sectors.

- Four industrial sectors account for three quarters of the CHP electrical capacity - chemicals (32 per cent of capacity), oil refineries (20 per cent), paper, publishing and printing (12½ per cent) and food, beverages and tobacco (8½ per cent). Capacity by sector is shown in Chart 6.3.

Chart 6.3: CHP electrical capacity by sector in 2002

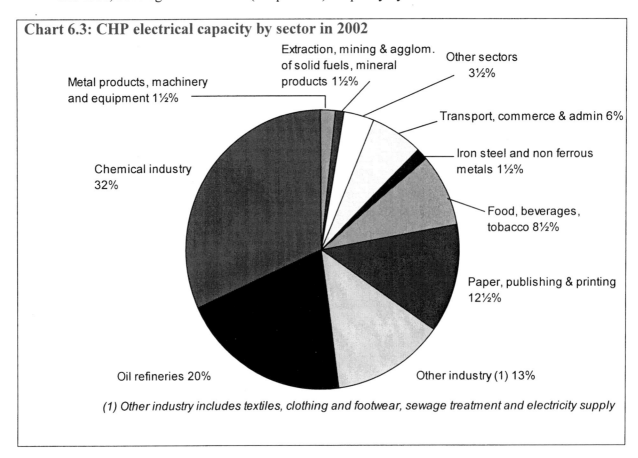

(1) Other industry includes textiles, clothing and footwear, sewage treatment and electricity supply

Table 6C: Number and capacity of CHP schemes installed in buildings by sector in 2002

	Number of schemes	Electrical capacity (MWe)	Heat capacity (MWth)
Leisure	435	42.4	69.9
Hotels	303	37.6	63.5
Health	222	105.5	228.3
Residential Group Heating	51	46.3	86.3
Universities	33	29.6	88.0
Offices	25	18.3	22.5
Education	23	10.3	26.1
Government Estate	14	11.1	17.8
Retail	8	5.8	4.6
Other *(1)*	7	15.1	23.4
Total	**1,121**	**322.0**	**630.4**

(1) Other includes: agriculture, airports, and domestic buildings

6.22   Table 6C gives a summary of the 1,121 schemes installed in the commercial, public sector and residential buildings.   These schemes form a major part of the "Transport, commerce and administration" and "Other" sectors in Tables 6.8 and 6.9. The vast majority of these schemes (98 per cent) are based on spark ignition reciprocating engines fuelled with natural gas, though the larger schemes use compression ignition reciprocating engines or gas turbines. The largest proportion of the capacity is in the health sector, mainly hospitals. Leisure and hotels account for more than half the total number of schemes. Table 6.9 gives details of the quantities of fuels used in each sector.

CHP performance by main prime mover

6.23   Table 6D gives a summary of the performance of schemes in 2002 by main prime mover type. Combined cycle gas turbines have the highest average operating hours at 5,773 hours. The average for all schemes of 5,111 hours is significantly higher than the equivalent in 2001 (4,743 hours).

6.24   The average electrical efficiency is 21 per cent and heat efficiency 52 per cent, giving an overall average of 72 per cent. The average electrical efficiency has increased compared to 2001, probably because of higher utilisation of the CHP.

Table 6D: A summary of scheme performance in 2002

	Typical operating hours per annum (Full load equivalent)	Average electrical efficiency (% GCV)	Average heat efficiency (% GCV)	Average overall efficiency (% GCV)	Average heat to power ratio	Average parasitic losses (% of electrical output)
Main prime mover in CHP plant						
Back pressure steam turbine	4,282	10	61	71	6.3	2.8
Pass out condensing steam turbine	3,594	13	61	74	4.7	5.8
Gas turbine	5,104	22	47	69	2.2	3.1
Combined cycle	5,773	25	49	74	2.0	1.6
Reciprocating engine	4,769	25	39	65	1.5	4.1
All schemes	**5,111**	**21**	**52**	**72**	**2.5**	**2.2**

CHP schemes which export and schemes with mechanical power output

6.25   For 2002, 97 CHP schemes have provided information on the amount of electricity they export (Table 6E). It is estimated that this accounts for almost all the electricity exported from schemes in 2002. Where a scheme that exports is Good Quality for only a portion of its capacity and output, the exports have been scaled back in the same way as power output has been scaled back (see paragraph 6.11, above). Exports accounted for about 30 per cent of power generation from CHP.

6.26   Table 6E also shows revised figures for exports for 2000 and 2001. In 2002, exports have increased by 7 per cent compared to 2001. Exports via licensed suppliers have decreased significantly (by 55 per cent) mainly due to low electricity prices.

Table 6E: Electrical exports from CHP

GWh

	2000	2001	2002
To part of same qualifying group (1)	152	494	401
To a firm NOT part of same qualifying group	2,242	1,537	4,702
To an electricity supplier	6,023	4,751	2,129
Customer not specified	41	2	8
Total	**8,458**	**6,784**	**7,240**

(1) A qualifying group is a group of two or more corporate consumers that are connected or related to each other, for example, as a subsidiary, or via a parent or holding company, or in terms of share capital.

6.27   Around 30 large schemes also export heat, some larger schemes to more than one customer. Together they supplied 7,184 GWh of heat, a moderate increase on 2001.

6.28   There are an estimated 11 schemes with mechanical power output. For those schemes, mechanical power accounts for around 14½ per cent of their capacity (Table 6F). These schemes are predominantly on petro-chemicals or steel sites, using by-product fuels in boilers to drive steam turbines. The steam turbine is used to provide mechanical rather than electrical power, driving compressors, blowers or fans, rather than an alternator.

Table 6F: CHP schemes with mechanical power output in 2002

	Unit	
Number of schemes		11
Total Power Capacity of these schemes (CHP_{TPC})	MWe	1,057
Mechanical power capacity of these schemes	MWe	153

Emissions savings

6.29   The calculation of emissions savings from CHP is important, given the substantial contribution of CHP to the Climate Change Programme, but complex given that CHP displaces a variety of fuels, technologies and sizes of plant. Using the methodology and assumptions outlined in Energy Trends www.dti.gov.uk/energy/inform/energy stats/. CHP saved 3.3 - 4.6 MtC in 2002 compared to equivalent electricity-only and heat-only generation. This is equivalent to 0.70 – 0.96 MtC per 1,000 MWe[1]. The carbon savings are higher than in 2001 because the relative increase in the use of gas fired CHP and the improvements in load factor.

---

[1] This range is obtained by assuming that electricity displaced is either at the average carbon intensity for the whole generating system, giving 0.70 MtC per 1,000 MWe, or at the carbon intensity of the fossil fuel basket, giving 0.96 MtC per 1,000 MWe.

Technical notes and definitions

6.30   These notes and definitions are in addition to the technical notes and definitions covering all fuels and energy as a whole in Chapter 1, paragraphs 1.24 to 1.58.

Data for 2002

6.31   The data are summarised from the results of a long term project being undertaken by Future Energy Solutions on behalf of the Department of Trade and Industry (DTI), the Department for the Environment, Food and Rural Affairs (Defra), and the Statistical Office of the European Communities (Eurostat). Data are included for CHP schemes installed in all sectors of the UK economy.

6.32   The project continues to be overseen by a Steering Group that comprises officials from the DTI, Defra, the Office of Gas and Electricity Markets (OFGEM) and the Combined Heat and Power Association (CHPA), all of whom have an interest in either the collection of information on CHP schemes or the promotion of the wider use of CHP in the UK.

6.33   Data for 2002 were based largely on data supplied to the CHPQA programme, supplemented by a survey carried out by the Office for National Statistics (ONS) between December 2002 and March 2003 of companies (other than major power producers) who generate their own electricity, either in CHP schemes or in electricity-only schemes. Information on the CHP plant included in the major power producers category comes from surveys conducted by DTI as part of the electricity statistics system. Owing to the difficulties in the iron and steel industry, separate statistics on fuel use in that industry have not been collected. The information on CHP in iron and steel is largely based on statistics collected in previous years.   Over half of CHP schemes and around 82 per cent of capacity are based on returns under CHPQA, while around 3 per cent of schemes and 6 per cent of CHP capacity are based on data from ONS. Data for schemes not applying for CHPQA and not included in the ONS survey (eg because they were below the cut off capacity for the survey) were interpolated from historical data.

Definitions of schemes

6.34   There are four principal types of CHP systems:

- **Steam turbine,** where steam at high pressure is generated in a boiler. In **back pressure steam turbine systems**, the steam is wholly or partly used in a turbine before being exhausted from the turbine at the required pressure for the site. In **pass-out condensing steam turbine systems**, a proportion of the steam used by the turbine is extracted at an intermediate pressure from the turbine with the remainder being fully condensed before it is exhausted at the exit. (Condensing steam turbines without passout and which do not utilise steam are not included in these statistics as they are not CHP). The boilers used in such schemes can burn a wide variety of fuels including coal, gas, oil, and waste-derived fuels. With the exception of waste-fired schemes, steam turbine plant has often been in service for several decades. Steam turbine schemes capable of supplying useful steam have electrical efficiencies of between 10 and 20 per cent, depending on size, and thus between 70 per cent and 30 per cent of the fuel input is available as useful heat. Steam turbines used in CHP applications typically range in size from a few MWe to over 100 MWe.

- **Gas turbine systems**, often aero-engine derivatives, where fuel (gas, or gas-oil) is combusted in the gas turbine and the exhaust gases are normally used in a waste heat boiler to produce usable steam, though the exhaust gases may be used directly in some process applications. Gas turbines range from 30kWe upwards, achieving electrical efficiency of 23 to 30 per cent (depending on size) and with the potential to recover up to 50 per cent of the fuel input as useful heat. They have been common in CHP since the mid 1980s. The waste heat boiler can include supplementary or auxiliary firing using a wide range of fuels, and thus the heat to power ratio of the scheme can vary.

- **Combined cycle systems**, where the plant comprises more than one prime mover. These are usually gas turbines where the exhaust gases are utilised in a steam generator, the steam from which is passed wholly or in part into one or more steam turbines. In rare cases reciprocating engines may be linked with steam turbines. Combined cycle is suited to larger installations of 7 MWe and over. They achieve higher electrical efficiency and a lower heat to power ratio than steam turbines or gas turbines. Recently installed combined cycle gas turbine (CCGT) schemes have achieved an electrical efficiency approaching 50 per cent, with 20 per cent heat recovery, and a heat to power ratio of less than 1:1.

- **Reciprocating engine systems** range from less than 100 kWe up to around 5 MWe, and are found in applications where production of hot water (rather than steam) is the main requirement, for example, on smaller industrial sites as well as in buildings. They are based on auto engine or marine engine derivatives converted to run on gas. Both compression ignition and spark ignition firing is used. Reciprocating engines operate at around 28 to 33 per cent electrical efficiency with around 50 per cent to 33 per cent of the fuel input available as useful heat. Reciprocating engines produce two grades of waste heat: high grade heat from the engine exhaust and low grade heat from the engine cooling circuits.

Determining fuel consumption for heat and electricity

6.35   In order to provide a comprehensive picture of electricity generation in the United Kingdom and the fuels used to generate that electricity, the energy input to CHP schemes has to be allocated between heat and electricity production. This allocation is notional and is not determinate.

6.36   The convention used to allocate the fuels to heat and electricity relates the split of fuels to the relative efficiency of heat and electricity supply. The efficiency of utility plant varies widely: electricity generation from as little as 25 per cent to more than 50 per cent and boilers from as little as 50 per cent to more than 90 per cent. Thus it is around twice as hard to generate a unit of electricity as it is to generate a unit of heat. Accordingly a simple convention can be implemented whereby twice as many units of fuel are allocated to each unit of electricity generated, as to each unit of heat supplied. This approach is consistent with the DEFRA Guidelines for Company Reporting on greenhouse gas emissions and for Negotiated Agreements on energy efficiency agreed between Government and industry as part of the Climate Change Levy (CCL) package. It recognises that in developing a CHP scheme, both the heat customer(s) and the electricity generator share in the savings, reflecting the fact that more than three-quarters of CHP build in the last few years has been supplied under an energy services arrangement.

6.37   The assumption in this convention that it is twice as hard to generate a unit of electricity as heat, is appropriate for the majority of CHP schemes. However, for some types of scheme (for example in the iron and steel sector) this allocation is less appropriate and can result in very high apparent heat efficiencies. These however are only notional efficiencies.

The effects on the statistics of using CHPQA

6.38   Paragraph 6.11 described how schemes were scaled back so that only CHP_{QPC} and CHP_{QPO} were included in the CHP statistics. This is illustrated in Table 6G. In 2002, 53 schemes have been scaled back. The power output from these schemes was scaled back from a total of 26,772 GWh to 5,435 GWh. The total fuel input to these schemes is 76,164 GWh of which 57,682 GWh is regarded as power only.

Table 6G: CHP capacity, output and fuel use which has been scaled back in 2002

	Units	
Number of schemes requiring scaling back		53
Total Power Capacity of these schemes (CHP_{TPC})	MWe	7,054
Qualifying Power Capacity of these schemes (CHP_{QPC})	MWe	1,279
Total power output of these schemes (CHP_{TPO})	GWh	26,772*
Qualifying Power Output of these schemes (CHP_{QPO})	GWh	5,435
Electricity regarded as "Power only" not from CHP (CHP_{TPO} - CHP_{QPO})	GWh	21,357
Total Fuel Input of these schemes (CHP_{TFI})	GWh	76,164
Fuel input regarded as being for "Power only" use ie not for CHP	GWh	57,682

*This figure includes generation from major power producers

Contacts: *Ann Gardiner, FES*
ann.gardiner@aeat.co.uk
01235 433343

Mike Janes (Statistician), DTI
mike.janes@dti.gsi.gov.uk
020-7215 5186

6.1 CHP installations by capacity and size range

	1998	1999	2000	2001	2002
Number of schemes (1)	**1,356r**	**1,383r**	**1,522r**	**1,561r**	**1,539**
Less than 100 kWe	627r	627r	667r	665r	664
100 kWe to 999 kWe	484	509r	593r	635r	625
1 MWe to 9.9 MWe	175	174	192r	189r	182
10.0 MWe and above	70	73	70r	72r	68
					MWe
Total capacity	**3,680**	**3,912r**	**4,730r**	**4,753r**	**4,742**
Less than 100 kWe	38	38	41	41	41
100 kWe to 999 kWe	119	127	145	155r	151
1 MWe to 9.9 MWe	742	740r	803r	766r	760
10.0 MWe and above	2,782	3,007r	3,741r	3,790r	3,791

(1) A site may contain more than one CHP scheme.

6.2 Fuel used to generate electricity and heat in CHP installations

					GWh
	1998	1999	2000	2001	2002
Fuel used to generate electricity (1)					
Coal (2)	3,357r	2,333r	1,524r	2,402r	2,360
Fuel oil	4,364	4,433	3,071r	2,810r	2,291
Natural gas	22,835r	27,075r	37,842r	32,672r	36,368
Renewable fuels (3)	1,173	1,187	943	1,048r	1,108
Other fuels (4)	9,589	9,238	10,530r	9,167r	9,520
Total all fuels	**41,318r**	**44,266r**	**53,908r**	**48,099r**	**51,646**
Fuel used to generate heat					
Coal (2)	9,565r	6,682r	3,845r	4,724r	4,831
Fuel oil	9,520	9,414	3,342	5,201r	3,303
Natural gas	31,808r	31,718r	37,618r	36,874r	39,223
Renewable fuels (3)	1,066	1,051	1,024	1,038r	1,180
Other fuels (4)	19,921	19,889	17,714r	18,496r	17,703
Total all fuels	**71,880r**	**68,753r**	**63,542r**	**66,333r**	**66,241**
Overall fuel use					
Coal (2)	12,922r	9,015r	5,369r	7,126r	7,191
Fuel oil	13,884	13,847	6,412r	8,010r	5,594
Natural gas	54,643r	58,793r	75,459r	69,546r	75,591
Renewable fuels (3)	2,239	2,238	1,967	2,086r	2,288
Other fuels (4)	29,510	29,127	28,243	27,663r	27,223
Total all fuels	**113,198r**	**113,019r**	**117,450r**	**114,432r**	**117,887**

(1) The allocation of fuel use between heat generation and electricity generation has been changed to match that used in CHPQA. See paragraphs 6.35 to 6.37 for an explanation of the method used.

(2) includes coke and semi-coke.

(3) Renewable fuels include: sewage gas; other biogases; municipal waste and refuse derived fuels.

(4) Other fuels include: process by-products, coke oven gas, blast furnace gas, gas oil and uranium.

6.3 Fuel used by types of CHP installation

GWh

	1998	1999	2000	2001	2002
Coal					
Back pressure steam turbine	7,937r	3,940r	2,333r	2,103r	1,920
Gas turbine	31	31	30	34	46
Combined cycle	498	271	347r	322r	328
Reciprocating engine	-	-	-	-	-
Pass out condensing steam turbine	4,456	4,774	2,659r	4,667r	4,898
Total coal	**12,922r**	**9,015r**	**5,369r**	**7,127r**	**7,191**
Fuel oil					
Back pressure steam turbine	2,642	2,215	555	553r	461
Gas turbine	410	503	651r	402	318
Combined cycle	4,756	4,798	4,361r	5,994r	4,061
Reciprocating engine	371	387	226	183r	281
Pass out condensing steam turbine	5,705	5,943	619	878	473
Total fuel oil	**13,884**	**13,847**	**6,412**	**8,010r**	**5,594**
Natural gas					
Back pressure steam turbine	9,334	7,613	6,116	5,810	5,333
Gas turbine	12,954	13,160	16,050r	13,206r	13,302
Combined cycle	20,332r	25,229r	39,256r	39,232r	45,108
Reciprocating engine	4,976r	5,659r	7,455r	7,433r	8,774
Pass out condensing steam turbine	7,048r	7,132r	6,583r	3,865r	3,074
Total natural gas	**54,644r**	**58,793r**	**75,459r**	**69,546r**	**75,591**
Renewable fuels (1)					
Back pressure steam turbine	289	119	8	10	10
Gas turbine	-	-	-	19	21
Combined cycle	-	20	20	23	65
Reciprocating engine	1,649	1,633	1,417	1,575	1,579
Pass out condensing steam turbine	301	466	522	459r	612
Total renewable fuels	**2,239**	**2,238**	**1,966**	**2,086r**	**2,288**
Other fuels (2)					
Back pressure steam turbine	5,518	5,537	4,847	5,811r	5,911
Gas turbine	2,229	2,244	3,185r	1,480r	1,321
Combined cycle	7,673r	7,514r	6,863r	7,389r	7,821
Reciprocating engine	109r	77	107	87	62
Pass out condensing steam turbine	13,981r	13,754r	13,241r	12,896r	12,108
Total other fuels	**29,509r**	**29,127**	**28,243r**	**27,663r**	**27,223**
Total - all fuels					
Back pressure steam turbine	25,720r	19,425r	13,859r	14,288r	13,634
Gas turbine	15,623	15,938	19,916r	15,141r	15,008
Combined cycle	33,259r	37,832r	50,847r	52,960r	57,383
Reciprocating engine	7,105r	7,756r	9,205r	9,278r	10,696
Pass out condensing steam turbine	31,491r	32,069r	23,623r	22,765r	21,166
Total all fuels	**113,198r**	**113,019r**	**117,450r**	**114,432r**	**117,887**

(1) Renewable fuels include: sewage gas; other biogases; municipal waste and refuse derived fuels.
(2) Other fuels include: process by-products, coke oven gas, blast furnace gas, gas oil and uranium.

6.4 CHP - electricity generated by fuel and type of installation

GWh

	1998	1999	2000	2001	2002
Coal					
Back pressure steam turbine	607r	278r	192r	151r	151
Gas turbine	4	5	6	6	7
Combined cycle	83	44	45	45	37
Reciprocating engine	-	-	-	-	-
Pass out condensing steam turbine	649	661	396	771r	745
Total coal	**1,343r**	**987r**	**639r**	**973r**	**939**
Fuel oil					
Back pressure steam turbine	210	181	54	51	52
Gas turbine	68	81	116r	84r	65
Combined cycle	639	625	1,245r	902r	768
Reciprocating engine	112	118	69	54r	69
Pass out condensing steam turbine	825	862	109	145r	68
Total fuel oil	**1,853**	**1,866**	**1,593r**	**1,236r**	**1,021**
Natural gas					
Back pressure steam turbine	681	557	515r	461	447
Gas turbine	3,050	3,185	4,022r	3,002r	2,915
Combined cycle	4,815r	6,765r	11,362r	10,134r	11,817
Reciprocating engine	1,464r	1,667r	2,237r	1,994r	2,270
Pass out condensing steam turbine	956r	961r	987r	431r	366
Total natural gas	**10,966r**	**13,135r**	**19,124r**	**16,022r**	**17,815**
Renewable fuels (1)					
Back pressure steam turbine	31	18	1	1	1
Gas turbine	-	-	-	3	4
Combined cycle	-	5	5	6	18
Reciprocating engine	409	408	370	365r	369
Pass out condensing steam turbine	49	48	46	57r	58
Total renewable fuels	**489**	**479**	**422**	**433r**	**451**
Other fuels (2)					
Back pressure steam turbine	733	734	624	661r	667
Gas turbine	327	336	536r	293r	259
Combined cycle	1,178r	975r	1,800r	1,186r	1,529
Reciprocating engine	37	25	35	28	19
Pass out condensing steam turbine	1,758r	1,719r	1,767r	1,737r	1,536
Total other fuels	**4,033**	**3,788**	**4,761r**	**3,905r**	**4,010**
Total - all fuels					
Back pressure steam turbine	2,262r	1,768r	1,385r	1,325r	1,317
Gas turbine	3,449	3,606	4,680r	3,388r	3,251
Combined cycle	6,715r	8,413r	14,457r	12,272r	14,169
Reciprocating engine	2,022r	2,219r	2,711r	2,441r	2,727
Pass out condensing steam turbine	4,237r	4,250r	3,306r	3,142r	2,772
Total all fuels	**18,684r**	**20,256r**	**26,539r**	**22,568r**	**24,236**

(1) Renewable fuels include: sewage gas; other biogases; municipal waste and refuse derived fuels.
(2) Other fuels include: process by-products, coke oven gas, blast furnace gas, gas oil and uranium.

6.5 CHP - electrical capacity by fuel and type of installation

MWe

	1998	1999	2000	2001	2002
Coal					
Back pressure steam turbine	160r	82r	63r	55r	48
Gas turbine	1	1	1	1	1
Combined cycle	15	8	8	8	6
Reciprocating engine	-	-	-	-	-
Pass out condensing steam turbine	134	176r	93r	195r	208
Total coal	**310r**	**267r**	**165r**	**259r**	**263**
Fuel oil					
Back pressure steam turbine	61	42	16	17	14
Gas turbine	21	25	31r	27r	24
Combined cycle	118	116	201r	251r	146
Reciprocating engine	28	27	20r	16	20
Pass out condensing steam turbine	178	185	24	33r	14
Total fuel oil	**405**	**395**	**291**	**344r**	**217**
Natural gas					
Back pressure steam turbine	184	173r	145r	149	136
Gas turbine	461	477	594r	528r	520
Combined cycle	964	1,238	1,785r	1,834r	2,026
Reciprocating engine	291r	336r	437r	473r	460
Pass out condensing steam turbine	184	177r	214r	97r	83
Total natural gas	**2,084r**	**2,401r**	**3,175r**	**3,082r**	**3,224**
Renewable fuels (1)					
Back pressure steam turbine	16	13	-	-	-
Gas turbine	-	-	-	-	1
Combined cycle	-	1	1	1	2
Reciprocating engine	91r	92r	86r	86	85
Pass out condensing steam turbine	17	18	18	16	18
Total renewable fuels	**124**	**124r**	**105r**	**104**	**105**
Other fuels (2)					
Back pressure steam turbine	134	134	111	109r	110
Gas turbine	101	107	129r	97r	92
Combined cycle	199r	170r	288r	295r	275
Reciprocating engine	10	8	11	9	8
Pass out condensing steam turbine	314r	306r	456r	455r	450
Total other fuels	**757**	**726**	**993r**	**965r**	**934**
Total - all fuels					
Back pressure steam turbine	554r	444r	336r	329r	308
Gas turbine	584	609	754r	653r	637
Combined cycle	1,295r	1,533r	2,282r	2,389r	2,455
Reciprocating engine	420r	463r	552r	584r	572
Pass out condensing steam turbine	827r	862r	804r	797r	772
Total all fuels	**3,680**	**3,912r**	**4,729r**	**4,753r**	**4,742**

(1) Renewable fuels include: sewage gas; other biogases; municipal waste and refuse derived fuels.
(2) Other fuels include: process by-products and uranium.

6.6 CHP - heat generated by fuel and type of installation

GWh

	1998	1999	2000	2001	2002
Coal					
Back pressure steam turbine	4,667r	2,650r	1,493r	1,342r	1,221
Gas turbine	19	19	17	18	27
Combined cycle	342	191	179	162	107
Reciprocating engine	-	-	-	-	-
Pass out condensing steam turbine	2,612	2,765	1,546	2,370r	2,510
Total coal	**7,640r**	**5,625r**	**3,235r**	**3,892r**	**3,866**
Fuel oil					
Back pressure steam turbine	175	1,485	399	395	335
Gas turbine	162	193	274r	231r	187
Combined cycle	2,549	2,593	2,460r	3,419r	2,105
Reciprocating engine	119	119	55r	59	73
Pass out condensing steam turbine	3,431	3,529	376	518	328
Total fuel oil	**8,016**	**7,920**	**3,564r**	**4,623r**	**3,028**
Natural gas					
Back pressure steam turbine	6,446	5,322	4,125	3,961r	3,568
Gas turbine	5,622	5,607	7,154r	6,462r	6,123
Combined cycle	10,200r	11,421r	19,097r	18,904r	22,035
Reciprocating engine	1,961r	2,317r	3,072r	3,321r	3,536
Pass out condensing steam turbine	5,010r	5,032r	4,380r	3,032r	2,530
Total natural gas	**29,239r**	**29,699r**	**37,828r**	**35,680r**	**37,792**
Renewable fuels *(1)*					
Back pressure steam turbine	62	36	4	5	5
Gas turbine	-	-	-	9	11
Combined cycle	-	16	16r	16	31
Reciprocating engine	633	634	514r	579	584
Pass out condensing steam turbine	193	165	253	223r	259
Total renewable fuels	**888**	**852**	**787r**	**832r**	**890**
Other fuels *(2)*					
Back pressure steam turbine	2,828	2,840	2,562	3,145r	3,216
Gas turbine	1,027	1,000	1,446r	838r	752
Combined cycle	4,082r	4,134	4,358r	3,934r	3,894
Reciprocating engine	39	24	41r	35	30
Pass out condensing steam turbine	8,468r	8,345	8,300r	8,046r	7,272
Total other fuels	**16,444**	**16,343**	**16,707r**	**15,998r**	**15,164**
Total - all fuels					
Back pressure steam turbine	14,177r	12,333r	8,582r	8,849r	8,345
Gas turbine	6,831	6,819	8,890r	7,559r	7,101
Combined cycle	17,173r	18,356r	26,111r	26,435r	28,172
Reciprocating engine	2,752r	3,094r	3,682r	3,993r	4,221
Pass out condensing steam turbine	19,713r	19,837r	14,856r	14,189r	12,899
Total all fuels	**62,227r**	**60,439r**	**62,121r**	**61,025r**	**60,738**

(1) Renewable fuels include: sewage gas; other biogases; municipal waste and refuse derived fuels.
(2) Other fuels include: process by-products and uranium.

6.7 CHP - heat capacity by fuel and type of installation

MWth

	1998	1999	2000	2001	2002
Coal					
Back pressure steam turbine	1,380r	742r	446r	405r	304
Gas turbine	3	3	3	3	4
Combined cycle	47	25	25	25	18
Reciprocating engine	-	-	-	-	-
Pass out condensing steam turbine	1,165	1,326	314	573	606
Total coal	**2,595r**	**2,096r**	**787r**	**1,005r**	**932**
Fuel oil					
Back pressure steam turbine	584	402	124	128	92
Gas turbine	73	90	103r	95r	89
Combined cycle	400	389	474r	572r	357
Reciprocating engine	34	34	21	20	22
Pass out condensing steam turbine	1,497	1,572	70	104	54
Total fuel oil	**2,588**	**2,486**	**791r**	**920r**	**613**
Natural gas					
Back pressure steam turbine	1,424	1,266	830r	817r	712
Gas turbine	1,183	1,140	1,286r	1,156r	1,082
Combined cycle	2,086r	2,592	3,315r	3,417r	3,709
Reciprocating engine	513	570r	774r	919r	886
Pass out condensing steam turbine	1,351	1,270r	820r	573r	395
Total natural gas	**6,557**	**6,838r**	**7,025r**	**6,883r**	**6,784**
Renewable fuels (1)					
Back pressure steam turbine	54	46	1	1	1
Gas turbine	-	-	-	2	2
Combined cycle	-	2	2	2	5
Reciprocating engine	142	150	138	140	144
Pass out condensing steam turbine	52	57	57	46	60
Total renewable fuels	**248**	**255**	**199**	**190**	**212**
Other fuels (2)					
Back pressure steam turbine	418	420	358	357	368
Gas turbine	416	411	466r	384r	369
Combined cycle	692r	641r	777r	796r	803
Reciprocating engine	11	7	11	9	12
Pass out condensing steam turbine	1,738r	1,645r	1,475r	1,459r	1,391
Total other fuels	**3,274**	**3,124**	**3,086r**	**3,006r**	**2,943**
Total - all fuels					
Back pressure steam turbine	3,859r	2,876r	1,758r	1,708r	1,477
Gas turbine	1,675	1,645	1,858r	1,640r	1,546
Combined cycle	3,224r	3,649r	4,593r	4,813r	4,891
Reciprocating engine	700	761r	944r	1,088r	1,063
Pass out condensing steam turbine	5,803r	5,870r	2,736r	2,755r	2,506
Total all fuels	**15,262r**	**14,800r**	**11,888r**	**12,004r**	**11,483**

(1) Renewable fuels include: sewage gas; other biogases; municipal waste and refuse derived fuels.
(2) Other fuels include: process by-products and uranium.

6.8 CHP capacity, output and total fuel use[1] by sector

	Unit	1998	1999	2000	2001	2002
Iron and steel and non ferrous metals						
Number of sites		6	6	6	7r	5
Electrical capacity	MWe	74	74	74	80r	63
Heat capacity	MWth	492	491	491	497r	286
Electrical output	GWh	494	492	486	493r	380
Heat output	GWh	2,375	2,361	2,377	2,197r	1,343
Fuel use	GWh	2,778	2,728	2,751	2,680r	1,818
of which : for electricity	GWh	833	826	818	853r	701
for heat	GWh	1,945	1,902	1,933	1,828r	1,117
Chemicals						
Number of sites		61	59	55	52r	52
Electrical capacity	MWe	1,248	1,243r	1,524r	1,528r	1,520
Heat capacity	MWth	6,605	6,340	4,022	4,034r	3,840
Electrical output	GWh	6,990	6,839	9,675	8,399r	8,130
Heat output	GWh	24,857	24,213	22,959r	22,006r	22,246
Fuel use	GWh	43,901	42,041	45,838	42,245r	42,126
of which : for electricity	GWh	15,299	14,897	20,390	17,922r	17,533
for heat	GWh	28,602	27,144	25,448	24,323r	24,592
Oil refineries						
Number of sites		12	13	10	10	9
Electrical capacity	MWe	740	870	986	984r	954
Heat capacity	MWth	3,414	3,648	2,995	3,098	3,066
Electrical output	GWh	3,712	4,017	5,710	4,214r	5,199
Heat output	GWh	15,521	15,699	14,667r	14,823r	14,873
Fuel use	GWh	28,622	29,495	25,249r	27,465r	28,872
of which : for electricity	GWh	9,184	9,845	11,676r	10,116r	12,022
for heat	GWh	19,438	19,649	13,574r	17,349r	16,850
Paper, publishing and printing						
Number of sites		38	37	36	35	35
Electrical capacity	MWe	470	472r	559r	529r	595
Heat capacity	MWth	1,506	1,422	1,331	1,316	1,388
Electrical output	GWh	2,579	3,023	3,827	3,413r	3,662
Heat output	GWh	7,399	7,166	9,065	8,852r	8,632
Fuel use	GWh	13,796	14,082	16,718	16,468r	16,698
of which : for electricity	GWh	5,493	6,239	7,526	7,129r	7,569
for heat	GWh	8,303	7,842	9,192	9,339r	9,130
Food, beverages and tobacco						
Number of sites		46r	46r	47r	46r	45
Electrical capacity	MWe	328r	400r	405r	392r	392
Heat capacity	MWth	1,448r	1,349r	1,166r	1,121r	1,090
Electrical output	GWh	1,378r	2,201r	2,113r	1,675r	1,920
Heat output	GWh	5,769r	5,143r	5,536r	5,102r	5,542
Fuel use	GWh	9,938r	10,523r	10,089r	8,706r	9,545
of which : for electricity	GWh	3,173r	4,652r	4,316r	3,401r	3,836
for heat	GWh	6,765r	5,872r	5,772r	5,305r	5,709
Metal products, machinery and equipment						
Number of sites		8	9	15r	16r	13
Electrical capacity	MWe	29	31	86r	81r	78
Heat capacity	MWth	52	60	90r	91r	64
Electrical output	GWh	126	153	523r	182r	200
Heat output	GWh	171	179	302r	388r	349
Fuel use	GWh	455	520	1,446r	821r	791
of which : for electricity	GWh	269	328	1,132r	392r	417
for heat	GWh	186	192	313r	429r	373

6.8 CHP capacity, output and total fuel use[1] by sector (continued)

	Unit	1998	1999	2000	2001	2002
Mineral products, extraction, mining and agglomeration of solid fuels						
Number of sites		6	6	10	10	10
Electrical capacity	MWe	24	24	56	56	59
Heat capacity	MWth	100	100	180r	180r	180
Electrical output	GWh	163	149	313r	242	225
Heat output	GWh	622	573	913	848r	819
Fuel use	GWh	1,053	989	1,592	1,349	1,326
of which : for electricity	GWh	361	339	666	495r	472
for heat	GWh	692	649	927	854r	854
Sewage treatment						
Number of sites		116r	112r	113r	113r	113
Electrical capacity	MWe	106r	107r	102r	102r	101
Heat capacity	MWth	164r	172r	160r	162r	162
Electrical output	GWh	465r	463r	428r	424r	430
Heat output	GWh	714r	711r	586r	654r	660
Fuel use	GWh	1,866r	1,840r	1,624r	1,782r	1,784
of which : for electricity	GWh	1,051r	1,043r	931r	997r	999
for heat	GWh	815r	797r	692r	786r	785
Electricity supply						
Number of sites		6	6	6	6	6
Electrical capacity	MWe	243	243	437r	470r	470
Heat capacity	MWth	321	321	370r	370r	398
Electrical output	GWh	781	774	874	1,157r	1,495
Heat output	GWh	1,098	1,077	1,500	1,837r	1,980
Fuel use	GWh	2,337	2,297	2,624	3,375r	4,136
of which : for electricity	GWh	1,333	1,316	1,397	1,869r	2,442
for heat	GWh	1,003	981	1,228	1,506r	1,694
Other industrial branches (2)						
Number of sites		17r	15r	17r	16r	15
Electrical capacity	MWe	43r	41r	58r	57r	56
Heat capacity	MWth	182r	148r	206r	181r	161
Electrical output	GWh	249r	229r	348r	333r	322
Heat output	GWh	629r	402r	528r	699r	647
Fuel use	GWh	1,304r	1,038r	1,135r	1,419r	1,337
of which : for electricity	GWh	555r	542r	600r	680r	653
for heat	GWh	749r	495r	534r	739r	684
Total industry						
Number of sites		316r	309r	315r	311r	303
Electrical capacity	MWe	3,305r	3,504r	4,288r	4,280r	4,286
Heat capacity	MWth	14,282r	14,051r	11,011r	11,049r	10,635
Electrical output	GWh	16,935r	18,338r	24,295r	20,530r	21,963
Heat output	GWh	59,155r	57,524r	58,432r	57,405r	57,090
Fuel use	GWh	106,049r	105,552r	109,065r	106,309r	108,432
of which : for electricity	GWh	37,551r	40,029r	49,452r	43,854r	46,643
for heat	GWh	68,499r	65,524r	59,612r	62,456r	61,789

6.8 CHP capacity, output and total fuel use[1] by sector (continued)

	Unit	1998	1999	2000	2001	2002
Transport, commerce and administration						
Number of sites		965r	993	1,110r	1,151r	1,141
Electrical capacity	MWe	227r	250r	268r	294r	287
Heat capacity	MWth	413r	450r	586r	658r	564
Electrical output	GWh	1,179r	1,226r	1,347r	1,338r	1,288
Heat output	GWh	1,568r	1,798r	2,219r	2,391r	2,268
Fuel use	GWh	4,109r	4,465r	4,870r	5,245r	6,271
of which : for electricity	GWh	2,471r	2,602r	2,645r	2,756r	3,338
for heat	GWh	1,637r	1,864	2,225r	2,469r	2,934
Other (3)						
Number of sites		76r	81r	97r	99r	95
Electrical capacity	MWe	147r	159r	174r	179r	169
Heat capacity	MWth	567r	299r	292r	298r	285
Electrical output	GWh	570r	692r	897r	700r	985
Heat output	GWh	1,504r	1,118r	1,470r	1,230r	1,381
Fuel use	GWh	3,041r	3,001r	3,515r	2,898r	3,184
of which : for electricity	GWh	1,296r	1,635r	1,811r	1,490r	1,665
for heat	GWh	1,744r	1,366r	1,705r	1,408r	1,518
Total CHP usage by all sectors						
Number of sites		1,357r	1,383r	1,522r	1,561r	1,539
Electrical capacity	MWe	3,680	3,912r	4,730r	4,753r	4,742
Heat capacity	MWth	15,262r	14,801r	11,888r	12,004r	11,483
Electrical output	GWh	18,684r	20,256r	26,539r	22,568r	24,236
Heat output	GWh	62,227r	60,439r	62,121r	61,025r	60,738
Fuel use	GWh	113,198r	113,019r	117,450r	114,432r	117,887
of which : for electricity	GWh	41,318r	44,266r	53,908r	48,099r	51,646
for heat	GWh	71,881r	68,753r	63,542r	66,333r	66,241

(1) The allocation of fuel use between electricity and heat is largely notional and the methodology is outlined in paragraphs 6.35 to 6.37.

(2) Other industry includes Textiles, clothing and footwear sector.

(3) Sectors included under Other are agriculture, community heating, leisure, landfill and incineration.

6.9 CHP - use of fuels by sector

GWh

	1998	1999	2000	2001	2002
Iron and steel and non ferrous metals					
Coal	172	89	97	97	-
Fuel oil	137	153	160	154	44
Natural gas	397	413	422	492r	283
Blast furnace gas	1,743	1,643	1,643	1,537	1,158
Coke oven gas	305	406	405	376	332
Other fuels (2)	24	24	24	24	-
Total iron and steel and non ferrous metals	**2,778**	**2,728**	**2,751**	**2,680r**	**1,818**
Chemicals					
Coal	7,876	4,821	2,416	4,479	4,473
Fuel oil	3,654	3,951	868	1,151r	586
Gas oil	74	78	80	98	75
Natural gas	20,345	21,689	31,116	25,816r	26,319
Refinery gas	347	347	393	59r	59
Renewable fuels (1)	-	-	-	19	21
Other fuels (2)	11,605	11,156	10,965	10,625r	10,593
Total chemical industry	**43,901**	**42,041**	**45,838**	**42,245r**	**42,126**
Oil refineries					
Fuel oil	8,303	8,404	4,596r	5,946	4,136
Gas oil	-	266	266	134	134
Natural gas	5,548	6,319	7,050r	7,787	10,491
Refinery gas	9,394	9,128	7,961r	7,526r	7,879
Other fuels (2)	5,377	5,377	5,377	6,072r	6,233
Total oil refineries	**28,622**	**29,495**	**25,249r**	**27,465**	**28,872**
Paper, publishing and printing					
Coal	2,130	1,777	731	654r	772
Fuel oil	430	474	366	361	313
Gas oil	17	79	21	43r	34
Natural gas	11,217	11,749	15,441	15,218r	15,387
Renewable fuels (1)	2	2	2	4	4
Other fuels	-	-	157	188	188
Total paper, publishing and printing	**13,796**	**14,082**	**16,718**	**16,468r**	**16,698**
Food, beverages and tobacco					
Coal	1,912r	1,806r	1,521r	1,292r	1,238
Fuel oil	570	465	194	184	192
Gas oil	50	45	56	66r	14
Natural gas	7,403r	8,205r	8,316r	7,162r	8,098
Renewable fuels (1)	2	2	2	2	2
Other fuels (2)	-	-	-	-	-
Total food, beverages and tobacco	**9,938r**	**10,523r**	**10,088r**	**8,706r**	**9,544**
Metal products, machinery and equipment					
Coal	32	20	32	32	-
Fuel oil	74	106	107	61r	92
Gas oil	1	1	-	-	-
Natural gas	347	395	1,306r	727r	698
Total metal products, machinery and equipment	**455**	**520**	**1,446r**	**821r**	**791**
Mineral products, extraction, mining and agglomeration of solid fuels					
Coal	-	-	69	61	133
Fuel oil	-	-	-	-	-
Natural gas	833	769	1,373	1,138	1,044
Coke oven gas	219	219	150	150	150
Total mineral products, extraction, mining and agglomeration of solid fuels	**1,053**	**989**	**1,592**	**1,349**	**1,326**

6.9 CHP - use of fuels by sector (cont'd)

GWh

	1998	1999	2000	2001	2002
Sewage treatment					
Fuel oil	126	116	71	71	71
Gas oil	-	-	30	30	30
Natural gas	115r	116r	114r	114r	114
Renewable fuels (1)	1,625	1,608	1,408	1,567	1,569
Total sewage treatment	**1,866r**	**1,840r**	**1,624r**	**1,782r**	**1,784**
Electricity supply					
Coal	178	178	178	178	216
Fuel oil	-	-	-	3	21
Natural gas	1,899	1,860	1,857	2,594r	3,721
Other fuels (2)	260	260	590	599r	179
Total electricity supply	**2,337r**	**2,297r**	**2,625r**	**3,374r**	**4,136**
Other industrial branches (3)					
Fuel oil	10	2	2	2	-
Gas oil	-	2	3r	1	11
Natural gas	1,289r	1,029r	1,125r	1,411r	1,320
Renewable fuels (1)	5	6	6	6	6
Total other industrial branches	**1,304r**	**1,038r**	**1,135r**	**1,419r**	**1,337**
Transport, commerce and administration					
Coal	30	30	30	34	46
Fuel oil	160	158	32	65	135
Gas oil	40	44	76	64	33
Natural gas	3,857	4,212	4,811	5,382	6,048
Refinery gas	1r	1r	1r	1r	1
Renewable fuels (1)	5	5	5	5	2
Other fuels (2)	6	6	2	2	7
Total transport, commerce and administration	**4,098**	**4,454**	**4,956**	**5,552**	**6,271**
Other (4)					
Coal	591	294r	294	300	315
Fuel oil	418	18	18	14	3
Gas oil	27	44	44	20	15
Natural gas	1,383r	2,027r	2,613r	2,032r	2,069
Renewable fuels (1)	600	615	543	484r	684
Other fuels (2)	22	3	3	49r	97
Total other	**3,041r**	**3,001r**	**3,515r**	**2,898r**	**3,184**
Total - all sectors					
Coal	12,922r	9,015r	5,369r	7,127r	7,191
Fuel oil	13,884	13,847	6,412r	8,010r	5,594
Gas oil	208	559	573	455r	346
Natural gas	54,643r	58,793r	75,459r	69,546r	75,591
Blast furnace gas	1,743	1,643	1,643	1,537	1,158
Coke oven gas	525	625	555	526	482
Refinery gas	9,741	9,476	8,355r	7,587r	7,939
Renewable fuels (1)	2,239	2,238	1,967	2,086r	2,288
Other fuels (2)	17,293	16,825	17,117	17,559r	17,297
Total CHP fuel use	**113,198r**	**113,019r**	**117,450r**	**114,432**	**117,887**

(1) Renewable fuels include: sewage gas; other biogases; municipal waste and refuse derived fuels.
(2) Other fuels include: process by-products and uranium.
(3) Other industry includes textiles, clothing and footwear.
(4) Sectors included under Other are agriculture, community heating, leisure, landfill and incineration.

Chapter 7
Renewable sources of energy

Introduction

7.1   This chapter provides information on the contribution of renewable energy sources to the United Kingdom's energy requirements. It includes sources that under some definitions would not be counted as a renewable source or would be counted only in part. This is to ensure that this Digest covers all sources of energy available in the United Kingdom. This chapter covers both the use of renewables to generate electricity and the burning of renewable fuels to produce heat either in boilers (or cookers) or in combined heat and power plants.

7.2   The data summarise the results of an ongoing study undertaken by the Future Energy Solutions (FES - part of AEA Technology (AEAT) Environment), on behalf of the Department of Trade and Industry, to update a database containing information on all relevant renewable energy sources in the United Kingdom. This database is called RESTATS, the Renewable Energy STATisticS database.

7.3   The study started in 1989, when all relevant renewable energy sources were identified and, where possible, information was collected on the amounts of energy derived from each source. The renewable energy sources identified were the following: active solar heating; photovoltaics; onshore and offshore wind power; wave power; large and small scale hydro; biofuels; geothermal aquifers. The technical notes at the end of this chapter define each of these renewable energy sources. The database now contains 14 years of data from 1989 to 2002.

7.4   The information contained in the database is collected by a number of methods. For larger projects, an annual survey is carried out in which questionnaires are sent to project managers. For technologies in which there are large numbers of small projects, the values given in this chapter are estimates based on information collected from a sub-sample of the projects. Further details about the data collection methodologies used in RESTATS, including the quality and completeness of the information, are given in the technical notes at the end of this chapter.

7.5   Commodity balances for renewable energy sources covering each of the last three years form the first three tables (Tables 7.1 to 7.3). These are followed by the 5-year table showing capacity of and electricity generation from renewable sources (Table 7.4), and a table summarising all the renewable orders (Table 7.5). Table 7.6 shows renewable sources used to generate electricity and heat in each of the last five years. A long-term trends commentary and table (Table 7.1.1) covering the use of renewables to generate electricity and heat is available on DTI's energy statistics web site www.dti.gov.uk/energy/inform/dukes/dukes2003/07longterm.pdf .

7.6   Unlike in the commodity balance tables in other chapters of the Digest, Tables 7.1 to 7.3 have zero statistical differences. This is because the data for each category of fuel are, in the main, taken from a single source where there is less likelihood of differences due to timing or measurement.

Renewables Obligation and Renewables Directive

7.7   In April 2002 the Renewables Obligation (RO) (and the analogous Renewables (Scotland) Obligation) came into effect[1]. It is an obligation on all electricity suppliers to supply a specific proportion of electricity from eligible renewable sources. Eligible sources include all those covered by this chapter but with specific exclusions. These are: existing hydro plant of over 20 MW; all plant

---

[1] Parliamentary approval of the Renewables Obligation Orders under The Utilities Act 2000 was given in March 2002.

using renewable sources built before 1990 (unless re-furbished); and energy from mixed waste combustion unless the waste is first converted to fuel using advanced conversion technology. Only the biodegradable fraction of any waste is eligible (in line with the EU Directive, see paragraph 7.8, below). All stations outside the United Kingdom (the UK includes its territorial waters and the continental shelf) are also excluded. In Table 7.4 a row gives total electricity generation on an RO basis. Strictly speaking the RO covers only Great Britain, but in these UK based statistics Northern Ireland renewable sources have been treated as if they were also part of the RO.

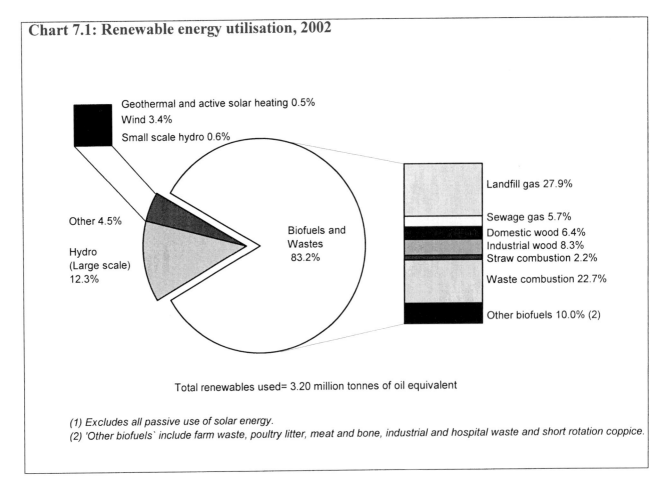

Chart 7.1: Renewable energy utilisation, 2002

Geothermal and active solar heating 0.5%
Wind 3.4%
Small scale hydro 0.6%

Other 4.5%

Hydro (Large scale) 12.3%

Biofuels and Wastes 83.2%

Landfill gas 27.9%
Sewage gas 5.7%
Domestic wood 6.4%
Industrial wood 8.3%
Straw combustion 2.2%
Waste combustion 22.7%
Other biofuels 10.0% (2)

Total renewables used= 3.20 million tonnes of oil equivalent

(1) Excludes all passive use of solar energy.
(2) 'Other biofuels' include farm waste, poultry litter, meat and bone, industrial and hospital waste and short rotation coppice.

7.8 The European Union's Renewables Directive (RD) (which came into force in October 2001) has a different definition of eligible renewables. The Directive's definition includes all those sources covered by this chapter except non-biodegradable wastes. FES has estimated the percentage of MSW that was non-biodegradable for all the years in the RESTATS database. For 2002 the estimate is that 34 per cent of MSW was non-biodegradable and all of waste tyres (but see paragraph 7.65). In Table 7.4 a further row gives total electricity generation on an RD basis.

7.9 In the past the main instruments for pursuing the development of renewables capacity were the Non Fossil Fuel Obligation (NFFO) Orders for England and Wales and for Northern Ireland, and the Scottish Renewable Orders (SRO). In this chapter the term "NFFO Orders" is used to refer to these instruments collectively. For projects contracted under NFFO Orders in England and Wales, details of capacity and generation were provided by the Non Fossil Purchasing Agency (NFPA). The Scottish Executive and Northern Ireland Electricity provided information on the Scottish and Northern Ireland NFFO Orders, respectively.

Renewables Targets
7.10 Thus since February 2000, the United Kingdom's renewables policy has consisted of four key strands:

- a new Renewables Obligation on all electricity suppliers in Great Britain to supply a specific proportion of electricity from eligible renewables;
- exemption of electricity from renewables[2] from the Climate Change Levy;
- an expanded support programme for new and renewable energy including capital grants and an expanded research and development programme;
- development of a regional strategic approach to planning and targets for renewables.

The aim of the Renewables Obligation (RO) is to increase the contribution of electricity from renewables in the UK so that by 2010, 10 per cent of licensed UK electricity sales should be from renewable sources eligible for the RO.

7.11   The EU Directive proposes that Member States adopt national targets for renewables that are consistent with reaching the overall EU target of 12 per cent of energy (22.1 per cent of electricity) from renewables by 2010. The proposed UK "share" of this target is that renewables sources eligible under the RD should account for 10 per cent of UK electricity **consumption** by 2010. Thus any imported electricity certified as coming from eligible renewable sources would count towards the RD target, but any electricity generated in the UK from eligible renewable sources but exported to another country would not. The Office of Gas and Electricity Markets (OFGEM) have advised that in 2002 1,668 GWh of imported electricity were certified as Climate Change Levy exempt and therefore count as eligible renewables.

7.12   Chart 7.2 and Table 7A show the growth in all sources of renewables generation since 1990. It includes progress towards the RO and RD 10 per cent targets. In 2002 the RO percentage showed continued growth. The percentage of UK electricity sales that were of electricity generated from sources eligible for the RO rose from 1.32 per cent in 2000 to 1.52 per cent in 2001 and 1.74 per cent in 2002. However, on the basis favoured by the Renewables Directive, the percentage of UK electricity consumption accounted for by RD eligible renewable sources rose from 2.52 per cent in 2000 to 2.87 per cent in 2001 and 3.19 per cent in 2002. The main reason for the large increase in the RD percentage in 2001 was the inclusion of imports of renewable sourced electricity over the interconnector with France (mainly hydro). In 2002 the further substantial increase was as a result of a consumption of electricity in the UK growing only marginally, while renewable sources increased more strongly. Generation from all renewables and wastes in the UK accounted for 2.96 per cent of UK electricity generation in 2002 (see paragraph 7.16, below).

Table 7A: Percentages of electricity derived from renewable sources			
	2000	2001	2002
Overall renewables percentage	2.75	2.62	2.96
Percentage on a Renewables Obligation basis	1.32	1.52	1.74
Percentage on a Renewables Directive basis	2.52	2.87	3.19

Commodity balances for renewables in 2002 (Table 7.1), 2001 (Table 7.2) and 2000 (Table 7.3)

7.13   Nine different categories of renewable fuels are identified in the commodity balances. Some of these categories are themselves groups of renewables because a more detailed disaggregation could disclose data for individual companies. The largest contribution is from biofuels and wastes, with large-scale hydro electricity production contributing the majority of the remainder as Chart 7.1 shows. Only 4½ per cent of renewable energy comes from renewable sources other than biofuels, wastes and large-scale hydro. These include solar, wind, small-scale hydro and geothermal aquifers.

7.14   78 per cent of the renewable energy produced in 2002 was transformed into electricity. This is an increase from 77 per cent in 2001 and 75 per cent in 2000. While biofuels and wastes appear to

---

[2] Electricity generated by hydro stations with a declared net capacity of more than 10 MW is not exempt from the Climate Change Levy.

dominate the picture when fuel inputs are being measured, hydro electricity dominates when the output of electricity is being measured as Table 7.4 shows. This is because on an energy supplied basis (see Chapter 5, paragraph 5.25) hydro (and also wind and wave) inputs are assumed to be equal to the electricity produced. For landfill gas, sewage sludge, municipal solid waste and other renewables a substantial proportion of the energy content of the input is lost in the process of conversion to electricity.

7.15   Overall, renewable sources, excluding passive uses of solar energy, provided 1.4 per cent of the United Kingdom's total primary energy requirements in 2002. This was 0.15 percentage points higher than in 2001, which in turn was 0.05 percentage points higher than in 2000.

Capacity of, and electricity generated from renewable sources (Table 7.4)
7.16   Table 7.4 shows the capacity of, and the amounts of electricity generated from, each renewable source. Total electricity generation from renewables in 2002 amounted to 11,444 GWh, 40 per cent of which was from large-scale hydro generation. Large-scale hydro generation was 19 per cent higher than the low levels of 2001, which were caused by low rainfall and snowfall. As a result all renewable sources provided 2.96 per cent of the electricity generated in the United Kingdom in 2001, 0.30 percentage points higher than in 2001. Chart 7.2 shows the growth in the proportion of electricity produced from renewable sources. It includes the progress towards the renewables targets set under the Renewables Obligation and Renewables Directive (see paragraphs 7.10 to 7.12 above).

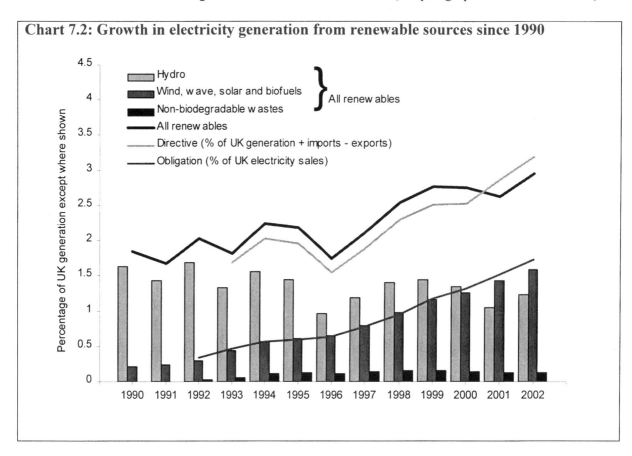

Chart 7.2: Growth in electricity generation from renewable sources since 1990

7.17   There was a 3½ per cent increase in the installed generating capacity of renewable sources in 2002, mainly as a result of a 25 per cent increase in wind capacity and a 5 per increase in the capacity fuelled by biofuels and wastes. Large-scale hydro capacity fell by 4 per cent as some stations were adapted to fall within the capacity limits specified by the renewables obligation.

7.18   Electricity generated from all renewable sources in the UK in 2002 was 13½ per cent greater than in 2001. Generation from renewables other than large-scale hydro in 2002 was 10 per cent higher than in 2001 and double the level in 1997.

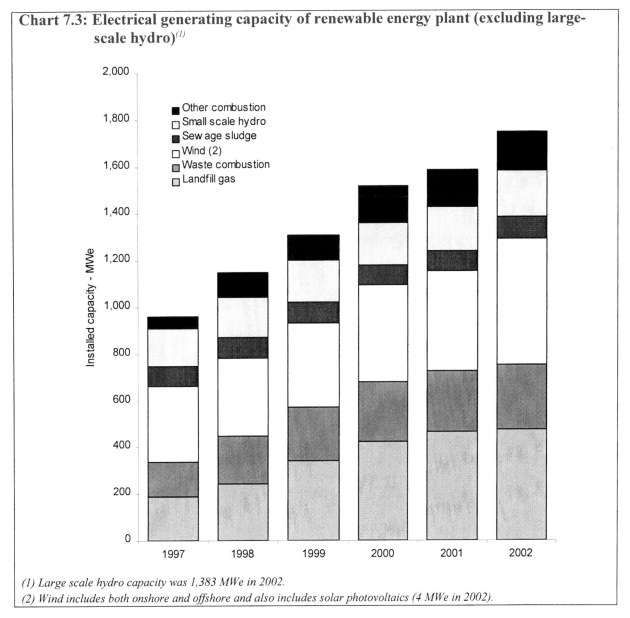

Chart 7.3: Electrical generating capacity of renewable energy plant (excluding large-scale hydro)[(1)]

Installed capacity - MWe

Legend:
- Other combustion
- Small scale hydro
- Sewage sludge
- Wind (2)
- Waste combustion
- Landfill gas

(1) Large scale hydro capacity was 1,383 MWe in 2002.
(2) Wind includes both onshore and offshore and also includes solar photovoltaics (4 MWe in 2002).

7.19   The renewables technology that showed the biggest growth in electricity output during 2002 was solar photovoltaics with an increase of nearly 50 per cent, although this was from a very low base and its overall contribution in 2002 was only 3 GWh. Next largest was wind (30½ per cent) followed by large-scale hydro (19 per cent – see paragraph 7.16, above). The increase in the other biofuels category (12 per cent) came largely from the co-firing of biomass with fossil fuels in a major power station (see paragraphs 7.70 and 7.71, below). Electricity from sewage sludge digestion grew by 9½ per cent while generation from landfill gas grew by 7 per cent as did generation from wastes.

7.20   Chart 7.3 (which covers all renewables capacity except large scale hydro) illustrates the continuing increase in the electricity generation capacity from all significant renewable sources. This upward trend in the capacity of new and renewable sources will continue as further projects already contracted under NFFO Orders come on line and recently consented offshore windfarms come on stream.

7.21   In 2002, 62½ per cent of electricity from renewables (excluding large-scale hydro) was generated under NFFO contracts. If ex-NFFO sites (NFFO 1 and 2 in England and Wales – see paragraphs 7.23 to 7.35, below) are included the proportion increases to 85 per cent. Table 7.4, however, includes both electricity generated outside of these contracts and electricity from large-scale hydro schemes and thus reports on total electricity generation from renewables. All electricity generated from renewables is also reported within the tables of Chapter 5 of this Digest (e.g. Table 5.6).

7.22   Plant load factors in Table 7.4 have been calculated in terms of installed capacity and express the average hourly quantity of electricity generated as a percentage of the average capacity at the beginning and end of the year. The overall figure is heavily influenced by the availability of hydro capacity during the year, which is in turn influenced by the amount of rainfall during the preceding period. Low rainfall in the winter of 2000/2001 led to 2001 having the lowest hydro load factors since 1996. Plant load factors for all generating plant in the UK are shown in Chapter 5, Table 5.9.

Renewable orders and operational capacity (Table 7.5)
7.23   In 1990, the first year of NFFO, projects contracted within NFFO accounted for about 34 per cent of the total capacity (excluding large-scale hydro); by 1998, this figure had risen to 86 per cent, but dropped to 50 per cent in 1999 due to the expiry of NFFO I and 2 contracts. However, in 2001 new NFFO capacity raised the proportion back to 61½ per cent but in 2002 NFFO capacity rose only slightly compared with the increase in Non-NFFO and the proportion slipped back to 60 per cent. 25 NFFO schemes totalling 63 MW (DNC) had begun to operate by the end of 2002 as shown in Chart 7.4.

(a)   Non Fossil Fuel Obligation (NFFO)
7.24   The 1989 Electricity Act empowered the Secretary of State to make orders requiring the Regional Electricity Companies in England and Wales (the RECs) to secure specified amounts of electricity from renewable energy sources.

7.25   Five NFFO Orders were made, of which the first in 1990 was set for a total of 102 MW DNC. This first order resulted in contracts for 75 projects for 152 MW DNC and provided a premium price for the electricity produced which was funded from a levy on electricity sales in England and Wales. (The bulk of this levy was used to support electricity from nuclear stations.)

7.26   The second Order, made in late 1991, was set for 457 MW DNC. This resulted in 122 separate contracts (for a total of 472 MW DNC) between the generators and the Non-Fossil Purchasing Agency (NFPA) which acted on behalf of the RECs. For landfill gas, sewage gas and waste-derived generation contracts were awarded at around 6p/kWh, while for wind-based generation a price of 11p/kWh was established. These prices reflected the limited period for the recovery of capital costs.

7.27   The third Order covers the period 1995 to 2014; this was for 627 MW DNC of contracted capacity at an average price of 4.35 p/kWh. The lower bid prices reflect the longer-term contracts, which are now available together with further developments which have led to improvements in the technologies. Taking into account factors such as the failure to gain planning permission it is estimated that about 300-400 MW DNC are likely to go forward for commissioning.

7.28   The fourth Order was announced in February 1997. Contracts have been let to 195 projects with a total DNC of 843 MW, at an average price of 3.46 p/kWh. In the fifth and largest Order, which was announced in September 1998, contracts have been let to 261 projects with a total DNC of 1,177.1 MW, at an average price of 2.71 p/kWh.

7.29   Since the expiry of the NFFO 1 and 2 contracts on 31 December 1998, these projects are no longer included in the monitoring of NFFO Orders and DTI no longer receive any status/output data on them from the NFPA. For some of these projects operational data have been obtained from other sources, while for the others estimates have been made based on output in 1998. For 2002 another source of information became available to us in the form of the Renewables Obligation data. This enabled Future Energy Solutions to identify, which former NFFO 1 and 2 schemes were applying for ROCs and therefore were still running. Of the 82 NFFO 1 and 2 projects identified in this way as still live, 26 were contracted under the first order and 56 under the second order. It is appreciated that there may be some ex NFFO 1 and 2 schemes that are continuing to operate but whose output is too small to qualify for ROCs and to that extent the estimates of NFFO capacity may be an underestimate.

7.30   As at the end of December 2002, 79 projects in the third Order were operational, with total capacities of 293 MW DNC. There were 77 schemes with a capacity of 196 MW DNC commissioned from the fourth Order projects and 65 schemes totalling 119 MW DNC from the fifth Order. Table 7.5 sets out the technologies and capacities of schemes in all five Orders.

Chart 7.4: Renewable generating capacity from NFFO and former NFFO contracts (including equivalents in Scotland and Northern Ireland) and capacity outside of NFFO

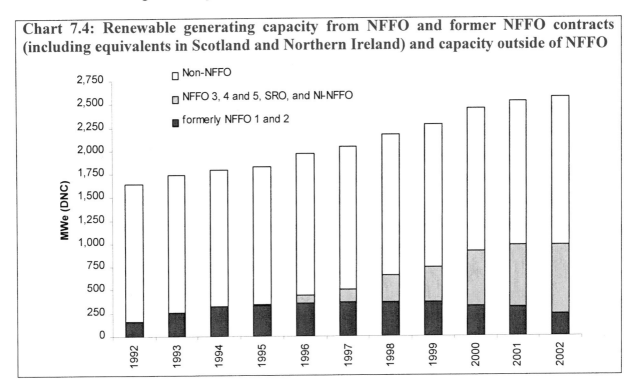

(b)   Scottish Renewable Order (SRO)
7.31   In Scotland, the first Renewables Order was made in 1994 for approximately 76 MW DNC of new capacity and comprising 30 schemes. Four generation technology bands were covered; 12 wind, 15 hydro, 2 waste-to-energy and 1 biomass. At the end of December 2002, 18 schemes were commissioned with a capacity of 47 MW DNC.

7.32   A second SRO was launched in 1995 and was made in March 1997 for 114 MW DNC of new capacity comprising 26 schemes, nine of which were waste to energy projects, nine were hydro projects, seven were wind projects and one was a biomass project. Under this Order, at the end of 2002 there were 11 commissioned schemes with a capacity of 48 MW DNC.

7.33   A third SRO was laid before Parliament in February 1999 for 145.4 MW DNC of new capacity comprising 53 schemes. Sixteen of these were waste to energy projects, five were hydro projects, twenty-eight were wind projects, one was a biomass project and three were wave energy projects. Under this Order, at the end of 2002 there were 9 commissioned schemes with a capacity of 21 MW DNC. Table 7.5 sets out the technologies and capacities of schemes in all three Scottish Orders.

(c)   Northern Ireland Non Fossil Fuel Obligation (NI NFFO)
7.34   In Northern Ireland, a first Order was made in March 1994 for approximately 16 MW DNC comprising 20 schemes. The contracted schemes were spread throughout Northern Ireland and were divided into three technology bands. There were 6 wind schemes of around 2 MW DNC each, totalling 12.7 MW DNC; 5 sewage gas projects totalling 0.56 MW DNC; and 9 small-scale hydro

schemes totalling 2.4 MW DNC. At the end of 2002, 14 schemes were commissioned with a capacity of 15 MW DNC.

7.35   A second NI Order was made in 1996 for 10 schemes, totalling 16 MW DNC. These comprised 2 wind schemes, 2 hydro schemes, 2 biomass, 1 biogas, 2 landfill gas and 1 municipal and industrial waste scheme, as shown in Table 7.5. At the end of 2002, 5 schemes were commissioned with a capacity of 3 MW DNC.

Renewable sources used to generate electricity and heat (Table 7.6).
7.36   Between 2001 and 2002 there was a decrease of 9½ per cent in the input of renewable sources into electricity generation. Biofuels and wastes grew by 7 per cent, hydro by 18 per cent and wind by 30 per cent.

7.37   Compared with 5 years earlier total inputs to electricity generation have grown by 78 per cent aided by a doubling of the use of biofuels and wastes and an **88** per cent increase in the use of wind.

7.38   Table 7.6 also shows the contribution from renewables to heat generation. Here only a small share comes from geothermal and active solar heating and from various wastes, while the main contribution is from wood burning.

Technical notes and definitions

7.39   Energy derived from renewable sources is included in the aggregate energy tables in Chapter 1 of this Digest. The main energy tables (Tables 7.1 to 7.3) present figures in the common unit of energy, the tonne of oil equivalent, which is defined in Chapter 1 paragraph 1.24. The gross calorific values and conversion factors used to convert the data from original units are given on page 205 of Annex A and inside the back cover flap. The statistical methodologies and conversion factors are in line with those used by the International Energy Agency and the Statistical Office of the European Communities. Primary electricity contributions from hydro and wind are expressed in terms of an electricity supplied model (see Chapter 5, paragraph 5.25). Electrical capacities in this chapter are now quoted as Installed capacities. However, in Chapter 5 Declared Net Capacity (DNC) of renewables is used when calculating the overall UK generating capacity. DNC takes into account the intermittent nature of the power output from some renewable sources (see paragraph 7.73, below).

7.40   The various renewable energy sources are described in the following paragraphs. This section also provides details of the quality of information provided within each renewables area, and the progress made to improve the quality of this information.

Use of existing solar energy
7.41   Nearly all buildings make use of some passive solar energy because they have windows or roof lights, which allow in natural light and provide a view of the surroundings. This existing use of passive solar energy is making a substantial contribution to the energy demand in the UK building stock. Passive solar design, in which buildings are designed to enhance solar energy use, results in additional savings in energy. A study in 1990, on behalf of the Department of Trade and Industry, estimated that this existing use saves 12.6 million tonnes of oil equivalent per year in the United Kingdom. This figure reflects an estimate of the net useful energy flow (heat and lighting) across windows and other glazing in the United Kingdom building stock. The figure is very approximate and, as in previous years, has therefore not been included in the tables in this chapter.

Active solar heating
7.42   Active solar heating employs solar collectors to heat water mainly for domestic hot water systems but also for swimming pools and other applications. Updated figures have been obtained by FES (on behalf of the Department of Trade and Industry). For 2002 an estimated 55.2 GWh for domestic hot water generation replaces gas heating; for swimming pools, an estimated 78.5 GWh generation for 2001 replaces gas (45 per cent), oil (45 per cent) or electricity (10 per cent).

Photovoltaics
7.43   Photovoltaics is the direct conversion of solar radiation into direct current electricity by the interaction of light with the electrons in a semiconductor device or cell. There has been a significant increase in capacity and generation of PV over the last year due to increased support from the Government. There is a Major Photovoltaic Demonstration Programme offering grants for small, medium and large-scale installations which is encouraging a significant number of new projects. This was preceded by a two-phase Domestic Field Trial, which has supported the installation of approximately 200 kW in the first phase and 500 kW in the second phase, and the Large Scale Field Trial for Public Buildings, which should result in another 700-800 kW capacity.

Onshore wind power
7.44   A wind turbine extracts energy from the wind by means of a rotor fitted with aerodynamic-section blades using the lifting forces on the blades to turn the rotor primary shaft. This mechanical power is used to drive an electrical generator. The figures included for generation from wind turbines are based on the installed capacities, together with an average capacity factor for the United Kingdom or, where figures are available, on actual generation.

7.45   There have been a total of 302 wind projects awarded contracts under NFFO. Many of these are new projects, so this has resulted in a considerable increase in electricity generation from wind since 1990. At the end of 2002, there were 79 wind generation projects operational under NFFO. More are anticipated to be commissioned over the next 2-3 years. The figures for wind in this chapter cover all known schemes in the United Kingdom. Wind capacity in 2002 was a factor of 1.6 greater than the capacity of 5 years earlier, while electricity generated from wind is a factor of 1.9 greater over the same period. This is attributed to improvement in technologies together with the better siting of wind farms.

Offshore wind power

7.46   The UK's offshore wind resource is vast, with the potential to provide more than the UK's current demand for electricity. Offshore wind speeds are higher than those onshore (typically up to 0.5m/s higher 10 km offshore) and also less turbulent. However, elevated inland sites can have higher wind speeds.

7.47   Due to the higher costs of installing each turbine offshore it is expected that, in general, the machines will be larger than their onshore counterparts (2 MW and above). This is driven by economics, with larger machine more cost effective per unit of electricity generated. The larger turbines also experience higher wind speeds, because taller towers put the rotors into the stronger winds. In addition, onshore constraints such as planning, noise effects and visual impact are likely to be reduced offshore. There are 18 sites with pre-lease agreements for offshore wind farms from Crown Estates. Scroby Sands applied for consent in 2001, the first to do so, but North Hoyle is expected to be first to come on stream in autumn 2003.

Wave power

7.48   Waves in the oceans are created by the interaction of winds with the surface of the sea. Because of the direction of the prevailing winds and the size of the Atlantic Ocean, the United Kingdom has wave power levels, which are amongst the highest in the world. Previously (since 1985), the Department of Trade and Industry's shoreline programme has concentrated on an oscillating water column device on the Hebridean island of Islay. This 75 kW experimental prototype came on line in late 1991 and has now been decommissioned. Three wave schemes won contracts under the third SRO for a declared net capacity of 2 MW. One of these contract holders, Wavegen, has built a new 500kW scheme called the LIMPET near to the site of the prototype. This plant is now operating. The other concepts are still under development and testing and will be deployed over the next few years.

Large scale hydro

7.49   In hydro schemes the turbines that drive the electricity generators are powered by the direct action of water either from a reservoir or from the run of the river. Large-scale hydro covers plants belonging to companies with an aggregate hydro capacity of 5 MWe and over. Most of the plants are located in Scotland and Wales and mainly draw their water from high-level reservoirs with their own natural catchment areas. The schemes report their output to the Department of Trade and Industry. The coverage of these large-scale hydro figures is the same as that used in the tables in the Chapter 5 of this Digest. The data exclude pumped storage stations (see paragraph 5.47). In 2002 large-scale hydro generated 19 per cent more electricity than in 2001 because precipitation was higher.

Small scale hydro

7.50   Electricity generation schemes belonging to companies with an aggregate hydro capacity below 5 MWe are classified as small scale. These are schemes being used for either domestic/farm purposes or for sale to the local regional electricity company. Data given for generation are actual figures where available, but otherwise are estimated using a typical load factor (based on NFFO schemes actual data), or the design load factor, where known. The estimated figures for 1998 and 1997 have been calculated using a load factor of 36 per cent, while those for 1996 have been calculated using a load factor of 28 per cent to reflect the reduction of generation due to the reduced rainfall. A new survey of small scale hydro sites was carried out in 1999 giving a more detailed picture of the current situation that formed the basis for estimates in 2000; a revised load factor of 38 per cent was used for 1999 and a factor of 33 per cent for 2000, 2001 and 2002 data. This was largely based on data provided for NFFO schemes. Small-scale hydro capacity has risen by 5.6 MWe compared with 2001.

Geothermal aquifers
7.51   Aquifers containing water at elevated temperatures occur in some parts of the United Kingdom at between 1,500 and 3,000 metres below the surface. This water can be pumped to the surface and used, for example, in community heating schemes. There is currently only one scheme operating in the UK at Southampton.

Biofuels
(a)   Landfill gas
7.52   Landfill gas is a methane-rich biogas formed from the decomposition of organic material in landfill. The gas can be used to fuel reciprocating engines or turbines to generate electricity or used directly in kilns and boilers. In other countries, the gas has been cleaned to pipeline quality or used as a vehicle fuel. Data on landfill gas exploitation are provided from LAMMCOS, the LAndfill gas Monitoring, Modelling and COmmunication System. This is a landfill gas database maintained by FES and containing information on all existing landfill gas exploitation schemes. Landfill gas exploitation has benefited considerably from the NFFO and this can be seen from the large rise in the amount of electricity generated since 1992. Further commissioning of landfill gas projects under NFFO will continue to increase the amount of electricity generated from this technology. In 2002, 13 new schemes came on line under NFFO.

(b)   Sewage sludge digestion
7.53   In all sewage sludge digestion projects, some of the gas produced is used to maintain the optimum temperature for digestion. In addition, many use combined heat and power (CHP) systems. The electricity generated is either used on site or sold under the NFFO. Information from these projects was provided from the CHAPSTAT Database, which is compiled and maintained by FES on behalf of the Department of Trade and Industry (See Chapter 6).

(c)   Domestic wood combustion
7.54   Domestic wood use includes the use of logs in open fires, "AGA"-type cooker boilers and other wood burning stoves. The figure given is an approximate estimate based on a survey carried out in 1989. A survey to provide current information was undertaken for 2001/02. Unfortunately, the results proved inconclusive and estimates for domestic wood use remain unchanged.

(d)   Industrial wood combustion
7.55   In 1997, the industrial wood figure (which includes sawmill residues, furniture manufacturing waste etc.) was included as a separate category for the first time. This was due to the availability of better data as a result of a survey carried out in 1996 on wood fired combustion plants above 400 kW thermal input. A follow-up survey was subsequently carried out for 2000. This survey highlighted that there were fewer sites (174) operating than in 1996 due to the imposition of more stringent emissions control.

(e)   Short rotation coppice
7.56   Short rotation willow coppice development is now becoming well established with demonstration projects underway in Northern Ireland and England. Under Northern Ireland's second Non-Fossil Fuel Renewable Energy order for electricity, two projects were live at the end of 2002.

7.57   In England, Project ARBRE in South Yorkshire was contracted under NFFO 3 to generate 10 MW of electricity of which 8 MW were to be exported to the local grid. This project has run into difficulties and has recently been sold to new owners who are currently evaluating their options on taking the project forward.

(f)   Straw combustion

7.58   Straw can be burnt in high temperature boilers, designed for the efficient and controlled combustion of solid fuels and biomass to supply heat, hot water and hot air systems. There are large numbers of these small-scale batch-fed whole bale boilers. The figures given are estimates based partly on 1990 information and partly on a survey of straw-fired boilers carried out in 1993-94. A 31 MW straw fired power station near Ely, Cambridgeshire was commissioned in 2000 and has been exporting electricity since September of that year.

(g)   Waste combustion

7.59   Domestic, industrial and commercial wastes represent a significant resource for materials and energy recovery. Wastes may be combusted, as received, in purpose built incinerators or processed into a range of refuse derived fuels for both on-site and off-site utilisation. The paragraphs below describe various categories of waste combustion in greater detail.

7.60   Nineteen waste-to-energy plants were in operation in 2002 burning municipal solid waste (MSW), refuse derived fuel (RDF) and general industrial waste (GIW).

7.61   **Municipal solid waste combustion:** Information was provided from the refuse incinerator operators in the United Kingdom that practice energy recovery. This included both direct combustion of unprocessed MSW and the combustion of RDF. In the latter, process waste can be partially processed to produce coarse RDF which can then be burnt in a variety of ways. By further processing the refuse, including separating off the fuel fraction, compacting, drying and densifying, it is possible to produce an RDF pellet. This pellet has around 60 per cent of the gross calorific value of British coal.

7.62   Information on projects in this area was obtained from data collected, using the RESTATS questionnaire, for 2002. The generation from MSW has been split between biodegradable sources and non-biodegradable sources using information on calorific values of the constituent parts. Approximately 66 per cent of generation from MSW was estimated to be from biodegradable sources.

7.63   **General industrial waste combustion:** Certain wastes produced by industry and commerce can be used as a source of energy for industrial processes or space heating. These wastes include general waste from factories such as paper, cardboard, wood and plastics.

7.64   A survey conducted in 2001 has highlighted that although there are 6 waste-to-energy plants burning GIW, these are all MSW facilities. As no sites are solely burning GIW for heat or electricity generation, this feedstock is being handled under the MSW category.

7.65   **Specialised waste combustion:** Specialised wastes arise as a result of a particular activity or process. Materials in this category include scrap tyres, hospital wastes, poultry litter, meal and bone and farm waste digestion. The large tyre incineration plant with energy recovery did not generate in 2002. Although part of waste tyre combustion is of biodegradable waste, because there is no agreed method of calculating the small biodegradable content, all of the generation from waste tyres has been included under non-biodegradable wastes when calculating renewables eligible for the RO and RD in this chapter.

7.66   Information on hospital waste incineration is based on the 1999 RESTATS survey carried out by ETSU on behalf of the Department of Trade and Industry.

7.67   One poultry litter combustion project started generating electricity in 1992; a second began in 1993. Both of these are NFFO projects. In addition, a small-scale CHP scheme began generating towards the end of 1990 however this has now closed due to new emissions regulations. A further NFFO scheme started generating in 1998 at Thetford, and during 2000 an SRO scheme began to generate. During 2000, 2001 and 2002 one of the earlier poultry litter projects was fuelled mainly by meat and bone. A new poultry litter scheme became fully operational in 2001.

7.68   Information on farm waste digestion in the United Kingdom is based on a survey carried out during 1991-1992 with a follow-up study in 1996. There was a farm digestion project generating electricity under the NFFO; its output was included in the commodity balances but is has now ceased to operate. Data collected from the 1996 survey were used to derive estimates for 1997 through to 2002.

(g)   Co-firing of biomass with fossil fuels

7.69   Co-firing of biomass with fossil fuels is now eligible under the RO, the first time that any renewable energy initiative has included co-firing. As the purpose of this was to enable markets and supply chains for biomass to develop, and not to support coal fired power stations, the following limits are placed on co-firing:

- only electricity generated before 1 April 2011 will be eligible;
- from 1 April 2006 at least 75 per cent of the biomass must consist of energy crops.

7.70   Co-firing of biomass fuel in fossil fuel power stations is not a new idea. Technically it has been examined and proven to various degrees in power stations worldwide. It has not been considered at the large power station scale in the UK until fairly recently but a number of utilities are now investigating use of a range of biomass products at various coal fired power station sites. The ability of coal station furnaces to cope with the introduction of such biomass is dependent on a number of factors including biomass composition and furnace design. Current trials are planned to look at possible substitution at up to 20 per cent on a thermal basis. However, the scale of implicit fuel preparation and plant transport systems may limit the scope for substitution in addition to coal furnace considerations. The 2002 data for biomass include biomass use at one UK coal-fired power station, although other stations have begun to burn biomass in 2003.

Combined Heat and Power

7.71   A Combined Heat and Power (CHP) plant is an installation where there is a simultaneous generation of usable heat and power (usually electricity) in a single process. Some CHP installations are fuelled either wholly or partially by renewable sources of energy. The main renewable sources that are used for CHP are biofuels particularly sewage gas.

7.72   Chapter 6 of this Digest summarises information on the contribution made by CHP to the United Kingdom's energy requirements in 1998 to 2002 using the results of annual studies undertaken to identify all CHP schemes. Included in Tables 6.1 to 6.9 of that chapter is information on the contribution of renewable sources to CHP generation in each year from 1998 to 2002. Corresponding data for 1996 and 1997 are available on the DTI web site. The information contained in those tables is therefore a subset of the data contained within the tables presented in this chapter.

Capacity and load factor

7.73   The electrical capacities are given in Table 7.4 as installed capacities i.e. the maximum continuous rating of the generating sets in the stations. In Chapter 5 and in Chapter 7 of previous Digests DNC (Declared Net Capacity) is used, i.e. the maximum continuous rating of the generating sets in the stations, less the power consumed by the plant itself, and reduced by a specified factor to take into account the intermittent nature of the energy source e.g. 0.43 for wind and 0.33 for shoreline wave. DNC represents the nominal maximum capability of a generating set to supply electricity to consumers.

7.74   Plant load factors have been calculated in terms of installed capacity (i.e. the maximum continuous rating of the generating sets in the stations) and express the average hourly quantity of electricity generated as a percentage of the average capacity at the beginning and end of the year.

Contact :   Steve Dagnall, Future Energy Solutions
steve.dagnall@aeat.co.uk
01235 433580

Mike Janes, DTI, Statistician
mike.janes@dti.gsi.gov.uk
020-7215 5186

7.1 Commodity balances 2002
Renewables and waste

Thousand tonnes of oil equivalent

	Wood waste	Wood	Poultry litter, meat and bone, straw, farm waste and SRC(3)	Sewage gas	Landfill gas
Supply					
Production	266	204	355	184	892
Other sources	-	-	-	-	-
Imports	-	-	-	-	-
Exports	-	-	-	-	-
Marine bunkers	-	-	-	-	-
Stock change (1)	-	-	-	-	-
Transfers	-	-	-	-	-
Total supply	266	204	355	184	892
Statistical difference (2)	-	-	-	-	-
Total demand	266	204	355	184	892
Transformation	66	-	283	130	879
Electricity generation	-	-	283	130	879
Major power producers	-	-	184	-	-
Autogenerators	-	-	99	130	879
Heat generation	66	-	-	-	-
Petroleum refineries	-	-	-	-	-
Coke manufacture	-	-	-	-	-
Blast furnaces	-	-	-	-	-
Patent fuel manufacture	-	-	-	-	-
Other	-	-	-	-	-
Energy industry use	-	-	-	-	-
Electricity generation	-	-	-	-	-
Oil and gas extraction	-	-	-	-	-
Petroleum refineries	-	-	-	-	-
Coal extraction	-	-	-	-	-
Coke manufacture	-	-	-	-	-
Blast furnaces	-	-	-	-	-
Patent fuel manufacture	-	-	-	-	-
Pumped storage	-	-	-	-	-
Other	-	-	-	-	-
Losses	-	-	-	-	-
Final consumption	200	204	72	53	14
Industry	200	-	-	-	14
Unclassified	200	-	-	-	14
Iron and steel	-	-	-	-	-
Non-ferrous metals	-	-	-	-	-
Mineral products	-	-	-	-	-
Chemicals	-	-	-	-	-
Mechanical engineering, etc	-	-	-	-	-
Electrical engineering, etc	-	-	-	-	-
Vehicles	-	-	-	-	-
Food, beverages, etc	-	-	-	-	-
Textiles, leather, etc	-	-	-	-	-
Paper, printing, etc	-	-	-	-	-
Other industries	-	-	-	-	-
Construction	-	-	-	-	-
Transport	-	-	-	-	-
Air	-	-	-	-	-
Rail	-	-	-	-	-
Road	-	-	-	-	-
National navigation	-	-	-	-	-
Pipelines	-	-	-	-	-
Other	-	204	72	53	-
Domestic	-	204	-	-	-
Public administration	-	-	-	53	-
Commercial	-	-	-	-	-
Agriculture	-	-	72	-	-
Miscellaneous	-	-	-	-	-
Non energy use	-	-	-	-	-

(1) Stock fall (+), stock rise (-).
(2) Total supply minus total demand.
(3) SRC is short rotation coppice.
(4) Municipal solid waste, general industrial waste and hospital waste.
(5) The amount of shoreline wave included is less than 0.1 ktoe.

7.1 Commodity balances 2002 (continued)

Renewables and waste

Thousand tonnes of oil equivalent

Waste(4) and tyres	Geothermal and active solar heat	Hydro	Wind and wave (5)	Total renewables	
					Supply
763	17	412	108	3,201	Production
-	-	-	-	-	Other sources
-	-	-	-	-	Imports
-	-	-	-	-	Exports
-	-	-	-	-	Marine bunkers
-	-	-	-	-	Stock change (1)
-	-	-	-	-	Transfers
763	**17**	**412**	**108**	**3,201**	**Total supply**
-	-	-	-	-	**Statistical difference (2)**
763	**17**	**412**	**108**	**3,201**	**Total demand**
672	-	412	108	2,555	**Transformation**
672	-	412	108	2,484	Electricity generation
90	-	338	-	611	Major power producers
582	-	74	108	1,873	Autogenerators
-	-	-	-	66	Heat generation
-	-	-	-	-	Petroleum refineries
-	-	-	-	-	Coke manufacture
-	-	-	-	-	Blast furnaces
-	-	-	-	-	Patent fuel manufacture
-	-	-	-	-	Other
-	-	-	-	-	**Energy industry use**
-	-	-	-	-	Electricity generation
-	-	-	-	-	Oil and gas extraction
-	-	-	-	-	Petroleum refineries
-	-	-	-	-	Coal extraction
-	-	-	-	-	Coke manufacture
-	-	-	-	-	Blast furnaces
-	-	-	-	-	Patent fuel manufacture
-	-	-	-	-	Pumped storage
-	-	-	-	-	Other
-	-	-	-	-	**Losses**
91	**17**	**-**	**-**	**646**	**Final consumption**
6	-	-	-	214	**Industry**
6	-	-	-	214	Unclassified
-	-	-	-	-	Iron and steel
-	-	-	-	-	Non-ferrous metals
-	-	-	-	-	Mineral products
-	-	-	-	-	Chemicals
-	-	-	-	-	Mechanical engineering, etc
-	-	-	-	-	Electrical engineering, etc
-	-	-	-	-	Vehicles
-	-	-	-	-	Food, beverages, etc
-	-	-	-	-	Textiles, leather, etc
-	-	-	-	-	Paper, printing, etc
-	-	-	-	-	Other industries
-	-	-	-	-	Construction
-	-	-	-	-	**Transport**
-	-	-	-	-	Air
-	-	-	-	-	Rail
-	-	-	-	-	Road
-	-	-	-	-	National navigation
-	-	-	-	-	Pipelines
85	17	-	-	432	**Other**
23	17	-	-	244	Domestic
43	-	-	-	97	Public administration
-	-	-	-	-	Commercial
-	-	-	-	72	Agriculture
19	-	-	-	20	Miscellaneous
-	-	-	-	-	**Non energy use**

7.2 Commodity balances 2001
Renewables and waste

	Wood waste	Wood	Poultry litter, meat and bone, straw, farm waste and SRC(3)	Sewage gas	Landfill gas
Supply					
Production	265	204	352r	168	836
Other sources	-	-	-	-	-
Imports	-	-	-	-	-
Exports	-	-	-	-	-
Marine bunkers	-	-	-	-	-
Stock change (1)	-	-	-	-	-
Transfers	-	-	-	-	-
Total supply	265	204	352r	168	836
Statistical difference (2)	-	-	-	-	-
Total demand	265	204	352r	168	836
Transformation	71	-	280r	119	822
Electricity generation	-	-	280r	119	822
Major power producers	-	-	166r	-	-
Autogenerators	-	-	114r	119	822
Heat generation	71	-	-	-	-
Petroleum refineries	-	-	-	-	-
Coke manufacture	-	-	-	-	-
Blast furnaces	-	-	-	-	-
Patent fuel manufacture	-	-	-	-	-
Other	-	-	-	-	-
Energy industry use	-	-	-	-	-
Electricity generation	-	-	-	-	-
Oil and gas extraction	-	-	-	-	-
Petroleum refineries	-	-	-	-	-
Coal extraction	-	-	-	-	-
Coke manufacture	-	-	-	-	-
Blast furnaces	-	-	-	-	-
Patent fuel manufacture	-	-	-	-	-
Pumped storage	-	-	-	-	-
Other	-	-	-	-	-
Losses	-	-	-	-	-
Final consumption	194	204	72	49	14
Industry	194	-	-	-	14
Unclassified	194	-	-	-	14
Iron and steel	-	-	-	-	-
Non-ferrous metals	-	-	-	-	-
Mineral products	-	-	-	-	-
Chemicals	-	-	-	-	-
Mechanical engineering, etc	-	-	-	-	-
Electrical engineering, etc	-	-	-	-	-
Vehicles	-	-	-	-	-
Food, beverages, etc	-	-	-	-	-
Textiles, leather, etc	-	-	-	-	-
Paper, printing, etc	-	-	-	-	-
Other industries	-	-	-	-	-
Construction	-	-	-	-	-
Transport	-	-	-	-	-
Air	-	-	-	-	-
Rail	-	-	-	-	-
Road	-	-	-	-	-
National navigation	-	-	-	-	-
Pipelines	-	-	-	-	-
Other	-	204	72	49	-
Domestic	-	204	-	-	-
Public administration	-	-	-	49	-
Commercial	-	-	-	-	-
Agriculture	-	-	72	-	-
Miscellaneous	-	-	-	-	-
Non energy use	-	-	-	-	-

(1) Stock fall (+), stock rise (-).
(2) Total supply minus total demand.
(3) SRC is short rotation coppice.

(4) Municipal solid waste, general industrial waste and hospital waste.
(5) The amount of shoreline wave included is less than 0.1 ktoe.

7.2 Commodity balances 2001 (continued)
Renewables and waste

Thousand tonnes of oil equivalent

Waste(4) and tyres	Geothermal and active solar heat	Hydro	Wind and wave (5)	Total renewables	
					Supply
703r	14	349	83	2,973r	Production
-	-	-	-	-	Other sources
-	-	-	-	-	Imports
-	-	-	-	-	Exports
-	-	-	-	-	Marine bunkers
-	-	-	-	-	Stock change (1)
-	-	-	-	-	Transfers
703r	14	349	83	2,973r	**Total supply**
-	-	-	-	-	**Statistical difference (2)**
703r	14	349	83	2,973r	**Total demand**
619	-	349	83	2,343r	**Transformation**
619	-	349	83	2,272r	Electricity generation
88	-	277	-	530r	Major power producers
531	-	72	83	1,742r	Autogenerators
-	-	-	-	71	Heat generation
-	-	-	-	-	Petroleum refineries
-	-	-	-	-	Coke manufacture
-	-	-	-	-	Blast furnaces
-	-	-	-	-	Patent fuel manufacture
-	-	-	-	-	Other
-	-	-	-	-	**Energy industry use**
-	-	-	-	-	Electricity generation
-	-	-	-	-	Oil and gas extraction
-	-	-	-	-	Petroleum refineries
-	-	-	-	-	Coal extraction
-	-	-	-	-	Coke manufacture
-	-	-	-	-	Blast furnaces
-	-	-	-	-	Patent fuel manufacture
-	-	-	-	-	Pumped storage
-	-	-	-	-	Other
-	-	-	-	-	**Losses**
84	14	-	-	631	**Final consumption**
6	-	-	-	214	**Industry**
6	-	-	-	214	Unclassified
-	-	-	-	-	Iron and steel
-	-	-	-	-	Non-ferrous metals
-	-	-	-	-	Mineral products
-	-	-	-	-	Chemicals
-	-	-	-	-	Mechanical engineering, etc
-	-	-	-	-	Electrical engineering, etc
-	-	-	-	-	Vehicles
-	-	-	-	-	Food, beverages, etc
-	-	-	-	-	Textiles, leather, etc
-	-	-	-	-	Paper, printing, etc
-	-	-	-	-	Other industries
-	-	-	-	-	Construction
-	-	-	-	-	**Transport**
-	-	-	-	-	Air
-	-	-	-	-	Rail
-	-	-	-	-	Road
-	-	-	-	-	National navigation
-	-	-	-	-	Pipelines
77r	14	-	-	417	**Other**
24	14	-	-	242	Domestic
43	-	-	-	93	Public administration
-	-	-	-	-	Commercial
-	-	-	-	72	Agriculture
10	-	-	-	10	Miscellaneous
-	-	-	-	-	**Non energy use**

7.3 Commodity balances 2000
Renewables and waste

	Wood waste	Wood	Poultry litter, meat and bone, straw, farm waste and SRC(3)	Sewage gas	Landfill gas
Supply					
Production	299	204	250r	169	731
Other sources	-	-	-	-	-
Imports	-	-	-	-	-
Exports	-	-	-	-	-
Marine bunkers	-	-	-	-	-
Stock change (1)	-	-	-	-	-
Transfers	-	-	-	-	-
Total supply	299	204	250r	169	731
Statistical difference (2)	-	-	-	-	-
Total demand	299	204	250r	169	731
Transformation	105	-	178r	120	718
Electricity generation	-	-	178r	120	718
Major power producers	-	-	143r	-	-
Autogenerators	-	-	35r	120	718
Heat generation	105	-	-	-	-
Petroleum refineries	-	-	-	-	-
Coke manufacture	-	-	-	-	-
Blast furnaces	-	-	-	-	-
Patent fuel manufacture	-	-	-	-	-
Other	-	-	-	-	-
Energy industry use	-	-	-	-	-
Electricity generation	-	-	-	-	-
Oil and gas extraction	-	-	-	-	-
Petroleum refineries	-	-	-	-	-
Coal extraction	-	-	-	-	-
Coke manufacture	-	-	-	-	-
Blast furnaces	-	-	-	-	-
Patent fuel manufacture	-	-	-	-	-
Pumped storage	-	-	-	-	-
Other	-	-	-	-	-
Losses	-	-	-	-	-
Final consumption	194	204	72	48	14
Industry	194	-	-	-	14
Unclassified	194	-	-	-	14
Iron and steel	-	-	-	-	-
Non-ferrous metals	-	-	-	-	-
Mineral products	-	-	-	-	-
Chemicals	-	-	-	-	-
Mechanical engineering, etc	-	-	-	-	-
Electrical engineering, etc	-	-	-	-	-
Vehicles	-	-	-	-	-
Food, beverages, etc	-	-	-	-	-
Textiles, leather, etc	-	-	-	-	-
Paper, printing, etc	-	-	-	-	-
Other industries	-	-	-	-	-
Construction	-	-	-	-	-
Transport	-	-	-	-	-
Air	-	-	-	-	-
Rail	-	-	-	-	-
Road	-	-	-	-	-
National navigation	-	-	-	-	-
Pipelines	-	-	-	-	-
Other	-	204	72	48	-
Domestic	-	204	-	-	-
Public administration	-	-	-	48	-
Commercial	-	-	-	-	-
Agriculture	-	-	72	-	-
Miscellaneous	-	-	-	-	-
Non energy use	-	-	-	-	-

(1) Stock fall (+), stock rise (-).
(2) Total supply minus total demand.
(3) SRC is short rotation coppice.

(4) Municipal solid waste, general industrial waste and hospital waste.

7.3 Commodity balances 2000 (continued)

Renewables and waste

Thousand tonnes of oil equivalent

Waste(4) and tyres	Geothermal & active solar heat	Hydro	Wind	Total renewables	
					Supply
647r	12	437	81	2,831r	Production
-	-	-	-	-	Other sources
-	-	-	-	-	Imports
-	-	-	-	-	Exports
-	-	-	-	-	Marine bunkers
-	-	-	-	-	Stock change (1)
-	-	-	-	-	Transfers
647r	12	437	81	2,831r	**Total supply**
-	-	-	-	-	**Statistical difference** (2)
647r	12	437	81	2,831r	**Total demand**
569r	-	437	81	2,209r	**Transformation**
569r	-	437	81	2,104r	Electricity generation
108r	-	372	-	624r	Major power producers
461r	-	65	81	1,480r	Autogenerators
-	-	-	-	105	Heat generation
-	-	-	-	-	Petroleum refineries
-	-	-	-	-	Coke manufacture
-	-	-	-	-	Blast furnaces
-	-	-	-	-	Patent fuel manufacture
-	-	-	-	-	Other
-	-	-	-	-	**Energy industry use**
-	-	-	-	-	Electricity generation
-	-	-	-	-	Oil and gas extraction
-	-	-	-	-	Petroleum refineries
-	-	-	-	-	Coal extraction
-	-	-	-	-	Coke manufacture
-	-	-	-	-	Blast furnaces
-	-	-	-	-	Patent fuel manufacture
-	-	-	-	-	Pumped storage
-	-	-	-	-	Other
-	-	-	-	-	**Losses**
78	12	-	-	622	**Final consumption**
6r	-	-	-	213	**Industry**
6r	-	-	-	213	Unclassified
-	-	-	-	-	Iron and steel
-	-	-	-	-	Non-ferrous metals
-	-	-	-	-	Mineral products
-	-	-	-	-	Chemicals
-	-	-	-	-	Mechanical engineering, etc
-	-	-	-	-	Electrical engineering, etc
-	-	-	-	-	Vehicles
-	-	-	-	-	Food, beverages, etc
-	-	-	-	-	Textiles, leather, etc
-	-	-	-	-	Paper, printing, etc
-	-	-	-	-	Other industries
-	-	-	-	-	Construction
-	-	-	-	-	**Transport**
-	-	-	-	-	Air
-	-	-	-	-	Rail
-	-	-	-	-	Road
-	-	-	-	-	National navigation
-	-	-	-	-	Pipelines
72r	12	-	-	409	**Other**
21	12	-	-	238	Domestic
40	-	-	-	88	Public administration
-	-	-	-	-	Commercial
-	-	-	-	72	Agriculture
11	-	-	-	11	Miscellaneous
-	-	-	-	-	**Non energy use**

7.4 Capacity of, and electricity generated from, renewable sources[1]

	1998	1999	2000	2001	2002
Installed Capacity (MWe) [11]					
Wind:					
Onshore	331.3	357.0	408.0	423.5	530.6
Offshore	-	-	3.8	3.8	3.8
Shoreline wave	-	-	0.5	0.5	0.5
Solar photovoltaics	0.6	1.2	2.0	2.8	4.2
Hydro:					
Small scale	171.1	176.7	183.6	188.7	194.2
Large scale [3]	1,413.0	1,413.0	1,419.0	1,440.0	1,383.0
Biofuels and wastes:					
Landfill gas	245.1	343.3	425.1	464.8	472.9
Sewage sludge digestion	89.8	91.3	85.3	85.0	96.0
Municipal solid waste combustion	204.1	229.6	253.2	260.0	278.9
Other [4]	108.0	108.0	157.0	157.0	165.7
Total biofuels and wastes	647.0	772.2	920.6	966.8	1,013.5
Total	**2,563.0**	**2,720.2**	**2,937.4**	**3,026.0**	**3,129.9**
Generation (GWh)					
Wind:					
Onshore [5]	877	850	945	960	1,251
Offshore [2]	-	-	1	5	5
Solar photovoltaics	-	1	1	2	3
Hydro:					
Small scale [5]	206	207	214	210	204
Large scale [3]	4,911	5,128	4,871	3,845	4,584
Biofuels:					
Landfill gas	1,185	1,703	2,188	2,507	2,679
Sewage sludge digestion	386	410	367	363	397
Municipal solid waste combustion [6]	849	856	840r	929r	958
Other [7]	234	460	438r	767r	870
Total biofuels	2,654	3,429	3,830r	4,576r	4,904
Wastes [8]	583	558	519r	479r	494
Total biofuels and wastes	3,237	3,987	4,348r	5,054r	5,397
Total generation [1]	**9,231**	**10,174**	**10,383r**	**10,077r**	**11,444**
Total renewables generation on an obligation basis [9]	**2,888**	**3,630**	**4,151r**	**4,885r**	**5,508**
Total renewables generation on a directive basis [9]	**8,648**	**9,615**	**9,862r**	**11,338r**	**12,618**
Load factors (per cent) [10]					
Onshore wind	30.7	28.2	28.2	26.4	29.9
Hydro	36.8	38.4	36.4	28.7	34.1
Biofuels and wastes	53.9r	55.2r	51.6r	55.3r	56.5
Total	**42.5r**	**44.0r**	**41.9r**	**38.6r**	**42.4**

(1) Includes some waste of fossil fuel origin.
(2) In 2000, 2001 and 2002 includes less than 0.05 GWh of electricity from shoreline wave.
(3) Excluding pumped storage stations. Capacities are as at the end of December.
(4) Includes the use of farm waste digestion, waste tyre, poultry litter, meat and bone and straw combustion, and short rotation coppice.
(5) Actual generation figures are given where available, but otherwise are estimated using a typical load factor or the design load factor, where known.
(6) Biodegradable part only.
(7) Includes the use of farm waste digestion, poultry litter combustion, meat and bone combustion, straw and short rotation coppice.
(8) Non-biodegradable part of municipal solid waste plus waste tyres.
(9) See paragraphs 7.7 and 7.8 for definitions.
(10) Load factors are calculated based on installed capacity at the beginning and the end of the year - see paragraph 7.74.
(11) Installed capacity is now shown in this table in place of DNC which was used in previous years - see paragraph 7.73.

7.5 Renewable orders and operational capacity

	Technology band	Contracted projects		Live projects operational at 31 December 2002 (1)	
		Number	Capacity MW	Number	Capacity MW
England and Wales					
NFFO - 1 (1990)	Hydro	26	11.85	9	2.95
	Landfill gas	25	35.50	8	16.56
	Municipal and industrial waste	4	40.63	4	44.62
	Other	4	45.48	2	25.38
	Sewage gas	7	6.45	2	8.67
	Wind	9	12.21	1	2.06
	Total (2)	**75**	**152.11**	**26**	**100.24**
NFFO - 2 (late 1991)	Hydro	12	10.86	1	0.07
	Landfill gas	28	48.45	13	22.33
	Municipal and industrial waste	10	271.48	2	31.50
	Other	4	30.15	1	12.50
	Sewage gas	19	26.86	16	14.22
	Wind	49	84.43	23	52.45
	Total (2)	**122**	**472.23**	**56**	**133.07**
NFFO - 3 (1995)	Energy crops and agricultural and forestry waste - gasification	3	19.06		
	Energy crops and agricultural and forestry waste - other	6	103.81	2	69.50
	Hydro	15	14.48	8	11.74
	Landfill gas	42	82.07	42	82.07
	Municipal and industrial waste	20	241.87	6	77.42
	Wind - large	31	145.92	10	41.02
	Wind - small	24	19.71	11	10.84
	Total	**141**	**626.90**	**79**	**292.58**
NFFO - 4 (1997)	Hydro	31	13.22	8	2.30
	Landfill gas	70	173.68	55	141.73
	Municipal and industrial waste - CHP	10	115.29	4	33.48
	Municipal and industrial waste - fluidised bed combustion	6	125.93		
	Wind - large	48	330.36	4	12.97
	Wind - small	17	10.33	5	3.27
	Anaerobic digestion of agricultural waste	6	6.58	1	1.43
	Energy crops and forestry waste gasification	7	67.34		
	Total	**195**	**842.72**	**77**	**195.18**
NFFO - 5 (1998)	Hydro	22	8.87	3	0.64
	Landfill gas	141	313.73	58	114.50
	Municipal and industrial waste	22	415.75		
	Municipal and industrial waste - CHP	7	69.97		
	Wind - large	33	340.16		
	Wind - small	36	28.67	4	3.65
	Total	**261**	**1,177.15**	**65**	**118.79**
NFFO Total		**794**	**3,271.11**	**303**	**839.86**

7.5 Renewable orders and operational capacity (continued)

Technology band	Contracted projects		Live projects operational at 31 December 2002 (1)	
	Number	Capacity MW	Number	Capacity MW
Scotland				
SRO - 1 (1994) Biomass	1	9.80	1	9.80
Hydro	15	17.25	8	7.82
Waste to Energy	2	3.78	2	3.78
Wind	12	45.60	7	25.13
Total	**30**	**76.43**	**18**	**46.53**
SRO - 2 (1997) Biomass	1	2.00		
Hydro	9	12.36	2	1.46
Waste to Energy	9	56.05	4	15.00
Wind	7	43.63	5	31.29
Total	**26**	**114.04**	**11**	**47.75**
SRO - 3 (1999) Biomass	1	12.90		
Hydro	5	3.90		
Waste to Energy	16	49.11	4	10.30
Wave	3	2.00	1	0.20
Wind - large	11	63.43	1	8.29
Wind - small	17	14.06	3	2.47
Total	**53**	**145.40**	**9**	**21.26**
SRO Total	**109**	**335.87**	**38**	**115.54**
Northern Ireland				
NI NFFO - 1 (1994) Hydro	9	2.37	8	2.33
Sewage gas	5	0.56		
Wind	6	12.66	6	12.66
Total	**20**	**15.60**	**14**	**14.99**
NI NFFO - 2 (1996) Biogas	1	0.25		
Biomass	2	0.30	2	0.30
Hydro	2	0.25	1	0.08
Landfill gas	2	6.25		
Municipal and industrial waste	1	6.65		
Wind	2	2.57	2	2.57
Total	**10**	**16.27**	**5**	**2.95**
NI NFFO Total	**30**	**31.87**	**19**	**17.94**
All NFFO and equivalents	**933**	**3,638.85**	**360**	**973.34**

(1) Sites that have closed and sites that are not currently using renewables as fuel have been excluded.

(2) The NFPA reported that at the end of December 2002 417 sites totalling 1,053.38 MW had gone live under NFFO, but this includes, all NFFO-1 and NFFO-2 sites for England and Wales, some of which have closed or are not currently using renewables as fuels. The following table compares the totals for live projects, above, with the overall NFFO total:

	Number	MW
All NFFO and equivalents	360	973.34
NFFO-1 no longer classed as live and operational	33	40.77
NFFO-2 no longer classed as live and operational	24	39.29
All live NFFO and equivalents	417	1,053.38

RENEWABLES

7.6 Renewable sources used to generate electricity and heat[1][2]

Thousand tonnes of oil equivalent

	1998	1999	2000	2001	2002
Used to generate electricity (3)					
Wind:					
Onshore	75.4	73.1	81.3	82.6r	107.6
Offshore	-	-	0.1	0.4	0.4
Solar photovoltaics	-	0.1	0.1	0.2	0.2
Hydro:					
Small scale	17.7	17.8	18.4	18.1	17.5
Large scale (4)	422.3	441.0	418.8	330.7	394.2
Biofuels and wastes:					
Landfill gas	388.8	558.4	717.6	822.2	878.5
Sewage sludge digestion	126.5	134.6	120.4	119.0	130.3
Municipal solid waste combustion (5)	346.5	345.0	350.1r	408.7r	443.7
Other (6)	76.3	157.0	177.9r	279.6r	283.3
Wastes (7)	273.8	238.5	219.4r	210.6r	228.6
Total biofuels and wastes	1,211.8	1,433.6	1,585.3r	1,840.1r	1,964.4
Total	**1,727.2**	**1,965.5**	**2,104.0r**	**2,272.0r**	**2,484.3**
Used to generate heat					
Active solar heating	9.1	9.4	11.1	13.2	16.1
Biofuels and wastes:					
Landfill gas	13.6	13.6	13.6	13.6	13.6
Sewage sludge digestion	54.1	54.2	48.3	49.4	53.4
Wood combustion - domestic	204.2	204.2	204.2	204.2	204.2
Wood combustion - industrial	436.9	367.7	298.6	264.6	265.6
Straw combustion, farm waste digestion and short rotation coppice	72.0	72.2	72.2	72.2	72.2
Municipal solid waste combustion (5)	24.1	32.0	40.6	46.5	53.8
Other (8)	40.6	37.5	37.3	37.1	37.1
Total biofuels and wastes	845.6	781.4	714.6	687.4	699.9
Geothermal aquifers	0.8	0.8	0.8	0.8	0.8
Total	**855.5**	**791.6**	**726.5**	**701.5**	**716.8**
Total use of renewable sources					
Solar heating and photovoltaics	9.1	9.5	11.2	13.4	16.3
Onshore and offshore wind	75.4	73.1	81.3r	83.0r	108.0
Hydro	440.0	458.8	437.3r	348.7r	411.7
Biofuels and wastes	2,057.4	2,214.9	2,299.9r	2,527.6r	2,664.3
Geothermal aquifers	0.8	0.8	0.8	0.8	0.8
Total	**2,582.7**	**2,757.1**	**2,830.5r**	**2,973.5r**	**3,201.1**

(1) Includes some waste of fossil fuel origin.

(2) See paragraphs 7.39 to 7.74 for technical notes and definitions of the categories used in this table

(3) For wind, solar PV and hydro, the figures represent the energy content of the electricity supplied but for biofuels the figures represent the ene content of the fuel used.

(4) Excluding pumped storage stations.

(5) Biodegradable part only.

(6) Includes electricity from farm waste digestion, poultry litter combustion, meat and bone combustion, straw and short rotation coppice.

(7) Non-biodegradable part of municipal solid waste plus waste tyres.

(8) Includes heat from waste tyre combustion, hospital waste combustion, and general industrial waste combustion.

Digest of United Kingdom Energy Statistics
2003

Annexes

Annex A: **Energy and commodity balances, conversion factors and calorific values**

Annex B: **Glossary**

Annex C: **Further sources**

Annex D: **Major events in the Energy Industry, 2001-2003**

Department of Trade and Industry

Annex A

Energy and commodity balances, conversion factors and calorific values

Balance principles

A.1　This Annex outlines the principles behind the balance presentation of energy statistics. It covers these in general terms. Fuel specific details are given in the appropriate chapters of this publication.

A.2　Balances are divided into two types, each of which performs a different function.

a) *commodity balance* – a balance for each energy commodity that uses the units usually associated with that commodity. By using a single column of figures, it shows the flow of the commodity from its sources of supply through to its final use. Commodity balances are presented in the individual fuel chapters of this publication.

b) *energy balance* - presents the commodity balances in a common unit and places them alongside one another in a manner that shows the dependence of the supply of one commodity on another. This is useful as some commodities are manufactured from others. The layout of the energy balance also differs slightly from the commodity balance. The energy balance format is used in Chapter 1.

A.3　Energy commodities can be either primary or secondary. Primary energy commodities are drawn (extracted or captured) from natural reserves or flows, whereas secondary commodities are produced from primary energy commodities. Crude oil and coal are examples of primary commodities, whilst petrol and coke are secondary commodities manufactured from them. For balance purposes, electricity may be considered to be both primary electricity (for example, hydro, wind) or secondary (produced from steam turbines using steam from the combustion of fuels).

A.4　Both commodity and energy balances show the flow of the commodity from its production, extraction or import through to its final use.

A.5　A simplified model of the commodity flow underlying the balance structure is given in Chart A.1. It illustrates how primary commodities may be used directly and/or be transformed into secondary commodities. The secondary fuels then enter final consumption or may also be transformed into another energy commodity (for example, electricity produced from fuel oil). To keep the diagram simple these "second generation" flows have not been shown.

A.6　The arrows at the top of the chart represent flows to and from the "pools" of primary and secondary commodities, from imports and exports and, in the case of the primary pool, extraction from reserves (eg the production of coal, gas and crude oil).

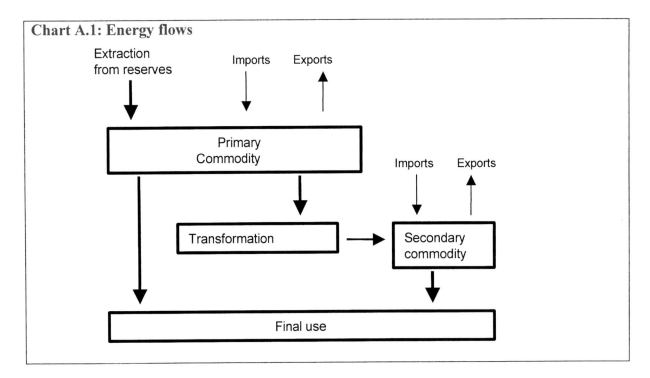

Chart A.1: Energy flows

Extraction from reserves

Imports

Exports

Primary Commodity

Imports

Exports

Transformation → Secondary commodity

Final use

Commodity balances (Tables 2.1 to 2.6, 3.1 to 3.6, 4.1, 5.1, and 7.1 to 7.3)
A.7   A commodity balance comprises a supply section and a demand section. The supply section gives available sources of supply (ie exports are subtracted). The demand section is divided into a transformation section, a section showing uses in the energy industries (other than for transformation) and a section covering uses by final consumers for energy or non-energy purposes. Final consumption for energy purposes is divided into use by sector of economic activity. The section breakdowns are described below.

Supply

Production
A.8   Production, within the commodity balance, covers indigenous production (extraction or capture of primary commodities) and generation or manufacture of secondary commodities. Production is always gross, that is, it includes the quantities used during the extraction or manufacturing process.

Other sources
A.9   Production from other sources covers sources of supply that do not represent "new" supply. These may be recycled products, recovered fuels (slurry or waste coal), or electricity from pumped storage plants. The production of these quantities will have been reported in an earlier accounting period or have already been reported in the current period of account. Exceptionally, the *Other sources* row in the commodity balances for ethane, propane and butane is used to receive transfers of these hydrocarbons from gas stabilisation plants at North Sea terminals. In this manner, the supplies of primary ethane, propane and butane from the North Sea are combined with the production of these gases in refineries, so that the disposals may be presented together in the balances.

Imports and exports
A.10   The figures for imports and exports relate to energy commodities moving into or out of the United Kingdom as part of transactions involving United Kingdom companies. Exported commodities are produced in the United Kingdom and imported commodities are for use within the United

Kingdom (although some may be re-exported before or after transformation). The figures thus exclude commodities either exported from or imported into HM Customs bonded areas or warehouses. These areas, although part of the United Kingdom, are regarded as being outside of the normal United Kingdom's customs boundary, and so goods entering into or leaving them are not counted as part of the statistics on trade used in the balances.

A.11   Similarly, commodities that only pass through the United Kingdom on their way to a final destination in another country are also excluded. However, for gas these transit flows are included because it is difficult to identify this quantity separately, without detailed knowledge of the contract information covering the trade. This means that for gas, there is some over statement of the level of imports and exports, but the net flows are correct.

A.12   The convention in these balances is that exports are shown with a negative sign.

Marine bunkers
A.13   These are deliveries of fuels (usually fuel oil or gas oil) to ships of any flag (including the United Kingdom) for consumption during the voyage to other countries. Marine bunkers are treated rather like exports and shown with a negative sign.

Stock changes
A.14   Additions to (- sign) and withdrawals from stocks (+ sign) held by producers and transformation industries correspond to withdrawals from and additions to supply, respectively.

Transfers
A.15   There are several reasons why quantities may be transferred from one commodity balance to another:
- a commodity may no longer meet the original specification and be reclassified;
- the name of the commodity may change through a change in use;
- to show quantities returned to supply from consumers. These may be by-products of the use of commodities as raw materials rather than fuels.

A.16   A quantity transferred from a balance is shown with a negative sign to represent a withdrawal from supply and with a positive sign in the receiving commodity balance representing an addition to its supply.

Total supply
A.17   The total supply available for national use is obtained by summing the flows above this entry in the balance.

Total demand
A.18   The various figures for the disposals and/or consumption of the commodities are summed to provide a measure of the demand for them. The main categories or sectors of demand are described in paragraphs A.32 to A.42.

Statistical difference
A.19   Any excess of supply over demand is shown as a statistical difference. A negative figure indicates that demand exceeds supply. Statistical differences arise when figures are gathered from a variety of independent sources and reflect differences in timing, in definition of coverage of the activity, or in commodity definition. Differences also arise for methodological reasons in the measurement of the flow of the commodity eg if there are differences between the volumes recorded by the gas producing companies and the gas transporting companies. A non-zero statistical difference

is normal and, provided that it is not too large, is preferable to a statistical difference of zero as this suggests that a data provider has adjusted a figure to balance the account.

Transformation

A.20   The transformation sector of the balance covers those processes and activities that transform the original primary (and sometimes secondary) commodity into a form which is better suited for specific uses than the original form. Most of the transformation activities correspond to particular energy industries whose main business is to manufacture the product associated with them. Certain activities involving transformation take place to make products that are only partly used for energy needs (coke oven coke) or are by-products of other manufacturing processes (coke oven and blast furnace gases). However, as these products and by-products are then used, at least in part, for their energy content they are included in the balance system.

A.21 The figures given under the activity headings of this sector represent the quantities used for transformation. The production of the secondary commodities will be shown in the *Production* row of the corresponding commodity balances.

Electricity generation

A.22   The quantities of fuels burned for the generation of electricity are shown in their commodity balances under this heading. The activity is divided into two parts, covering the major power producers (for whom the main business is the generation of electricity for sale) and autogenerators (whose main business is not electricity generation but who produce electricity for their own needs and may also sell surplus quantities). The amounts of fuels shown in the balance represent the quantities consumed for the gross generation of electricity. Where a generator uses combined heat and power plant, the figures include only the part of the fuel use corresponding to the electricity generated.

A.23   In relation to autogenerators' data, the figures for quantities of fuel used for electricity generation appear under the appropriate fuel headings in the *Transformation* sector heading for *Autogenerators,* whilst the electricity generated appears in the *Electricity* column under *Production.* A breakdown of the information according to the branch of industry in which the generation occurs is not shown in the balance but is given in Chapter 1, Table 1.9. The figures for energy commodities consumed by the industry branches shown under final consumption include all use of electricity, but exclude the fuels combusted by the industry branches to generate the electricity.

Heat generation

A.24   The quantities of fuel burned to generate heat that is sold under the provision of a contract to a third party are shown in their commodity balances under this heading. It includes heat that is generated and sold by combined heat and power plants and by community heating schemes (also called district heating).

Petroleum refineries

A.25   Crude oil, natural gas liquids and other oils needed by refineries for the manufacture of finished petroleum products are shown under this heading.

Coke manufacture and blast furnaces

A.26   Quantities of coal for coke ovens and all fuels used within blast furnaces are shown under this heading. The consumption of fuels for heating coke ovens and the blast air for blast furnaces are shown under "Energy industry use".

Patent fuel manufacture

A.27   The coals and other solid fuels used for the manufacture of solid patent fuels are reported under this heading.

Other

A.28   Any minor transformation activities not specified elsewhere are captured under this heading.

Energy industry use

A.29   Consumption by both extraction and transformation industries to support the transformation process (but not for transformation itself) are included here according to the energy industry concerned. Typical examples are the consumption of electricity in power plants (eg for lighting, compressors and cooling systems) and the use of extracted gases on oil and gas platforms for compressors, pumps and other uses. The headings in this sector are identical to those used in the transformation sector with the exception of *Pumped storage*. In this case, the electricity used to pump the water to the reservoir is reported.

Losses

A.30   This heading covers the intrinsic losses that occur during the transmission and distribution of electricity and gas (including manufactured gases). Other metering and accounting differences for gas and electricity are within the statistical difference, as are undeclared losses in other commodities.

Final consumption

A.31   *Final consumption* covers both final energy consumption (by different consuming sectors) and the use of energy commodities for non-energy purposes, that is *Non energy use*. Final consumption occurs when the commodities used are not for transformation into secondary commodities. The energy concerned disappears from the account after use. Any fuel used for electricity generation by final consumers is identified and reported separately within the transformation sector. When an enterprise generates electricity, the figure for final consumption of the industrial sector to which the enterprise belongs includes its use of the electricity it generates itself (as well as supplies of electricity it purchases from others) but does not include the fuel used to generate that electricity.

A.32   The classification of consumers according to their main business follows, as far as practicable, the *Standard Industrial Classification (SIC1992)*. The qualifications to, and constraints on, the classification are described in the technical notes to Chapter 1, paragraphs 1.24 to 1.58. Table 1E in Chapter 1 shows the breakdown of final consumers used, and how this corresponds to the SIC1992.

Industry

A.33   Two sectors of industry (iron and steel and chemicals) require special mention because the activities they undertake fall across the transformation, final consumption and non-energy classifications used for the balances. Also, the data permitting an accurate allocation of fuel use within each of these major divisions are not readily available.

Iron and steel

A.34   The iron and steel industry is a heavy energy user for transformation and final consumption activities. Figures shown under final consumption for this industry branch reflect the amounts that remain after quantities used for transformation and energy sector own use have been subtracted from the industry's total energy requirements. Use of fuels for transformation by the industry may be identified within the transformation sector of the commodity balances.

A.35   The amounts of coal used for coke manufacture by the iron and steel industry are in the transformation sector of the coal balance. Included in this figure is the amount of coal used for coke manufacture by the companies outside of the iron and steel industry, ie solid fuel manufacturers. The corresponding production of coke and coke oven gas may be found in the commodity balances for these products. The use of coke in blast furnaces is shown in the commodity balance for coke, and the gases produced from blast furnaces and the associated basic oxygen steel furnaces are shown in the production row of the commodity balance for blast furnace gas.

A.36   Fuels used for electricity generation by the industry are included in the figures for electricity generation by autogenerators and are not distinguishable as being used by the iron and steel sector in the balances. Electricity generation and fuel used for this by broad industry group are given in Table 1.9.

A.37   Fuels used to support coke manufacture and blast furnace gas production are included in the quantities shown under *Energy industry use*. These gases and other fuels do not enter coke ovens or blast furnaces, but are used to heat the ovens and the blast air supplied to furnaces.

Chemicals
A.38   The petro-chemical industry uses hydrocarbon fuels (mostly oil products and gases) as feedstock for the manufacture of its products. Distinguishing the energy use of delivered fuels from their non-energy use is complicated by the absence of detailed information. The procedures adopted to estimate the use are described in paragraphs A.41 and A.42 under *Non energy use*.

Transport
A.39   Figures under this heading are almost entirely quantities used strictly for transport purposes. However, the figures recorded against road transport usually include some fuel that is actually consumed in some "off-road" activities. Similarly, figures for railway fuels include some amounts of burning oil not used directly for transport purposes. Transport sector use of electricity includes all electricity used in industries classified to SIC1992 Groups 60 to 63. Fuels supplied to cargo and passenger ships undertaking international voyages are reported as *Marine bunkers* (see paragraph A.13). Supplies to fishing vessels are included under "agriculture".

Other sectors
A.40   The classification of all consumers groups under this heading, except *domestic*, follows *SIC1992* and is described in Table 1E in Chapter 1. The consistency of the classification across different commodities cannot be guaranteed because the figures reported are dependent on what the data suppliers can provide.

Non energy use
A.41   The non energy use of fuels may be divided into two types. They may be used directly for their physical properties eg lubricants or bitument used for road surfaces, or by the petro-chemical industry as raw materials for the manufacture of goods such as plastics. In their use by the petro-chemical industry, relatively little combustion of the fuels takes place and the carbon and/or hydrogen they contain are largely transferred into the finished product. However, in some cases heat from the manufacturing process or from combustion of by-products may be used. Data for this energy use are rarely available. Depending on the feedstock, non energy consumption is either estimated or taken to be the deliveries to the chemicals sector.

A.42   Both types of non energy use are shown under the *Non energy use* heading at the foot of the balances.

The energy balance (Tables 1.1 to 1.3)

Principles

A.43   The energy balance conveniently presents:

- an overall view of the United Kingdom's energy supplies;
- the relative importance of each energy commodity;
- dependence on imports;
- the contribution of our own fossil and renewable resources;
- the interdependence of commodities on one another.

A.44   The energy balance is constructed directly from the commodity balances by expressing the data in a common unit, placing them beside one another and adding appropriate totals. Heat sold is also included as a fuel. However, some rearrangement of the commodity balance format is required to show transformation of primary into secondary commodities in an easily understood manner.

A.45   Energy units are widely used as the common unit, and the current practice for the United Kingdom and the international organisations which prepare balances is to use the tonne of oil equivalent or a larger multiple of this unit, commonly thousands. One tonne of oil equivalent is defined as 10^7 kilocalories (41.868 gigajoules). The tonne of oil equivalent is another unit of energy like the gigajoule, kilocalorie or kilowatt hour, rather than a physical quantity. It has been chosen as it is easier to visualise than the other units. Due to the natural variations in heating value of primary fuels such as crude oil, it is rare that one tonne of oil has an energy content equivalent to one tonne of oil equivalent, however it is generally within a few per cent of the heating value of a tonne of oil equivalent. The energy figures are calculated from the natural units of the commodity balances by multiplying by factors representing the calorific (heating) value of the fuel. The gross calorific values of fuels are used for this purpose. When the natural unit of the commodity is already an energy unit (electricity in kilowatt hours, for example) the factors are just constants, converting one energy unit to another.

A.46   Most of the underlying definitions and ideas of commodity balances can be taken directly over into the energy balance. However, production of secondary commodities and, in particular, electricity are treated differently and need some explanation. The components of the energy balance are described below, drawing out the differences of treatment compared with the commodity balances.

Primary supply

A.47   Within the energy balance, the production row covers only extraction of primary fuels and the generation of primary energy (hydro, nuclear, wind). Note the change of row heading from *Production* in the commodity balances to *Indigenous production* in the energy balance. Production of secondary fuels and secondary electricity are shown in the transformation sector and not in the indigenous production row at the top of the balance.

A.48   For fossil fuels, indigenous production represents the marketable quantity extracted from the reserves. Indigenous production of *Primary electricity* comprises hydro-electricity, wind and nuclear energy. The energy value for hydro-electricity is taken to be the energy content of the electricity produced from the hydro power plant and not the energy available in the water driving the turbines. A similar approach is adopted for electricity from wind generators. The electricity is regarded as the primary energy form because there are currently no other uses of the energy resource "upstream" of the generation. The energy value attached to nuclear electricity is discussed in paragraph A.52.

A.49   The other elements of the supply part of the balance are identical to those in the commodity balances. In particular, the sign convention is identical, so that figures for exports and international marine bunkers carry negative signs. A stock build carries a negative sign to denote it as a withdrawal from supply whilst a stock draw carries a positive sign to show it as an addition to supply.

A.50   The *Primary supply* is the sum of the figures above it in the table, taking account of the signs, and expresses the national requirement for primary energy commodities from all sources and foreign supplies of secondary commodities. It is an indicator of the use of indigenous resources and external energy supplies. Both the amount and mixture of fuels in final consumption of energy commodities in the United Kingdom will differ from the primary supply. The "mix" of commodities in final consumption will be much more dependent on the manufacture of secondary commodities, in particular electricity.

Transformation

A.51   Within an energy balance the presentation of the inputs to and outputs from transformation activities requires special mention, as it is carried out using a compact format. The transformation sector also plays a key role in moving primary electricity from its own column in the balance into the electricity column, so that it can be combined with electricity from fossil fuelled power stations and the total disposals shown.

A.52   Indigenous production of primary electricity comprises nuclear electricity, hydro electricity and electricity from wind generation. Nuclear electricity is obtained by passing steam from nuclear reactors through conventional steam turbine sets. The heat in the steam is considered to be the primary energy available and its value is calculated from the electricity generated using the average thermal efficiency of nuclear stations, currently 37.58 in the United Kingdom. The electrical energy from hydro and wind is transferred from the *Primary electricity* column to the *Electricity* column using the *transfers* row because electricity is the form of primary energy and no transformation takes place. However, because the form of the nuclear energy is the steam from the nuclear reactors, the energy it contains is shown entering electricity generation and the corresponding electricity produced is included with all electricity generation in the figure, in the same row, under the *Electricity* column.

A.53   Quantities of fuels entering transformation activities (fuels into electricity generation and heat generation, crude oil into petroleum product manufacture (refineries), or coal into coke ovens) are shown with a negative sign to represent the input and the resulting production is shown as a positive number.

A.54   For electricity generated by Major power producers, the inputs are shown in the *Major power producers* row of the *coal, manufactured fuel, primary oils, petroleum products, gas, renewables* and *primary electricity* columns. The total energy input to electricity generation is the sum of the values in these first seven columns. The *Electricity* column shows total electricity generated from these inputs and the transformation loss is the sum of these two figures, given in the *Total* column.

A.55   Within the transformation sector, the negative figures in the *Total* column represent the losses in the various transformation activities. This is a convenient consequence of the sign convention chosen for the inputs and outputs from transformation. Any positive figures represent a transformation gain and, as such, are an indication of incorrect data.

A.56   In the energy balance, the columns containing the input commodities for electricity generation, heat generation and oil refining are separate from the columns for the outputs. However, for the transformation activities involving solid fuels this is only partly the case. Coal used for the manufacture of coke is shown in the coke manufacture row of the transformation section in the coal column, but the related coke and coke oven gas production are shown combined in the *Manufactured fuels* column. Similarly, the input of coke to blast furnaces and the resulting production of blast furnace gas are not identifiable and have been combined in the *Manufactured fuels* column in the *Blast furnace* row. As a result, only the net loss from blast furnace transformation activity appears in the column.

A.57   The share of each commodity or commodity group in primary supply can be calculated from the table. This table also shows the demand for primary as well as foreign supplies. Shares of primary supplies may be taken from the *Primary supply* row of the balance. Shares of fuels in final consumption may be calculated from the final consumption row.

Energy industry use and final consumption
A.58   The figures for final consumption and energy industry use follow, in general, the principles and definitions described under commodity balances in paragraphs A.29 to A.42.

Standard conversion factors

1 tonne of oil equivalent (toe)	= 10^7 kilocalories
	= 396.83 therms
	= 41.868 GJ
	= 11,630 kWh
100,000 British thermal units (Btu)	= 1 therm

The following prefixes are used for multiples of joules, watts and watt hours:

kilo (k)	= 1,000	or 10^3
mega (M)	= 1,000,000	or 10^6
giga (G)	= 1,000,000,000	or 10^9
tera (T)	= 1,000,000,000,000	or 10^{12}
peta (P)	= 1,000,000,000,000,000	or 10^{15}

WEIGHT

1 kilogramme (kg)	= 2.2046 pounds (lb)
1 pound (lb)	= 0.4536 kg
1 tonne (t)	= 1,000kg
	= 0.9842 long ton
	= 1.102 short ton (sh tn)
1 Statute or long ton	= 2,240 lb
	= 1.016 t
	= 1.102 sh tn

VOLUME

1 cubic metre (cu m)	= 35.31 cu ft
1 cubic foot (cu ft)	= 0.02832 cu m
1 litre	= 0.22 Imperial gallons (UK gall)
1 UK gallon	= 8 UK pints
	= 1.201 US gallons
	= 4.54609 litres
1 barrel	= 159.0 litres
	= 34.97 UK gal
	= 42 US gal

LENGTH

1 mile	= 1.6093 kilometres
1 kilometre (km)	= 0.62137 miles

TEMPERATURE

1 scale degree Celsius (C) = 1.8 scale degrees Fahrenheit (F)

For conversion of temperatures: °C = 5/9 (°F −32); °F = 9/5 °C +32

Average conversion factors for petroleum

	Imperial gallons per tonne	Litres per tonne		Imperial gallons per tonne	Litres per tonne
Crude oil:			Gas/diesel oil:		
Indigenous	264	1,199	Gas oil	256	1,163
Imported	260	1,181	Marine diesel oil	255	1,157
Average of refining throughput	262	1,192			
			Fuel oil:		
Ethane	601	2,730	All grades	227	1,031
Propane	435	1,975	Light fuel oil:		
Butane	377	1,715	1% or less sulphur	231	1,048
Naphtha (l.d.f.)	304	1,382	>1% sulphur	231	1,048
			Medium fuel oil:		
Aviation gasoline	307	1,397	1% or less sulphur	238	1,083
			>1% sulphur	225	1,025
Motor spirit:			Heavy fuel oil:		
All grades	300	1,362	1% or less sulphur	220	1,002
Unleaded Super	299	1,361	>1% sulphur	222	1,009
Premium	299	1,357			
Ultra low sulphur petrol	300	1,362			
Lead replacement petrol	299	1,361	Lubricating oils:		
			White	251	1,142
Middle distillate feedstock	205	930	Greases	252	1,147
Kerosene:			Other	248	1,127
Aviation turbine fuel	275	1,251	Bitumen	214	974
Burning oil	275	1,251	Petroleum coke	185	843
			Petroleum waxes	271	1,231
DERV fuel: all	265	1,203	Industrial spirit	274	1,247
0.005% or less sulphur	265	1,203	White spirit	222	1,282
>0.005% sulphur	261	1,187			

Note: The above conversion factors, which for refined products have been compiled by the UK Petroleum Industry Association, apply to the year 2002, and are only approximate for other years.

A.1 Estimated average gross calorific values of fuels

	GJ per tonne		GJ per tonne
Coal:		**Renewable sources:**	
All consumers (weighted average) *(1)*	26.9	Domestic wood *(2)*	10.0
Power stations *(1)*	26.1	Industrial wood *(3)*	11.9
Coke ovens *(1)*	30.5	Straw	15.0
Low temperature carbonisation plants		Poultry litter	8.8
and manufactured fuel plants	30.5	Meat and bone	18.6
Collieries	29.7	General industrial waste	16.0
Agriculture	28.5	Hospital waste	14.0
Iron and steel	30.4	Municipal solid waste *(4)*	9.5
Other industries (weighted average)	26.5	Refuse derived waste *(4)*	18.5
Non-ferrous metals	25.0	Short rotation coppice *(5)*	10.6
Food, beverages and tobacco	30.0	Tyres	32.0
Chemicals	25.1		
Textiles, clothing, leather etc.	29.9	**Petroleum:**	
Pulp, paper, printing etc.	28.9	Crude oil (weighted average)	45.7
Mineral products	27.0	Petroleum products (weighted average)	45.9
Engineering (mechanical and		Ethane	50.7
electrical engineering and			
vehicles)	30.7	Butane and propane (LPG)	49.4
Other industries	28.4	Light distillate feedstock for gasworks	47.6
		Aviation spirit and wide cut gasoline	47.3
		Aviation turbine fuel	46.2
Domestic		Motor spirit	47.1
House coal	31.1	Burning oil	46.2
Anthracite and dry steam coal	33.9	Gas/diesel oil (DERV)	45.6
Other consumers	30.1	Fuel oil	43.4
Imported coal (weighted average)	27.6	Power station oil	43.4
Exports (weighted average)	31.7	Non-fuel products (notional value)	42.7

			MJ per cubic metre
Coke (including low temperature	29.8	Natural gas *(6)*	39.8
carbonisation cokes)		Coke oven gas	18.0
Coke breeze	24.8	Blast furnace gas	3.0
Other manufactured solid fuel	30.9	Landfill gas	38.6
		Sewage gas	38.6

(1) Applicable to UK consumption - based on calorific value for home produced coal plus imports and, for "All consumers" net of exports.

(2) Based on a 50 per cent moisture content.

(3) Average figure covering a range of possible feedstock.

(4) Average figure based on survey returns.

(5) On an "as received" basis. On a "dry" basis 18.6 GJ per tonne.

(6) The gross calorific value of natural gas can also be expressed as 11.056 kWh per cubic metre. This value represents the average calorific value seen for gas when extracted. At this point it contains not just methane, but also some other hydrocarbon gases (ethane, butane, propane). These gases are removed before the gas enters the National Transmission System for sale to final consumers. As such, this calorific value will differ from that readers will see quoted on their gas bills.

Note: The above estimated average gross calorific values apply only to the year 2002. For calorific values of fuels in earlier years see Table A.2 and previous issues of this Digest. See the notes in Chapter 1, paragraph 1.52 regarding net calorific values. The calorific values for coal other than imported coal are based on estimates provided by the main coal producers, but with some exceptions as noted on Table A.2. The calorific values for petroleum products have been calculated using the method described in Chapter 1, paragraph 1.27. The calorific values for coke oven gas and blast furnace gas are provided by the Iron and Steel Statistics Bureau (ISSB).

Data reported in this Digest in 'thousand tonnes of oil equivalent' have been prepared on the basis of 1 tonne of oil equivalent having an energy content of 41.868 gigajoules (GJ), (1 GJ = 9.478 therms) - see notes in Chapter 1, paragraphs 1.24 to 1.26.

A.2 Estimated average gross calorific values of fuels, 1980, 1990 and 1998 to 2002

GJ per tonne (gross)

	1980	1990	1998	1999	2000	2001	2002
Coal							
All consumers *(1)(2)*	25.6	25.5	26.1	26.2	26.2	26.1	26.1
All consumers - home produced plus imports minus exports *(1)*	..	..	27.2	27.0	27.0	26.9r	26.9
Power stations *(2)*	23.8	24.8	25.4	25.5	25.6	25.4	25.4
Power stations - home produced plus imports *(1)*	..	..	25.8	25.9	26.0	26.1r	26.1
Coke ovens *(2)*	30.5	30.2	31.3	31.5	31.2	31.5	31.3
Coke ovens - home produced plus imports *(1)*	..	..	32.0	30.5	30.4	30.5	30.5
Low temperature carbonisation plants and manufactured fuel plants	19.1	29.2	30.5	30.1	30.3	30.3	30.5
Collieries	27.0	28.6	29.6	29.3	29.6	29.8	29.7
Agriculture	30.1	28.9	28.5	28.9	29.2	29.0	28.5
Iron and steel industry *(3)*	29.1	28.9	31.3	30.7	30.7	30.4r	30.4
Other industries *(1)*	27.1	27.8	26.9	26.7	26.7r	26.6r	26.5
Non-ferrous metals	..	23.1	24.5	25.1	25.1	24.9	25.0
Food, beverages and tobacco	28.6	28.1	29.7	29.1	29.5	29.3	30.0
Chemicals	25.8	27.3	28.9	27.2	28.7	27.1	25.1
Textiles, clothing, leather & footwear	27.5	27.7	30.2	28.0	30.4	30.0	29.9
Pulp, paper, printing, etc.	26.5	27.9	29.0	27.7	28.7	28.8	28.9
Mineral products *(4)*	..	28.2	26.6	26.7	27.0r	27.0r	27.0
Engineering *(5)*	27.7	28.3	29.4	29.3	29.3	29.3	30.7
Other industry *(6)*	28.4	28.5	30.1	29.1	30.2	30.5	28.4
Unclassified	..	27.1	..	..	..	..	..
Domestic							
House coal	30.1	30.2	30.9	30.9	30.9	30.9	31.1
Anthracite and dry steam coal	33.3	33.6	34.1	33.5	33.6	33.9	33.9
Other consumers	27.5	27.5	29.2	25.3	29.2	29.2	30.1
Imported coal *(1)*	..	28.3	29.2	28.2	28.0	27.6r	27.6
of which Steam coal	..	..	27.0	26.8	26.6	26.7r	26.5
Coking coal	..	..	32.0	30.4	30.4	30.4	30.4
Anthracite	..	..	32.0	31.2	31.2	31.1r	31.5
Exports *(1)*	..	29.0	30.8	31.7	32.0	32.1	31.7
of which Steam coal	..	..	30.1	32.1	31.0	30.7	30.0
Anthracite	..	..	31.4	31.5	32.6	32.7	32.6
Coke *(7)*	28.1	28.1	29.8	29.8	29.8	29.8	29.8
Coke breeze	24.4	24.8	24.8	24.8	24.8	24.8	24.8
Other manufactured solid fuels *(1)*	27.6	27.6	30.7	30.9	30.8	30.6	30.9
Petroleum							
Crude oil *(1)*	45.2	45.6	45.7	45.7	45.7	45.7	45.7
Liquified petroleum gas	49.6	49.4	49.4	49.4	49.4	49.4	49.4
Ethane	52.3	50.6	50.7	50.7	50.7	50.7	50.7
LDF for gasworks/Naphtha	47.8	47.9	47.7	47.7	47.7	47.6	47.6
Aviation spirit and wide-cut gasoline (AVGAS & AVTAG)	47.2	47.3	47.3	47.3	47.3	47.3	47.3
Aviation turbine fuel (AVTUR)	46.4	46.2	46.2	46.2	46.2	46.2	46.2
Motor spirit	47.0	47.0	47.0	47.1	47.0	47.1	47.1
Burning oil	46.5	46.2	46.2	46.2	46.2	46.2	46.2
Vaporising oil	45.9	45.9	..	..	..	..	..
Gas/diesel oil (including DERV)	45.5	45.4	45.5	45.6	45.6	45.6	45.6
Fuel oil	42.8	43.2	43.2	43.2	43.1	43.5	43.4
Power station oil	42.8	43.2	43.2	43.2	43.1	43.5	43.4
Non-fuel products (notional value)	42.2	43.2	43.3	43.4	43.8	42.8	42.7
Petroleum coke	..	39.5	35.8	35.8	35.8	35.8	35.8
Orimulsion *(8)*	..	29.7	..	..	..	..	..

(1) Weighted averages.

(2) Home produced coal only.

(3) For 2001 and 2002 almost entirely sourced from imports.

(4) Based on information provided by the British Cement Industry Association; almost all coal used by this sector in the latest 3 years

(5) Mechanical engineering and metal products, electrical and instrument engineering and vehicle manufacture.

(6) Includes construction.

(7) Since 1995 the source of these figures has been the ISSB.

(8) Orimulsion use ceased in 1997.

Annex B
Glossary

Advanced gas-cooled reactor (AGR)
A type of nuclear reactor cooled by carbon dioxide gas.

Anthracite
Within this publication, anthracite is coal classified as such by UK coal producers and importers of coal. Typically it has a high heat content making it particularly suitable for certain industrial processes and for use as a domestic fuel.

Anthropogenic
Produced by human activities.

Associated Gas
Natural gas found in association with crude oil in a reservoir, either dissolved in the oil or as a cap above the oil.

Autogeneration
Generation of electricity by companies whose main business is not electricity generation, the electricity being produced mainly for that company's own use.

Aviation spirit
A light hydrocarbon oil product used to power piston-engined aircraft power units.

Aviation turbine fuel
The main aviation fuel used for powering aviation gas-turbine power units (jet aircraft engine).

Benzole
A colourless liquid, flammable, aromatic hydrocarbon by-product of the iron and steel making process. It is used as a solvent in the manufacture of styrenes and phenols but is also used as a motor fuel.

Biogas
Energy produced from the anaerobic digestion of sewage and industrial waste.

Bitumen
The residue left after the production of lubricating oil distillates and vacuum gas oil for upgrading plant feedstock. Used mainly for road making and construction purposes.

Blast furnace gas
Mainly produced and consumed within the iron and steel industry. Obtained as a by-product of iron making in a blast furnace, it is recovered on leaving the furnace and used partly within the plant and partly in other steel industry processes or in power plants equipped to burn it. A similar gas is obtained when steel is made in basic oxygen steel converters, this gas is recovered and used in the same way.

Breeze
Breeze can generally be described as coke screened below 19 mm (¾ inch) with no fines removed, but the screen size may vary in different areas and to meet the requirements of particular markets.

BNFL
British Nuclear Fuels plc.

Burning oil
A refined petroleum product, with a volatility in between that of motor spirit and gas diesel oil primarily used for heating and lighting.

Butane
Hydrocarbon (C_4H_{10}), gaseous at normal temperature, but generally stored and transported as a liquid. Used as a component in Motor Spirit to improve combustion, and for cooking and heating (see LPG).

Calorific values (CVs)
The energy content of a fuel can be measured as the heat released on complete combustion. The SI (Système International - see note below) derived unit of energy and heat is the Joule. This is the energy per unit volume of the fuel and is often measured in GJ per tonne. The energy content can be expressed as an upper (or gross) value and a lower (or net) value. The difference between the two values is due to the release of energy from the condensation of water in the products of combustion. Gross calorific values are used throughout this publication.

CO$_2$
Carbon dioxide. Carbon dioxide contributes about 60 per cent of the potential global warming effect of man-made emissions of greenhouse gases. Although this gas is naturally emitted by living organisms, these emissions are offset by the uptake of carbon dioxide by plants during photosynthesis; they therefore tend to have no net effect on atmospheric concentrations. The burning of fossil fuels, however, releases carbon dioxide fixed by plants many millions of years ago, and thus increases its concentration in the atmosphere.

Coke oven coke
The solid product obtained from carbonisation of coal, principally coking coal, at high temperature, it is low in moisture and volatile matter. Used mainly in iron and steel industry.

Coke oven gas
Gas produced as a by-product of solid fuel carbonisation and gasification at coke ovens, but not from low temperature carbonisation plants. Synthetic coke oven gas is mainly natural gas which is mixed with smaller amounts of blast furnace and basic oxygen steel furnace gas to produce a gas with almost the same quantities as coke oven gas.

Coking coal
Within this publication, coking coal is coal sold by producers for use in coke ovens and similar carbonising processes. The definition is not therefore determined by the calorific value or caking qualities of each batch of coal sold, although calorific values tend to be higher than for steam coal. Not all coals form cokes. For a coal to coke it must exhibit softening and agglomeration properties, ie the end product must be a coherent solid.

Colliery methane
Methane released from coal seams in deep mines which is piped to the surface and consumed at the colliery or transmitted by pipeline to consumers.

Combined cycle gas Turbine (CCGT)
Combined cycle gas turbine power stations combine gas turbines and steam turbines which are connected to one or more electrical generators in the same plant. The gas turbine (usually fuelled by natural gas or oil) produces mechanical power (to drive the generator)

and heat in the form of hot exhaust gases. These gases are fed to a boiler, where steam is raised at pressure to drive a conventional steam turbine, which is also connected, to an electrical generator.

Combined Heat and Power (CHP) CHP is the simultaneous generation of usable heat and power (usually electricity) in a single process. The term CHP is synonymous with cogeneration and total energy, which are terms often used in the United States or other Member States of the European Community. The basic elements of a CHP plant comprise one or more prime movers driving electrical generators, where the steam or hot water generated in the process is utilised via suitable heat recovery equipment for use either in industrial processes, or in community heating and space heating. For further information see paragraph 6.31.

Conventional thermal power stations These are stations which generate electricity by burning fossil fuels to produce heat to convert water into steam, which then powers steam turbines.

Cracking/conversion A refining process using combinations of temperature, pressure and in some cases a catalyst to produce petroleum products by changing the composition of a fraction of petroleum, either by splitting existing longer carbon chain or combining shorter carbon chain components of crude oil or other refinery feedstock's. Cracking allows refiners to selectively increase the yield of specific fractions from any given input petroleum mix depending on their requirements in terms of output products.

Crude oil A mineral oil consisting of a mixture of hydrocarbons of natural origins, yellow to black in colour, of variable density and viscosity.

DERV Diesel engined road vehicle fuel used in internal combustion engines that are compression-ignited (see gas diesel oil).

Distillation A process of separation of the various components of crude oil and refinery feedstocks using the different temperatures of evaporation and condensation of the different components of the mix received at the refineries.

DNC Declared net capacity and capability are used to measure the maximum power available from generating stations at a point in time. See paragraphs 5.50, 5.51 and 7.73 for a fuller definition.

Downstream Used in oil and gas processes to cover the part of the industry after the production of the oil and gas. For example, it covers refining, supply and trading, marketing and exporting.

Embedded Generation Embedded generation is electricity generation by plant which has been connected to the distribution networks of the public electricity distributors rather than directly to the National Grid Company's transmission systems. Typically they are either smaller stations located on industrial sites, or combined heat and power plant, or renewable energy plant such as wind farms, or refuse burner generators. The category also includes some domestic generators such as those with electric solar panels. For a description of the current structure of the electricity industry in the UK see paragraphs 5.3 to 5.8 of Chapter 5.

Energy use

Energy use of fuel mainly comprises use for lighting, heating or cooling, motive power and power for appliances. See also non-energy use.

ESA

European System of National and Regional Accounts. An integrated system of economic accounts which is the European version of the System of National Accounts (SNA).

EESs

The Energy Efficiency Commitment (formerly known as Energy Efficiency Standards of Performance) is an obligation placed on all energy suppliers to offer help and advice to their customers to improve the energy efficiency of their homes.

Ethane

A light hydrocarbon gas (C_2H_6) in natural gas and refinery gas streams (see LPG).

EUROSTAT

Statistical Office of the European Communities (SOEC).

Exports

For some parts of the energy industry, statistics on trade in energy related products can be derived from two separate sources. Firstly, figures can be reported by companies as part of systems for collecting data on specific parts of the energy industry (e.g. as part of the system for recording the production and disposals of oil from the UK continental shelf). Secondly, figures are also available from the general systems that exist for monitoring trade in all types of products operated by HM Customs & Excise.

Feedstock

In the refining industry, a product or a combination of products derived from crude oil, destined for further processing other than blending. It is distinguished from use as a chemical feedstock etc. See non-energy use.

Final energy Consumption

Energy consumption by final user - i.e. which is not being used for transformation into other forms of energy.

Fossil fuels

Coal, natural gas and fuels derived from crude oil (for example petrol and diesel) are called fossil fuels because they have been formed over long periods of time from ancient organic matter.

Fuel oils

The heavy oils from the refining process; used as fuel in furnaces and boilers of power stations, industry, in domestic and industrial heating, ships, locomotives, metallurgic operations, and industrial power plants etc.

Fuel oil - Light

Fuel oil made up of heavier straight-run or cracked distillates and used in commercial or industrial burner installations not equipped with pre-heating facilities.

Fuel oil - Medium	Other fuel oils, sometimes referred to as bunker fuels, which generally require pre-heating before being burned, but in certain climatic conditions do not require pre-heating.

Fuel oil - Heavy Other heavier grade fuel oils which in all situations require some form of pre-heating before being burned.

Fuel poverty The common definition of a fuel poor household is one needing to spend in excess of 10 per cent of household income to achieve a satisfactory heating regime (21°C in the living room and 18°C in the other occupied rooms).

Gas Diesel Oil The medium oil from the refinery process; used as a fuel in diesel engines (i.e. internal combustion engines that are compression-ignited), burned in central heating systems and used as a feedstock for the chemical industry.

GDP Gross Domestic Product.

GDP deflator An index of the ratio of GDP at current prices to GDP at constant prices. It provides a measure of general price inflation within the whole economy.

Gigajoule (GJ) A unit of energy equal to 10^9 joules (see note on joules below).

Gigawatt (GW) A unit of electrical power, equal to 10^9 watts.

Gigawatt hour (GWh) Unit of electrical energy, equal to 0.0036 TJ. A 1 GW power station running for one hour produces 1 GWh of electrical energy.

Heat sold Heat (or steam) that is produced and sold under the provision of a contract. Heat sold is derived from heat generated by Combined Heat and Power (CHP) plants and from community heating schemes without CHP plants.

HMCE HM Customs and Excise.

Imports See the first paragraph of the entry for exports above. Before the 1997 edition of the Digest, the term "arrivals" was used to distinguish figures derived from the former source from those import figures derived from the systems operated by HM Customs & Excise. To make it clearer for users, a single term is now being used for both these sources of figures (the term imports) as this more clearly states what the figures relate to, which is goods entering the UK.

International Energy Agency (IEA) The IEA is an autonomous body located in Paris which was established in November 1974 within the framework of the Organisation for Economic Co-operation and Development (OECD) to implement an international energy programme.

Indigenous production For oil this includes production from the UK Continental Shelf both onshore and offshore.

Industrial spirit	Refined petroleum fractions with boiling ranges up to 200°C dependent on the use to which they are put – e.g. seed extraction, rubber solvents, perfume etc.
Joules	A joule is a generic unit of energy in the conventional SI system (see note on SI below). It is equal to the energy dissipated by an electrical current of 1 ampere driven by 1 volt for 1 second; it is also equal to twice the energy of motion in a mass of 1 kilogram moving at 1 metre per second.
Landfill gas	The methane-rich biogas formed from the decomposition of organic material in landfill.
LDF	Light distillate feedstock.
Liquefied petroleum Gas (LPG)	Gas usually propane or butane, derived from oil and put under pressure so that it is in liquid form. Often used to power portable cooking stoves or heaters and to fuel some types of vehicle, e.g. some specially adapted road vehicles, forklift trucks.
Lead Replacement Petrol (LRP)	An alternative to Leaded Petrol containing a different additive to lead (in the UK usually potassium based) to perform the lubrication functions of lead additives in reducing engine wear.
Lubricating oils	Refined heavy distillates obtained from the vacuum distillation of petroleum residues. Includes liquid and solid hydrocarbons sold by the lubricating oil trade, either alone or blended with fixed oils, metallic soaps and other organic and/or inorganic bodies.
Magnox	A type of gas-cooled nuclear fission reactor developed in the UK, so called because of the magnesium alloy used to clad the uranium fuel.
Major power producers	Companies whose prime purpose is the generation of electricity (paragraph 5.46 of Chapter 5 gives a full list of major power producers).
Motor spirit	Blended light petroleum product used as a fuel in spark-ignition internal combustion engines (other than aircraft engines).
Natural gas	Natural gas is a mixture of naturally occurring gases found either in isolation, or associated with crude oil, in underground reservoirs. The main component is methane; ethane, propane, butane, hydrogen sulphide and carbon dioxide may also be present, but these are mostly removed at or near the well head in gas processing plants.
Naphtha	(Light distillate feedstock) – Petroleum distillate boiling predominantly below 200°C.
Natural gas - compressed	Natural gas that has been compressed to reduce the volume it occupies to make it easier to transport other than in pipelines. Whilst other petroleum gases can be compressed such that they move into liquid form, the volatility of natural gas is such that liquefaction cannot be achieved without very high pressures and low temperatures being used.

As such, the compressed form is more usually used as a "half-way house".

Natural gas liquids (NGLs) A mixture of liquids derived from natural gas and crude oil during the production process, including propane, butane, ethane and gasoline components (pentanes plus).

NETA New Electricity Trading Arrangements - In England and Wales these arrangements replaced "the pool" from 27 March 2001. The arrangements are based on bi-lateral trading between generators, suppliers, traders and customers and are designed to be more efficient, and provide more market choice.

Non-energy use Includes fuel used for chemical feedstock, solvents, lubricants, and road making material.

NFFO Non Fossil Fuel Obligation. The 1989 Electricity Act empowers the Secretary of State to make orders requiring the Regional Electricity Companies in England and Wales to secure specified amounts of electricity from renewable sources.

NO$_X$ Nitrogen oxides. A number of nitrogen compounds including nitrogen dioxide are formed in combustion processes when nitrogen in the air or the fuel combines with oxygen. These compounds can add to the natural acidity of rainfall.

OFGEM The regulatory office for gas and electricity markets.

Orimulsion An emulsion of bitumen in water that can be used as a fuel in some power stations.

ONS Office for National Statistics.

OTS Overseas Trade Statistics of the United Kingdom.

Patent fuel A composition fuel manufactured from coal fines by shaping with the addition of a binding agent (typically pitch). The term manufactured solid fuel is also used.

Petrochemical feedstock All petroleum products intended for use in the manufacture of petroleum chemicals. This includes middle distillate feedstock of which there are several grades depending on viscosity. The boiling point ranges between $200°C$ and $400°C$.

Petroleum cokes Carbonaceous material derived from hydrocarbon oils, uses for which include metallurgical electrode manufacture and in the manufacture of cement.

Petroleum wax Includes paraffin wax, which is a white crystalline hydrocarbon material of low oil content normally obtained during the refining of lubricating oil distillate, paraffin scale, slack wax, microcrystalline wax and wax emulsions.

Photovoltaics
The direct conversion of solar radiation into electricity by the interaction of light with the electrons in a semiconductor device or cell.

Plant capacity
The maximum power available from a power station at a point in time (see also paragraph 5.50 of Chapter 5).

Plant loads, demands and efficiency
Measures of how intensively and efficiently power stations are being used. These terms are defined in paragraphs 5.52 and 5.53 of Chapter 5.

PPRS
Petroleum production reporting system. Licensees operating in the UK Continental Shelf are required to make monthly returns on their production of hydrocarbons (oil and gas) to the DTI. This information is recorded in the PPRS, which is used to report flows, stocks and uses of hydrocarbon from the well-head through to final disposal from a pipeline or terminal (see paragraphs F.29 to F.31 of Annex F on DTI's energy statistics website).

Process oils
Partially processed feedstocks which require further processing before being classified as a finished product suitable for sale. They can also be used as a reaction medium in the production process.

Primary fuels
Fuels obtained directly from natural sources, e.g. coal, oil and natural gas.

Primary electricity
Electricity obtained other than from fossil fuel sources, e.g. nuclear, hydro and other non-thermal renewables. Imports of electricity are also included.

Propane
Hydrocarbon containing three carbon atoms (C_3H_8), gaseous at normal temperature, but generally stored and transported under pressure as a liquid.

PWR
Pressurised water reactor. A nuclear fission reactor cooled by ordinary water kept from boiling by containment under high pressure.

Reforming
Processes by which the molecular structure of different fractions of petroleum can be modified. It usually involves some form of catalyst, most often platinum, and allows the conversion of lower grades of petroleum product into higher grades, improving their octane rating. It is a generic term for processes such as cracking, cyclization, dehydrogenation and isomerisation. These processes generally led to the production of hydrogen as a by-product, which can be used in the refineries in some desulphurization procedures.

Refinery fuel
Petroleum products produced by the refining process that are used as fuel at refineries.

Renewable energy sources
Renewable energy includes solar power, wind, wave and tide, and hydroelectricity. Solid renewable energy sources consist of wood, straw and waste, whilst gaseous renewable consist of landfill gas and sewage gas.

Reserves	With oil and gas these relate to the quantities identified as being present in underground cavities. The actual amounts that can be recovered depend on the level of technology available and existing economic situations. These continually change; hence the level of the UK's reserves can change quite independently of whether or not new reserves have been identified.
RPI	Retail Price Index (RPI) is published by the Office for National Statistics. RPI is calculated using prices collected on a day near the middle of the month.
SI (Système International)	Refers to the agreed conventions for the measurement of physical quantities.
SIC	Standard Industrial Classification in the UK. Last revised in 1992 and known as SIC92, replaced previous classifications SIC80 and SIC68. Now compatible with European Union classification NACE Rev1 (Nomenclature générale des activités économiques dans les Communautés européennes as revised in October 1990).
Secondary fuels	Fuels derived from natural primary sources of energy. For example electricity generated from burning coal, gas or oil is a secondary fuel, as are coke and coke oven gas.
Steam coal	Within this publication, steam coal is coal classified as such by UK coal producers and by importers of coal. It tends to be coal having lower calorific values; the type of coal that is typically used for steam raising.
SO_2	Sulphur Dioxide. Sulphur dioxide is a gas produced by the combustion of sulphur-containing fuels such as coal and oil.
Synthetic coke oven gas	Mainly a natural gas, which is mixed with smaller amounts of blast furnace, and BOS (basic oxygen steel furnace) gas to produce a gas with almost the same quantities as coke oven gas.
Temperature correction	The temperature corrected series of total inland fuel consumption indicates what annual consumption might have been if the average temperature during the year had been the same as the average for the years 1961 to 1990.
Thermal Sources of Electricity	These include coal, oil, natural gas, nuclear, landfill gas, sewage gas, municipal solid waste, farm waste, tyres, poultry litter, short rotation coppice, straw, coke oven gas, blast furnace gas, and waste products from chemical processes.
Tonne of oil equivalent (toe)	A common unit of measurement which enables different fuels to be compared and aggregated. (See paragraphs 1.24 to 1.25 of Chapter 1 for further information).
Tars	Viscous materials usually derived from the destructive distillation of coal which are by-products of the coke and iron making processes.

Therm	A common unit of measurement similar to a tonne of oil equivalent which enables different fuels to be compared and aggregated. (see Annex A.)
Thermal efficiency	The thermal efficiency of a power station is the efficiency with which heat energy contained in fuel is converted into electrical energy. It is calculated for fossil fuel burning stations by expressing electricity supplied as a percentage of the total energy content of the fuel consumed (based on average gross calorific values). For nuclear stations it is calculated using the quantity of heat released as a result of fission of the nuclear fuel inside the reactor.
UKCS	United Kingdom Continental Shelf.
UKPIA	UK Petroleum Industry Association. The trade association for the UK petroleum industry.
Ultra low sulphur Diesel (ULSD)	A grade of diesel fuel which has a much lower sulphur content (less than 0.005 per cent or 50 parts per million) and of a slightly higher volatility than ordinary diesel fuels. As a result it produces fewer emissions when burned. As such it enjoys a lower rate of excise duty in the UK than ordinary diesel (by 3 pence per litre) to promote its use. Virtually 100 per cent of sales of DERV fuel in the UK are ULSD.
Ultra low sulphur Petrol (ULSP)	A grade of motor spirit with a similar level of sulphur to ULSD. (less than 0.005 per cent or 50 parts per million). In the March 2000 Budget it was announced that a lower rate of excise duty than ordinary petrol for this fuel would be introduced during 2000, which was increased to 3 pence per litre in the March 2001 Budget. It has quickly replaced ordinary premium grade unleaded petrol in the UK market place.
Upstream	A term to cover the activities related to the exploration, production and delivery to a terminal or other facility of oil or gas for export or onward shipment within the UK.
VAT	Value added tax.
Watt (W)	The conventional unit to measure a rate of flow of energy. One watt amounts to 1 joule per second.
White spirit	A highly refined distillate with a boiling range of about 150°C to 200°C used as a paint solvent and for dry cleaning purposes etc.

Annex C
Further sources of United Kingdom energy publications

Some of the publications listed below give shorter term statistics, some provide further information about energy production and consumption in the United Kingdom and in other countries, and others provide more detail on a country or fuel industry basis. The list also covers recent publications on energy issues and policy, including statistical information, produced or commissioned by the DTI. The list is not exhaustive and the titles of publications and publishers may alter. Unless otherwise stated, all titles are available from The Stationery Office and can be ordered through Government Bookshops and can be found on the DTI Web site at www.dti.gov.uk/energy/inform/.

Department of Trade and Industry publications on energy

Energy Statistics
Monthly, quarterly and annual statistics on production and consumption of overall energy and individual fuels in the United Kingdom together with energy prices is available in MS Excel format on the internet at www.dti.gov.uk/energy/inform/energy_stats/.

Energy Trends
Quarterly publication. Covers all major aspects of energy. Provides a comprehensive picture of energy production and use. Contains analysis of data and articles covering energy issues. Available on subscription, with Quarterly Energy Prices publication, from EMU3-SID2, Department of Trade and Industry, Bay 232, 1 Victoria Street, London, SW1H 0ET, tel. 020-7215 2697/2698.

Quarterly Energy Prices
Quarterly publication. From June 2001 replaced energy prices information formerly available in the monthly publication Energy Trends and the annual Digest of UK Energy Statistics. Contains tables, charts and commentary covering energy prices to domestic and industrial consumers for all the major fuels as well as presenting comparisons of fuel prices in the European Union and G7 countries. Available on subscription, with Energy Trends publication, from EMU3-SID2, Department of Trade and Industry, Bay 232, 1 Victoria Street, London, SW1H 0ET, tel. 020-7215 2697/2698.

Energy Sector Indicators 2003
This is a set of indicators grouped into 12 sections covering different aspects of the energy sector. The content is designed to show the extent to which secure, diverse and sustainable supplies of energy to UK Businesses and consumers at competitive prices are ensured. Available free from EMU3-SID2, Department of Trade and Industry, Bay 232, 1 Victoria Street, London, SW1H 0ET, tel. 020-7215 2697/2698.

UK Energy in Brief
This booklet summarises the latest statistics on energy production, consumption and prices in the United Kingdom. The figures are taken from "Digest of UK Energy Statistics". Available free from EMU3-SID2, Department of Trade and Industry, Bay 232, 1 Victoria Street, London, SW1H 0ET, tel. 020-7215 2697/2698.

Development of the Oil and Gas Resources of the United Kingdom

> Publication of Development of UK Oil and Gas Resources, commonly known as the "Brown Book", ended with the 2001 edition. That edition, as well as more up-to-date information on the UK offshore industry, is available via DTI's Oil and Gas website: www.og.dti.gov.uk.

Industrial Energy Markets: Energy markets in UK manufacturing industry 1973 to 1993 - Energy Paper 64

> Using tables of data drawn from the 1989 Purchases Inquiry conducted by the Office for National Statistics, the report, which updates one produced in 1989, sets out the implications for the trends in industrial energy consumption over the period from 1973 to 1993. Available from The Stationery Office, tel 0870 600 5522. Not available on the Internet.

Energy Consumption in the UK

> Energy Consumption in the United Kingdom, brings together statistics from a variety of sources to produce a comprehensive review of energy consumption in the UK since the 1970s. This booklet describes the key trends in energy consumption in the UK since 1970 with a particular focus on trends since 1990. It includes an analysis of the factors driving the changes in energy consumption, the impact of increasing activity, increased efficiency, and structural change in the economy, while detailed tables can be found on the internet. The information is presented in five sections covering firstly overall energy consumption, then energy consumption in the transport, domestic, industrial and service sectors. Available free from EMU3-SID2, Department of Trade and Industry, Bay 232, 1 Victoria Street, London, SW1H 0ET, tel. 020-7215 2697/2698.

Energy Projections for the UK:- Energy Paper 68

> This paper presents the results of an exercise to update the Government's projections of future UK energy demand and related emissions of carbon and sulphur dioxides to 2020. It builds on work issued as a working paper in March 2000 and its projections underpin the Climate Change Programme launched by the DETR in November 2000. The paper contributes to policy development and assessment of the UK's efforts to meet its national and international greenhouse gases targets. Available from The Stationery Office, tel 0870 600 5522.

Social Effects of Energy Liberalisation: The UK Experience

> This paper reviews the impact of liberalisation of the energy markets, and the effects on the fuel industries, the consumer and the environment. Available free from EMU3-SID2, Department of Trade and Industry, Bay 232, 1 Victoria Street, London, SW1H 0ET, tel. 020-7215 2697/2698.

Energy Liberalisation Indicators in Europe: A preliminary report of a study carried out by OXERA for the Governments of the UK and the Netherlands.

> This paper presents preliminary results from a study carried out by OXERA on behalf of the Governments of the UK and the Netherlands. The study develops a set of indicators, within a hierarchical structure, for monitoring the development of competition in gas and electricity markets across Europe. The study mainly concentrates on the electricity market and presents some preliminary results for a subset of European countries including the UK and Netherlands. Available free from EMU3-SID2, Department of Trade and Industry, Bay 232, 1 Victoria Street, London, SW1H 0ET, tel. 020-7215 2697/2698.

Energy Liberalisation Indicators in Europe: A consultation paper based on a study carried out by OXERA for the Governments of the UK and the Netherlands.

> This consultation paper sets out the methodology used and presents results for a subset of European countries including the UK and the Netherlands. Available free from EMU3-SID2, Department of Trade and Industry, Bay 232, 1 Victoria Street, London SW1H 0ET, tel. 020-7215 2697/2698.

Social, Environmental and Security of Supply Policies in a Competitive Energy Market: A Review of Delivery Mechanisms in the United Kingdom, Summary Paper

This paper outlines the UK experience so far in using competitive energy markets to deliver social, environmental and security of supply policies. It highlights the benefits that have emerged from this approach and sets out the instruments the Government has used to enhance policy delivery. Available free from EMU3-SID2, Department of Trade and Industry, Bay 232, 1 Victoria Street, London, SW1H 0ET, tel. 020-7215 2697/2698.

The UK Fuel Poverty Strategy: November 2001

Produced by the The Department of Trade and Industry and Department for the Environment, Food and Rural Affairs (DEFRA). The strategy sets out the Government's objectives, policies and targets for alleviating fuel poverty in the UK over the next 10 years. Available free from Department of Trade and Industry, Orderline, Admail 528, London, SW1W 8YT, tel. 0870 1502 500, Fax 0870 1502 333, E-mail: publications@dti.gsi.gov.uk.

The UK Fuel Poverty Strategy, 1st Annual Progress Report 2003

Produced by the Department of Trade and Industry and Defra in association with the Devolved Administrations. This report sets out what progress has been made on tackling fuel poverty following the publication of the UK Fuel Poverty Strategy in November 2001. It is accompanied by detailed annexes published on the DTI web site at www.dti.gov.uk/energy/consumers/fuel_poverty/index.shtml Available free from Department of Trade and Industry, Orderline, Admail 528, London, SW1W 8YT, tel. 0870 1502 500, Fax 0870 1502 333, E-mail: publications@dti.gsi.gov.uk

Energy Policy – key issues for consultation

Consultation report produced by the The Department of Trade and Industry, Department of Trade and Industry and Depatment for Transport and Rural Affairs. This booklet is aimed at energy stakeholders ie consumer organisations, business, unions, environmental groups and others who have a particular expertise or interest in energy issues and invites comments on the main issues which the Government will need to consider in producing a White Paper including its energy policy objectives, its underlying energy policy and the practical steps needed to implement these. Available free from Department of Trade and Industry, Orderline, Admail 528, London SW1W 8YT, tel. 0870 1502 500, Fax 08701 502 333. E-mail: publications@dti.gsi.gov.uk.

Energy– Its impact on the environment and society

This booklet outlines the environmental and social impacts of energy production and use. It includes information on carbon dioxide and other emissions, the environmental consequences of energy production and supply activities and an analysis of the drivers of energy demand. It also covers the evolution and impact of competition in the energy market, quality of service and fuel poverty. Available free from EMU3-SID2, Department of Trade and Industry, Bay 232, 1 Victoria Street, London SW1H 0ET, tel. 020-7215 2697/2698.

Energy White Paper

The Government's Energy White Paper, "*Our energy future - creating a low carbon economy*", was published by the Secretary of State for Trade and Industry on 24 February 2003. The report addresses the challenges facing energy, by setting out a long-term strategic vision for energy policy. It is the product of extensive consultative and analytical work and has over 6,500 contributions. The White Paper is available on the DTI web site at www.dti.gov.uk/energy/whitepaper/index.shtml and in hard copy from The Stationery Office.

Other publications including energy information

General

Basic Statistics of the Community (annual); *Statistical Office of the European Communities*

Digest of Environmental Statistics (annual); *Department of the Environment, Food and Rural Affairs (Defra)*

Digest of Welsh Statistics (annual); *Welsh Office* (available from ESS Division, Welsh Office, Cathays Park, Cardiff)

Eurostatistics - Data for Short Term Analysis; *Statistical Office of the European Communities*

Monthly Digest of Statistics; *Office for National Statistics*

Northern Ireland Annual Abstract of Statistics (annual); *Department of Finance and Personnel,* (available from the Policy & Planning Unit, Department of Finance & Personnel, Stormont, Belfast BT4 3SW)

Overseas Trade Statistics of the United Kingdom; *H.M. Customs & Excise*
- Business Monitor MM20 (monthly) (extra-EU trade only)
- Business Monitor MM20A (monthly) (intra and extraEU
- trade data, relatively limited level of production detail)
- Business Monitor MQ20 (quarterly) (intra-EU trade only)
- Business Monitor MA20 (annual) (intra- and extra-EU trade);

Purchases Inquiry 1989, 1994-1998; Office *for National Statistics*

Rapid Reports - energy and industry (ad hoc); *Statistical Office of the European Communities*

Regional Trends (annual); *Office for National Statistics*

Scottish Abstract of Statistics (annual); *Scottish Office*

United Kingdom Minerals Yearbook (annual); *British Geological Survey* (available from the British Geological Survey, Keyworth, Nottingham, NG12 5GG)

Yearbook of Regional Statistics (annual); *Statistical Office of the European Communities*

Energy

Annual Bulletin of General Energy Statistics for Europe; *United Nations Economic Commission for Europe*

BP Statistical Review of World Energy (annual); (available from The Editor, BP Statistical Review, The British Petroleum Company plc, Corporate Communications Services, Britannic House, 1 Finsbury Circus, London EC2M 7BA)

Energy - Monthly Statistics; *Statistical Office of the European Communities*

Energy Balances of OECD Countries (annual); *OECD International Energy Agency*

Energy Statistics and Balances of OECD Countries (annual); *OECD International Energy Agency*

Energy Statistics and Balances of Non-OECD Countries (annual); *OECD International Energy Agency*

Energy - Yearly Statistics; *Statistical Office of the European Communities*

UN Energy Statistics Yearbook (annual); *United Nations Statistical Office*

Coal

Annual Bulletin of Coal Statistics for Europe; *United Nations Economic Commission for Europe*

Annual Reports and Accounts of The Coal Authority and the private coal companies; (*apply to the Headquarters of the company concerned*)

Coal Information (annual); *OECD International Energy Agency*

Oil and gas

Annual Bulletin of Gas Statistics for Europe; *United Nations Economic Commission for Europe*

BP Review of World Gas (annual); (*available from British Petroleum Company plc, Corporate Communications Services, Britannic House, 1 Finsbury Circus, London EC2M 7BA*)

Annual Reports and Accounts of National Grid Transco, Centrica and other independent gas supply companies; (contact *the Headquarters of the company concerned directly)*

Oil and Gas Information (annual); *OECD International Energy Agency*

Quarterly Oil Statistics and Energy Balances; *OECD International Energy Agency*

UK Petroleum Industry Statistics Consumption and Refinery Production (annual and quarterly); *Institute of Petroleum (available from IP, 61 New Cavendish Street, London W1M 8AR)*

Electricity

Annual Bulletin of Electric Energy Statistics for Europe; *United Nations Economic Commission for Europe*

Annual Reports and Accounts of the Electricity Supply Companies, Distributed Companies and Generators; *(apply to the Headquarters of the company concerned)*

Annual Report of the Office of Electricity Regulation;   OFGEM

Electricity Supply in OECD Countries; *OECD International Energy Agency*

National Grid Company - Seven Year Statement - (annual) *National Grid Transco - For further details telephone 01203 423065*

Operation of Nuclear Power Stations (annual); *Statistical Office of the European Communities*

UK Electricity (annual); *Electricity Association plc (available from the Electricity Association plc, 30 Millbank, London SW1P 4RD)*

Electricity Information (annual); *OECD International Energy Agency*

Prices

Energy Prices (annual); *Statistical Office of the European Communities* (summarises price information published in the European Commissions Weekly Oil Price, and half-yearly Statistics in Focus on Gas Prices and Electricity Prices)

Energy Prices and Taxes (quarterly); *OECD International Energy Agency*

Electricity prices (annual); *Eurostat*

Gas prices (annual); *Eurostat*

Environment

Digest of Environmental Statistics (Annual); *Department of the Environment, Food and Rural Affairs (Defra).*

Indicators of Sustainable Development for the United Kingdom; *Department of the Environment, Food and Rural Affairs (Defra)*

Quality of life counts, Indicators for a strategy for sustainable development for the United Kingdom: a baseline assessment; *Department of the Environment, Food and Rural Affairs (Defra)*

Environment Statistics (annual).; *Eurostat*

UK Environment (adhoc/one-off release); *Department of the Environment, Food and Rural Affairs (Defra)*

Renewables

New and Renewable Energy, Prospects for the 21st Century. A series of consultation papers reports on the outcome of the review conducted by the Government and the possible ways forward in implementing the Government's new drive for renewables. Available on the DTI website and via publications@dti

Fuel Poverty

English House Condition Survey – 1996 Energy Report:- Produced by the Department of the Environment, Food and Rural Affairs. This report presents the detailed findings of the 1996 English House Condition Survey (EHCS) on the energy efficiency and thermal performance of the stock, energy action by occupants and landlords and the potential for future energy and carbon savings.

Useful energy related websites

The DTI website can be found at http://www.dti.gov.uk, the energy information and statistics website is at http://www.dti.gov.uk/energy/inform/index.shtml

Other Government websites

Central Office of Information	www.nds.coi.gov.uk
Customs and Excise	www.hmce.gov.uk
Department for Environment, Food and Rural Affairs	www.defra.gov.uk
HM Government Online	www.ukonline.gov.uk/
Department for Transport	www.dft.gov.uk
National Statistics	www.statistics.gov.uk
Northern Ireland Departments	www.northernireland.gov.uk
Office of the Deputy Prime Minister	www.odpm.gov.uk
Ofgem	www.ofgem.gov.uk
Scottish Executive	www.scotland.gov.uk
Scottish Parliament	www.scottish.parliament.uk
The National Assembly for Wales	www.wales.gov.uk/
UK Parliament	www.parliament.uk

Other useful energy related websites

BP	www.bp.com/index.asp
British Wind Energy Association	www.bwea.com
Building Research Establishment	www.bre.co.uk
Coal Authority	www.coal.gov.uk/
Electricity Association	www.electricity.org.uk
Energywatch	www.energywatch.org.uk/
Europa (European Union Online)	www.europa.eu.int/
Eurostat	www.europa.eu.int/comm/eurostat/
Future Energy Solutions	www.future-energy solutions.com
Institute of Energy	www.dti.gov.uk/JEMU
Institute of Petroleum	www.petroleum.co.uk
Interconnector (UK) Ltd	www.iuk-isis.com
International Energy Agency	www.iea.org
Iron and Steel Statistics Bureau	www.issb.co.uk/
NETCEN (Air quality estimates)	www.airquality.co.uk
The Stationery Office	www.the-stationery-office.co.uk/
UK Offshore Operators Association (UKOOA)	www.ukooa.co.uk/
UK Petroleum Industry Association	www.ukpia.com
United Nations Statistics Division	www.unstats.un.org/unsd/default.htm
US Department of Energy	www.energy.gov
US Energy Information Administration	www.eia.doe.gov

Annex D
Major events in the Energy Industry

2003

Energy White Paper

On 24 February 2003 the Government published its Energy White Paper "Our energy future – creating a low carbon economy". The White Paper set out a new energy policy, designed to deal with the three major challenges that confront the UK's energy system: the challenge of climate change, the challenge of declining indigenous energy supplies, and the need to keep the UK's energy infrastructure up to date with changing technologies and needs.

To address these challenges, the White Paper set four new goals for energy policy: to put the United Kingdom on a path to cut carbon dioxide emissions by some 60 per cent by about 2050, with real progress by 2020; to maintain the reliability of energy supplies; to promote competitive energy markets in the UK and beyond, helping to raise the rate of sustainable economic growth and improve UK productivity; and to ensure that every home is adequately and affordably heated.

For the first time, the environment was put at the heart of Government's energy policy, causing energy efficiency and renewables to feature prominently in the White Paper, as the main ways of delivering carbon cuts. A new Europe-wide emissions trading scheme to be introduced in 2005 will create a powerful incentive to producers and consumers to use less energy and to switch to lower or zero-carbon forms of electricity.

Fuel Poverty Advisory Group

The first report to ministers by the Fuel Poverty Advisory Group (FPAG) was also published on 4 March 2003. The Group made several recommendations, the key ones of which were:

- The Government should annually review progress towards targets and the adequacy of existing policies.
- Current programmes will not be sufficient to meet the Government target for England by 2010; they need to be increased by at least 50 per cent.

The Government welcomed this report, and will be working with the Group to take their recommendations forwards.

Fuel Poverty Annual Report

On 4 March 2003, the Government published its first annual progress report on the UK Fuel poverty strategy: www.dti.gov.uk/energy/consumers/fuel_poverty/index.shtml . The report showed that encouraging progress had been made: the number of UK households in fuel poverty was down from around 5½ million in 1996 to around 3 million in 2001. However, it recognised that there was still a along way to go and that some difficult problems lie ahead.

Included in the report are a number of detailed annexes (published on the internet), which set out fuel poverty figures and various other indicators to show how related issues are progressing.

Energy Efficiency

In the 2003 Budget in April the Government noted that economic growth and social progress must be balanced with action to protect and improve the environment. One of the main areas in which the Government confirmed that it would be undertaking further consultation was on specific measures to encourage household energy efficiency, following on from an earlier consultation on the use of economic instruments to promote energy efficiency in the domestic sector.

Oil and Gas

US firm Apache (a new entrant to the UKCS) purchased the Forties oil field from BP in January 2003. This reflects the continuing changing nature of the North Sea as an area for investment and demonstrates the opportunities that still exist for new investors in the UK Continental Shelf. Originally one of the largest oil fields in the UKCS, and - as of 2002 - producing around 45,000 barrels of oil a day, Forties continues to make a significant contribution to overall UK oil production.

In February 2003, to encourage a wider range of bids for offshore oil and gas exploration licences, the DTI enhanced the licensing system to include a new "promote" licence in the 21st Offshore Licensing Round. This new type of licence is offered at a 10th of the price of a traditional licence for the first 2 years of its term and is aimed at attracting smaller newcomers wishing to find oil and gas. Its introduction has led to a good response in the 21st Round and an increase in licence applications. More information can be found on the Oil and Gas website: www.og.dti.gov.uk .

Electricity

In January 2003, Powergen announced the closure at the end of March of two already partly mothballed coal-fired power stations that it had acquired from TXU in October 2002, namely Drakelow and High Marnham. It said it would also mothball two 675 MW oil-fired units at Grain and one 450 MW gas fired unit at Killingholme, the three of which had already earmarked for mothballing in the previous autumn but had kept running to provide electricity for the former TXU customers it had acquired.

In May 2003, Centrica completed the acquisition of Lakeland Power's Roosecote Power Station (229 MW), which had suspended operations in November 2002. Scottish and Southern Energy announced that they are to buy the distribution network operator, Midland Electricity from Aquila Networks.

Nuclear

At the end of March 2003 BNFL's Calder Hall nuclear power station closed.

2002

Climate Change levy

In the Chancellor's 2002 Budget statement he strengthened the existing policy to support business energy efficiency by announcing proposals to:

- Freeze the climate change levy rates;